WORKED EXAMPLES
IN
PROBABILITY AND
DISTRIBUTION THEORY

By

F. D. J. DUNSTAN, M.A., M.Sc., D.Phil.
A. B. J. NIX, B.Sc., Ph.D.
J. F. REYNOLDS, M.A., Ph.D.
R. J. ROWLANDS, B.Sc., Ph.D.

Lecturers at
University College, Cardiff

RND PUBLICATIONS

First published in 1981 by
RND PUBLICATIONS
6 The Avenue, Whitchurch, Cardiff CF4 2EG.

Copyright©1981 RND PUBLICATIONS

CONTENTS

———

Preface

This book contains over 350 worked examples in probability and distribution theory. The problems range from elementary exercises to those suitable for Scholarship and first-year University examinations, and are taken from the companion volume entitled Introductory Statistics Volume 1: Probability and Distribution Theory.

Each problem is solved in full detail and sometimes alternative solutions are given. The methods used for a solution are those appropriate to the relevant section and do not use concepts from later sections. While this does not always lead to the quickest solution it is felt that this is preferable from a teaching point of view.

A selection of tables, reprinted from RND Statistical Tables is given at the end of the book.

F. D. J. DUNSTAN
A. B. J. NIX
J. F. REYNOLDS
R. J. ROWLANDS

Cardiff 1981

1

Descriptive Statistics

Miscellaneous Problems

1. Classify each of the following types of data. For example,
   children's shoe size data are certainly ordinal but are they also
   interval data?

   (i)   Hat sizes.

   (ii)   Barometric pressures.

   (iii)   Preferences for classical or pop music.

   (iv)   Religious faiths.

   (v)   Weights of people.

   (vi)   Shoe sizes of children.

   (vii)   Registration years of cars.

   (viii) Masses of pebbles on a beach.

   (ix)   Grades of students sitting an examination.

   (x)   People's Intelligence Quotients.

   (i)   Ratio. Hat sizes are proportional to the circumference of
           the head and so correspond to lengths.

   (ii)   Ratio. All arithmetic operations are permissible.

   (iii)   Categorical.

   (iv)   Categorical.

   (v)   Ratio.

   (vi)   Interval. Sizes are measured on a linear scale.

   (vii)   Interval. They are not ratio as division does not make
           sense. In 1980 a car made in 1970 was twice as old as one
           made in 1975.

   (viii) Ratio.

   (ix)   Ordinal. Grades may not cover equal ranges of marks.

   (x)   Ordinal. They are not necessarily interval data, but attempts have been made to produce testing procedures for which this is the case.

2. The heights in cm of 80 third-form students are listed below.

149	157	151	148	161	150	160	147	149	151
150	150	154	148	152	150	152	150	158	152
158	138	142	146	148	150	153	152	159	162
151	141	153	149	148	140	149	151	145	152
155	148	146	138	150	151	146	149	143	155
163	148	147	147	146	153	146	153	152	156
152	156	151	154	147	155	152	145	149	150
154	147	155	152	160	150	148	150	150	150

Taking classes with class boundaries 137.5, 139.5, 141.5,....., 159.5, 161.5, 163.5, find the following.

(i)   The frequency distribution and cumulative frequency distribution of heights in tabular form.

(ii)   The histogram of the heights of students.

(iii)   The cumulative frequency polygon.

(iv)   The median.

(v)   The upper and lower quartiles.

(vi)   The semi-interquartile range.

(vii)   The mode.

(viii) The mean.

(ix)   The standard deviation.

(i)   We obtain the frequency distribution shown.

Class	Class Mark	Frequency	Cumulative Frequency
137.5-139.5	138.5	2	2
139.5-141.5	140.5	2	4
141.5-143.5	142.5	2	6
143.5-145.5	144.5	2	8
145.5-147.5	146.5	10	18
147.5-149.5	148.5	13	31
149.5-151.5	150.5	18	49
151.5-153.5	152.5	13	62
153.5-155.5	154.5	7	69
155.5-157.5	156.5	3	72
157.5-159.5	158.5	3	75
159.5-161.5	160.5	3	78
161.5-163.5	162.5	2	80

(ii)

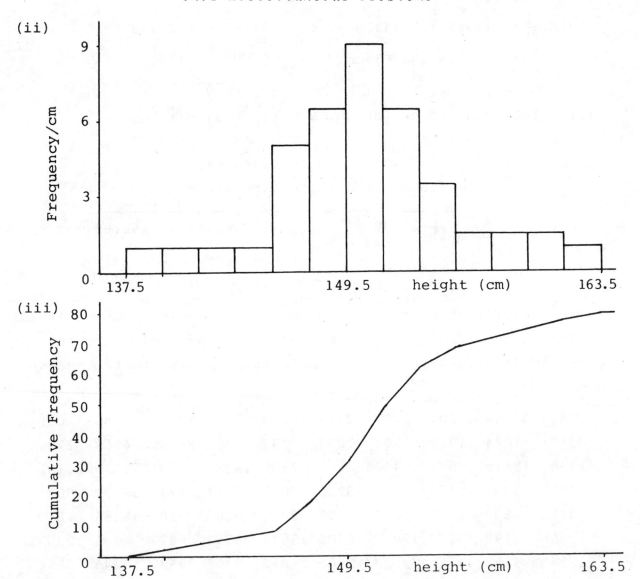

(iii)

(iv)   The median class is 149.5-151.5 as the 40.5th value is in this class.   The median is $149.5 + \frac{9.5}{18} \times 2 = 150.5\dot{5}$ cm.

(v)   The upper quartile is the 60.75th observation,

i.e. $151.5 + (60.75-49) \times \frac{2}{13} = 153.31$ cm.

The lower quartile is $147.5 + \frac{(20.25-18)}{13} \times 2 = 147.85$ cm.

(vi)   Semi-interquartile range $= \frac{153.31-147.85}{2} = 2.73$ cm.

(vii)   By symmetry in the diagram, the mode is 150.5 cm.

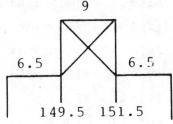

(viii)   The mean is $\frac{1}{80} \sum_{i=1}^{80} x_i = 150.56$ cm, where $x_1, \ldots, x_{80}$ are the observations.   Using the frequency distribution the mean is

3

$$\frac{1}{80}(2\times138.5 + 2\times140.5 + \dots + 3\times160.5 + 2\times162.5)$$

$$= 150.65 \text{ cm.}$$

(ix) The standard deviation, $s = \sqrt{\frac{1}{80}\sum_{i=1}^{80} x_i^2 - \bar{x}^2}$

$$= 4.944 \text{ cm.}$$

Using the frequency distribution it is

$$s = \sqrt{\frac{1}{80}(2\times138.5^2 + \dots + 2\times162.5^2) - 150.65^2}$$

$$= 4.937 \text{ cm.}$$

3. A manufacturer of electrical components tests 100 components to destruction to find their lifetimes. The data below are the observed lifetimes of these components, measured to the nearest hour.

5416	32364	33201	2767	7347	4570	7186	12383	29295	618
33441	11044	1317	11583	37097	883	7757	22185	4559	2731
17086	15115	911	15452	643	2235	14385	9131	1325	21182
19887	5759	5977	1305	3935	7817	5841	1799	32292	8681
7185	8830	2689	3332	7667	3971	107	36389	19165	1813
7666	2699	13683	17062	6700	15629	30754	6924	336	2357
17945	9393	17186	2543	9400	9896	7862	20582	5546	694
774	6536	52	16293	4452	4029	1943	2569	1955	8947
20756	8130	6125	9881	22980	6480	3022	43020	3326	140
9771	24268	206	5069	3960	1878	12706	11871	2500	553

Taking classes with class boundaries 0, 1000, 5000, 13000, 29000, 61000, find the following.

(i)   The frequency distribution and cumulative frequency distribution of lifetimes in tabular form.

(ii)   The histogram of the lifetimes.

(iii)   The cumulative frequency polygon.

(iv)   The median.

(v)   The upper and lower quartiles.

(vi)   The semi-interquartile range.

(vii)   The mode.

(viii) The mean.

(ix)   The standard deviation.

Explain why equal class intervals are not suitable for these data.

(i)

Class	Classmark	Frequency	Cumulative Frequency
0-1000	500	12	12
1000-5000	3000	27	39
5000-13000	9000	34	73
13000-29000	21000	18	91
29000-61000	45000	9	100

(ii) To construct the histogram we must divide the frequencies by the class intervals, obtaining

$$\frac{12}{1000}, \frac{6.75}{1000}, \frac{4.25}{1000}, \frac{1.125}{1000}, \frac{.28125}{1000}.$$

The histogram is

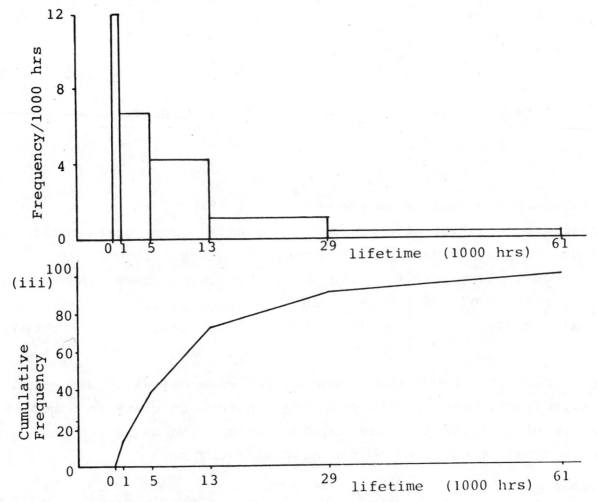

(iv) The median is the 50.5th observation and is

$$5000 + \frac{50.5-39}{73-39} \times 8000 = 7705.9 \text{ hr.}$$

(v) Upper quartile $= 13000 + \frac{75.75-73}{91-73} \times 16000 = 15444.4$ hr.

Lower quartile $= 1000 + \frac{25.25-12}{39-12} \times 4000 = 2963.0$ hr.

(vi) Semi-interquartile range $= \frac{1}{2}(15444.4-2963.0) = 6240.7$ hr.

5

(vii)   As the class intervals are unequal the modal class is the one
with the highest frequency per 1000 hours. From the histogram,
it is the class 0-1000. As this is an 'end-class', the
construction for the mode breaks down. However, the shape of
the histogram suggests the mode is closer to 0 than to 1000.

(viii) Using the raw data $\bar{x} = \frac{1}{100}\sum_{i=1}^{100} x_i = 9986.9$ hr.

Using the frequency distribution

$\bar{x} = (12\times500 + 27\times3000 + 34\times9000 + 18\times21000 + 9\times45000)/100$

$= 11760$ hr.

(ix)   Using the raw data

$$s = \sqrt{\frac{1}{100}\sum_{i=1}^{100} x_i^2 - \bar{x}^2} = 9800.2 \text{ hr},$$

while use of the frequency distribution gives

$$s = \sqrt{\frac{1}{100}(12\times500^2 + \ldots + 9\times45000^2) - 11760^2}$$

$$= 12382.7 \text{ hr}.$$

The discrepancies in the values obtained by the two methods
arise from the lack of symmetry in the data. The approximation of
using the grouped data is often poor in this situation.

Equal class intervals are unsuitable here because there is a
concentration of small values and a few widely scattered large ones.
Equal intervals would result in many classes having zero frequency.

In an education study the same mathematics examination was given to
a third-form class in School A and a third-form class in School B.
The results of the test are as shown below, the marks indicating
the percentage obtained to the nearest integer.

School A.

53	58	64	61	60	56	70	65	69	61
59	60	62	67	61	55	58	69	63	62
55	59	63	59	62	61	60	64	63	61

School B.

47	73	65	66	52	57	58	60	69	56
55	61	63	62	71	54	57	61	67	56
62	68	69	76	60	61	59	66	65	55

(i)   Represent this information graphically by constructing two histograms, one for each school.

(ii) Calculate the mean and standard deviation of the marks for each school.

(iii) Is there any evidence to suggest that one school may be setting children whilst the other has a policy of mixed ability teaching?

Taking classes 46-50, 51-55,..., 76-80 the frequency distributions for the marks from Schools A and B are as follows.

Class	46-50	51-55	56-60	61-65	66-70	71-75	76-80
School A		3	9	14	4		
School B	1	4	8	8	6	2	1

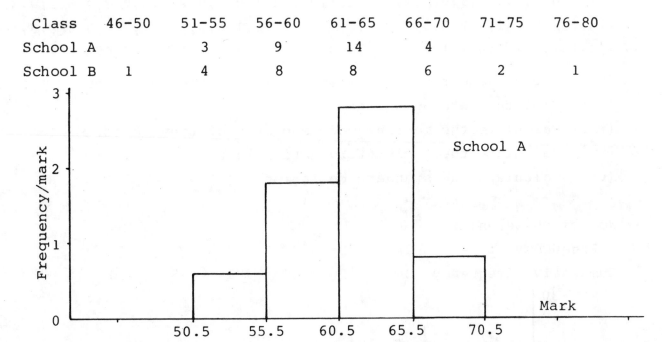

Note that in constructing the histogram we take the class boundaries as 45.5, 50.5, 55.5,.... The heights are the frequencies divided by the class interval 5.

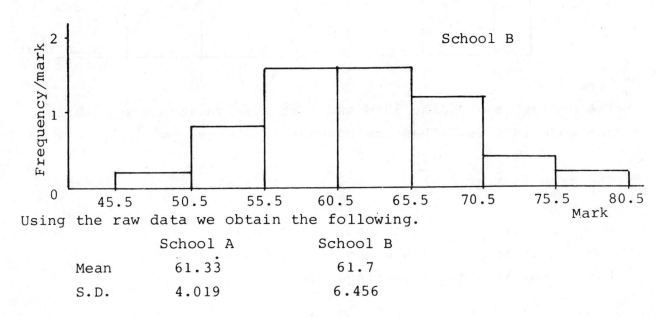

Using the raw data we obtain the following.

	School A	School B
Mean	61.33	61.7
S.D.	4.019	6.456

7

using the formulae

$$\bar{x} = \frac{1}{30}\sum_{i=1}^{30}x_i, \quad s = \sqrt{\frac{1}{30}\sum_{i=1}^{30}x_i^2 - \bar{x}^2}.$$

The schools produce similar mean marks but the standard deviation in school B is considerably higher, suggesting a greater range of standard of performance.

5. 100 married couples were asked how many children they had. The data are listed below.

0,1,1,0,2,3,2,0,1,0,0,2,2,0,3,4,3,0,1,1,0,2,0,2,1,2,2,3,4,5,2,0,3,1,
1,2,0,2,5,0,1,0,2,3,5,4,0,2,0,1,1,3,2,2,1,0,5,1,3,1,2,2,0,4,0,3,1,1,
2,0,3,2,1,1,2,0,1,1,2,4,3,3,2,0,1,0,2,1,2,3,1,2,0,1,2,0,5,4,2,1.

(i)   Present the frequency distribution in tabular form.
(ii)   Plot the data as a line diagram.
(iii)   Calculate the median, mode and mean of these data.
(iv)   Calculate the semi-interquartile range.
(v)   Calculate the standard deviation.

No. of children, i	0	1	2	3	4	5
Frequency, f_i	24	25	27	13	6	5
Cumulative frequency	24	49	76	89	95	100

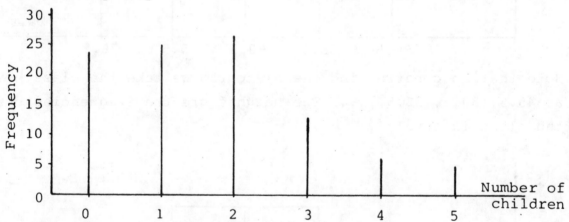

The median is 2 as the 50th and 51st observations are both 2.

The mode is 2 as it has the highest frequency.

The mean is $\bar{x} = \dfrac{1}{100}\sum_{i=1}^{100}x_i = \dfrac{1}{100}\sum_{i=0}^{5}if_i = 1.67$.

Upper quartile = 2   (75th and 76th both 2).

Lower quartile = 1   (25th and 26th both 1).

Hence semi-interquartile range = $\frac{1}{2}$.

$$\text{Standard deviation} = \sqrt{\frac{1}{100}\sum_{i=1}^{100} x_i^2 - 1.67^2}$$

$$= \sqrt{\frac{1}{100}\sum_{i=0}^{5} i^2 f_i - 1.67^2}$$

$$= 1.386.$$

6. The heads of English departments in 1000 schools were asked to assess their library facilities. Each teacher chose a reply on the following five-point scale,

Library facility	Score
Very bad	1
Less than adequate	2
Adequate	3
Good	4
Very good	5

and the resulting frequency distribution is shown below.

Score	1	2	3	4	5
Frequency	150	450	200	70	30

(i) Represent the information graphically.

(ii) Indicate the centre of the distribution using an appropriate measure.

(iii) Find the lower and upper quartiles.

(iv) What interpretation would you give to the interquartile range?

(i) There is clearly an ordering implicit in the scores and so we take the data to be ordinal. A line diagram can be drawn.

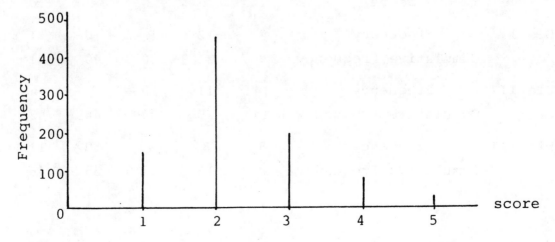

(ii) With ordinal data the median is an appropriate measure of the centre of the distribution. Here it is 2 since the 500th and 501st values are 2. An alternative measure is the mode, again 2.

(iii)   Upper quartile = 3,
           lower quartile = 2.

(iv) The interquartile range is only 1 and so there is an fair degree of agreement about the quality of their facilities.

7. A professional gambler buys 3 new dice. To test them, he throws each 60 times with the following results.

Die I
1,3,4,6,3,2,3,1,5,4,5,2,3,4,6,2,1,5,6,4,2,5,3,6,1,5,6,2,2,3,
1,2,6,5,5,4,1,4,6,1,3,6,5,3,2,4,4,2,4,2,6,5,1,1,2,5,4,3,2,5.

Die II
3,1,2,5,1,3,2,1,6,2,1,4,6,5,2,3,1,4,5,2,1,4,2,3,6,5,3,2,1,4,
2,3,1,6,4,2,3,1,1,6,1,5,4,6,2,3,1,6,4,2,3,6,5,4,1,5,3,4,1,5.

Die III
6,3,5,4,1,2,4,5,6,3,5,4,6,1,3,5,4,6,6,1,2,6,3,4,2,6,3,2,1,4,
5,3,1,6,4,5,1,3,2,6,4,5,6,5,1,6,1,5,6,2,5,3,4,2,3,5,6,4,2,6.

Construct, for each die, a cumulative frequency table and draw (on the same axes) a cumulative frequency polygon for each. The gambler now asserts that an 'ideal' die should give each value 10 times in 60 throws. Plot, on your graph, the cumulative frequency polygon given by such an 'ideal' die. Which die gives the most satisfactory results?

	Score	1	2	3	4	5	6
Die I	Frequency	9	12	9	10	11	9
	Cumulative Frequency	9	21	30	40	51	60
Die II	Frequency	14	11	10	9	8	8
	Cumulative Frequency	14	25	35	44	52	60
Die III	Frequency	8	8	9	10	11	14
	Cumulative Frequency	8	16	25	35	46	60

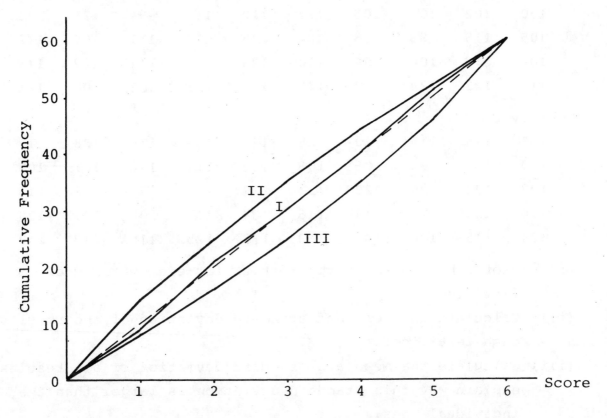

The cumulative frequency polygon of an 'ideal' die is shown by the dotted line. Die I clearly gives the results closest to the 'ideal' die.

8. Three fertiliser brands A,B,C were tested at 50 farms to compare their effectiveness. Each farmer prepared three similar plots of ground to grow a common variety of corn. Each fertiliser was allocated a plot at each farm and an agreed amount of that fertiliser was used. The yield, in suitable units, of corn per hectare for all farms is shown below.

Variety A

98	125	77	102	105	107	112	108	102	89
115	96	119	86	85	108	89	88	100	100
103	95	99	105	107	103	117	102	92	111
97	94	83	90	104	110	96	115	105	94
122	96	94	103	90	97	101	91	95	100

Variety B

110	116	96	101	102	113	106	110	126	117
130	102	107	108	112	110	113	94	125	91
105	115	88	118	104	108	116	111	109	112
108	113	106	104	110	128	116	111	122	115
113	122	124	100	120	106	121	103	100	121

Variety C

120	125	115	120	128	121	138	116	128	117
120	132	95	108	108	140	111	118	121	105
127	122	120	129	122	120	119	125	132	113
116	127	127	114	116	134	116	108	147	120
124	115	130	142	133	135	125	115	118	112

(i)   Plot a histogram of the results for each variety of fertiliser.

(ii)   Calculate the mean and standard deviation of the results for each fertiliser.

(iii) Calculate the mean and standard deviation of all results and explain why this standard deviation is larger than the individual ones.

(i)   Take as classes 71-80, 81-90, ..., 141-150.
       The following frequency distributions are obtained.

Class	Classmark	Frequency of A	Frequency of B	Frequency of C	Total Frequency
71-80	75.5	1	0	0	1
81-90	85.5	8	1	0	9
91-100	95.5	17	5	1	23
101-110	105.5	16	19	3	38
111-120	115.5	6	16	22	44
121-130	125.5	1	9	15	25
131-140	135.5	0	0	7	7
141-150	145.5	0	0	2	2

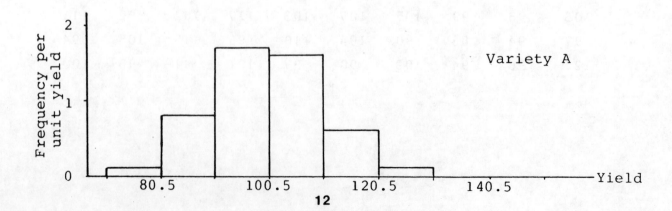

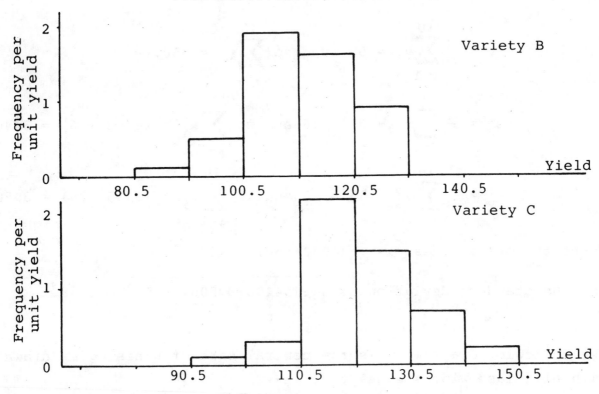

(ii) Using the raw data we find:

	Variety A	Variety B	Variety C	All varieties
Mean	100.44	110.76	121.78	110.99
Standard Deviation	10.12	9.21	9.88	13.07

These could also be found approximately using the frequency distributions in (i).

(iii) The standard deviation of the combined results is larger because it is the result of pooling three different distributions. Each variety has results which are fairly close to the mean for the variety but the combined distribution is spread more widely as the variety means are all different.

9. The 30 children in a class were given a mathematics examination. The 20 boys had a mean mark of 52 and standard deviation 4, while the 10 girls had a mean mark of 55 and standard deviation of 5. Calculate the mean and standard deviation of the marks of all 30 children.

Let the marks of the boys be $x_1, \ldots, x_{20}$ and those of the girls be $y_1, \ldots, y_{10}$.

$$\bar{x} = \frac{1}{20} \sum_{i=1}^{20} x_i = 52 \quad \text{and so} \quad \sum_{i=1}^{20} x_i = 20 \times 52 = 1040.$$

$$\bar{y} = \frac{1}{10}\sum_{i=1}^{10} y_i = 55 \quad \text{and so} \quad \sum_{i=1}^{10} y_i = 550.$$

$$s_x^2 = \frac{1}{20}\sum_{i=1}^{20} x_i^2 - 52^2 = 16 \quad \text{and so} \quad \sum_{i=1}^{20} x_i^2 = 20(52^2+16) = 54400.$$

$$s_y^2 = \frac{1}{10}\sum_{i=1}^{10} y_i^2 - 55^2 = 25 \quad \text{and so} \quad \sum_{i=1}^{10} y_i^2 = 10(55^2+25) = 30500.$$

Hence the overall mean is $\frac{1}{30}(1040+550) = 53$,

and the standard deviation is $\sqrt{\frac{1}{30}(54400+30500) - 53^2} = 4.58$.

10. The following diagram shows the central part of a histogram drawn with all class widths equal to 1.

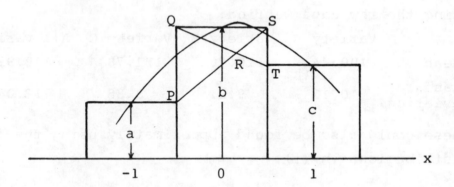

Suppose that the quadratic curve

$$y = A + Bx + Cx^2$$

passes through the three points $(-1,a)$, $(0,b)$ and $(1,c)$ as shown. Show that

$$B = \frac{(c-a)}{2} \quad \text{and} \quad C = \frac{(a+c-2b)}{2}.$$

Deduce, by completing the square of the above quadratic, that the maximum value of y occurs when

$$x = \frac{(c-a)}{2(2b-a-c)}.$$

By considering the similar triangles PQR, RST, show that the point R shown in the figure has this x-coordinate.

[This justifies the construction for finding the mode of a frequency distribution.]

14

Substituting the points $(-1,a)$, $(0,b)$ and $(1,c)$ in

$$y = A+Bx+Cx^2$$

we obtain

$$a = A-B+C$$
$$b = A$$
$$c = A+B+C.$$

Solving these, $A = b$, $B = \dfrac{c-a}{2}$ and $C = c-b-\dfrac{c-a}{2} = (a+c-2b)/2$.

Consider the quadratic $y = Cx^2+Bx+A$

$$y = C(x^2 + \frac{B}{C}x + \frac{A}{C})$$
$$= C(x + \frac{B}{2C})^2 + A - \frac{B^2}{4C}.$$

C is negative as a and c are both less than b, and so y is maximised when $(x + \dfrac{B}{2C})^2$ is as small as possible, that is when

$$x + \frac{B}{2C} = 0$$
$$\text{i.e. } x = \frac{-B}{2C} = \frac{c-a}{2(2b-a-c)}.$$

Clearly triangles PQR and RST are similar.

Hence $\dfrac{RU}{PQ} = \dfrac{RV}{ST}$

i.e. $\dfrac{RU}{b-a} = \dfrac{RV}{b-c}.$

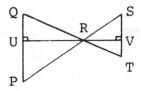

Now if z is the x-coordinate of R, $RU = \frac{1}{2}+z$, $RV = \frac{1}{2}-z$.

Therefore $(b-c)(z+\frac{1}{2}) = (b-a)(\frac{1}{2}-z)$, and, solving,

$$z = \frac{c-a}{2(2b-a-c)} \quad \text{as required.}$$

Thus in using the construction to find the mode we are fitting a quadratic through the midpoints of the tops of the three columns of the histogram and calculating the value at which it attains its maximum value.

2

Probability

Exercises 2.1 Introduction

1. The sample space S of an experiment is $S = \{0,1,2,3,4,5,6,7,8,9,10\}$ and events A, B and C are defined as follows:

$$A = \{0,1,2,4,7,8,9\},$$
$$B = \{0,3,4,5,9,10\},$$
$$C = \{0,2,4,6,8,10\}.$$

List the outcomes in the following events.

(i) $A \cup B$, (ii) $B \cup C$, (iii) $A \cap B'$.

Verify that $A \cap (B \cup C)$ and $(A \cap B) \cup (A \cap C)$ are equal here.

(i) $A \cup B = \{0,1,2,3,4,5,7,8,9,10\}$.

(ii) $B \cup C = \{0,2,3,4,5,6,8,9,10\}$.

(iii) $A \cap B' = \{1,2,7,8\}$, $A \cap (B \cup C) = \{0,2,4,8,9\}$,

   $A \cap B = \{0,4,9\}$, $A \cap C = \{0,2,4,8\}$.

   Thus $(A \cap B) \cup (A \cap C) = \{0,2,4,8,9\} = A \cap (B \cup C)$ as required.

2. In a group of 100 people, 58 are men, 60 are married and 32 are Welsh. There are 14 Welsh men, 21 married Welsh people, 25 married men and 8 married Welsh men. Draw a Venn diagram to illustrate these data, and find the number of unmarried Welsh women in the group.

Let Me, Ma and W denote respectively Men, Married and Welsh in the diagram. The numbers are inserted in each region, starting with the 8 common to all three sets. Adding, we find 98 included in at least one set and so 2 are not in any of the three sets.

   The number of unmarried Welsh women is 5 ($W \cap Me' \cap Ma'$).

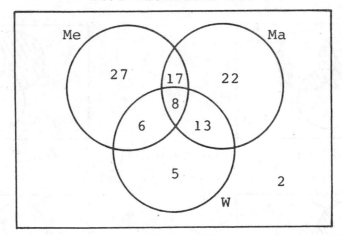

3. A coin is tossed 4 times and the result of each toss is noted.
   Write down the sample space using H for head and T for tail.

¶ {HHHH, HHHT, HHTH, HHTT, HTHH, HTHT, HTTH, HTTT, THHH, THHT, THTH,
   THTT, TTHH, TTHT, TTTH, TTTT}.
   [N.B. It is useful, in writing out all the possibilities, to
   identify H with 0 and T with 1 (or vice versa). The sequences of
   letters then represent the integers 0-15 in binary form.]

4. Use Venn diagrams to show that each of the following equalities is
   true for all events A,B,C.
   (i) $(A \cap B)' = A' \cup B'$,   (ii) $(A \cup B)' = A' \cap B'$,
   (iii) $A \cup (B \cap C) = (A \cup B) \cap (A \cup C)$,   (iv) $A \cap (B \cup C) = (A \cap B) \cup (A \cap C)$.

¶ The shaded area in each diagram represents the set indicated.

(i)

(ii)

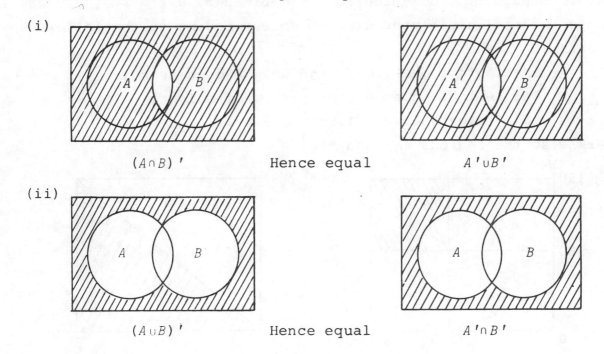

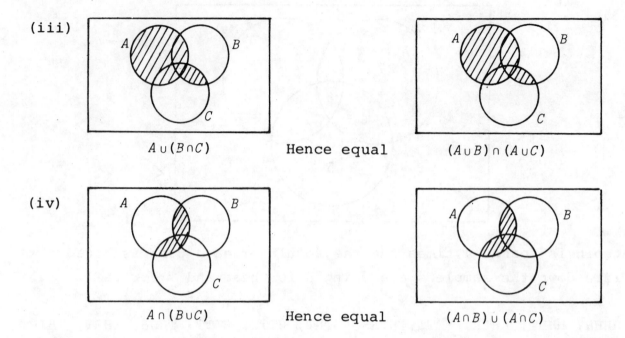

(iii) $A \cup (B \cap C)$ Hence equal $(A \cup B) \cap (A \cup C)$

(iv) $A \cap (B \cup C)$ Hence equal $(A \cap B) \cup (A \cap C)$

5. Two unknown volumes of water are maintained at temperatures of 30°C and 60°C respectively. If the two volumes are mixed and the resulting temperature recorded, what is the sample space for this experiment?

Let t°C be the temperature of the mixture. Since t clearly lies between 30 and 60, the sample space is $\{t: 30 < t < 60\}$.

6. The height (h) in metres and weight (w) in kilograms of each person in a population are recorded and plotted with respect to co-ordinate axes. Considering only the region defined by $0 \leqslant h \leqslant 3$, $0 \leqslant w \leqslant 150$, shade the regions in your diagram corresponding to the following events:

> A: height over 1.75m and weight over 80 kg,
> B: weight under 0.5 kg per cm of height,
> C: height between 1.5m and 2.0m.

Mark also the regions $A \cap B$ and $B \cap C'$.

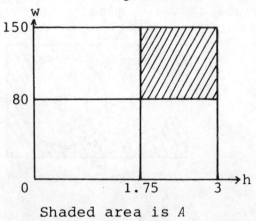

Shaded area is A

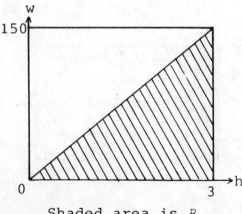

Shaded area is B

18

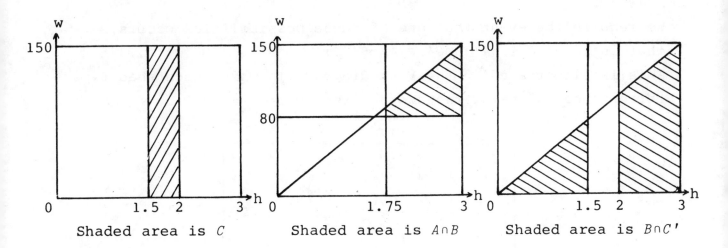

Shaded area is C Shaded area is $A \cap B$ Shaded area is $B \cap C'$

7. A coin is tossed until a head is obtained. Write down the sample space.

¶   {H, TH, TTH, TTTH, TTTTH, ...}
The sample space contains an infinite number of elements since the first H is not certain to appear within any given (finite) number of tosses.

8. A man tosses a coin until he gets either 3 heads in succession or 2 tails (not necessarily in succession). Write down the sample space.

¶ S = {TT, HTT, HHTT, THT, HTHT, HHTHT, THHT, HTHHT, HHTHHT, HHH, THHH, HTHHH, HHTHHH}.

9. Let A,B,C be 3 events. Express the following events in set notation.
         (i) A,B,C all occur,
         (ii)   at least one of A,B,C occurs,
         (iii) exactly one of A,B,C occurs,
         (iv)   not more than 2 of A,B,C occur.

¶   (i)   The event that A,B and C all occur is the intersection of them, by definition, and is written as $A \cap B \cap C$.
   (ii)   By definition the event that at least one occurs, that is A or B or C (or more than one) occurs, is $A \cup B \cup C$.
   (iii) The event that A occurs and B and C do not is $A \cap B' \cap C'$. Similarly the event that B occurs and A and C do not is $A' \cap B \cap C'$ and the event that C occurs while A and B do not is

19

$A'\cap B'\cap C$.

We require the event that one of these possibilities occurs, that is $(A\cap B'\cap C')\cup(A'\cap B\cap C')\cup(A'\cap B'\cap C)$.

This is illustrated in the Venn diagram, in which each shaded part corresponds to one of the above three events.

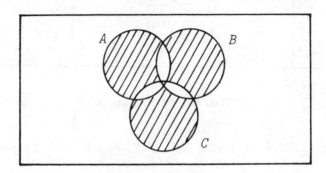

(iv)   The event 'not more than 2' is the complement of 'exactly 3', and 'exactly 3' is $A\cap B\cap C$. Thus the required event is $(A\cap B\cap C)'$.

10. A sample space S is defined by $S = \{(x,y): 0 \leqslant x \leqslant 10, 0 \leqslant y \leqslant 5\}$ and A,B are events defined by
$$A = \{(x,y): 0 \leqslant x \leqslant 5, 3 \leqslant y \leqslant 5\},$$
$$B = \{(x,y): 0 \leqslant x \leqslant 10, 0 \leqslant y \leqslant 3\}.$$

Sketch the events

(i) B',   (ii) A',   (iii) $A\cap B$,   (iv) $(A\cup B)'$.

¶   (i) Shaded area is B'

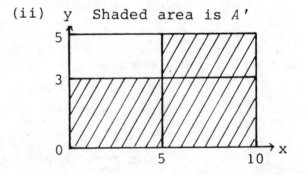

(ii)   Shaded area is A'

(iii)   Line segment is $A\cap B$

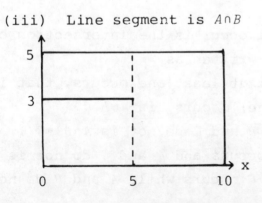

(iv)

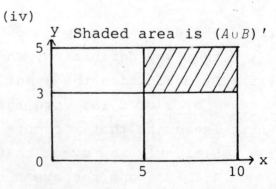

Shaded area is $(A\cup B)'$

20

Exercises 2.2 Definition of Probability

1. A fair coin is tossed twice. List the sample space and find
   (i) the probability that one head and one tail are obtained,
   (ii) the probability that a head precedes a tail.

¶ The sample space is $S = \{HH, HT, TH, TT\}$. As the four outcomes are equally likely

$$P(1H \text{ and } 1T) = \frac{\text{no. of outcomes giving 1H and 1T}}{4} = \frac{2}{4} = \frac{1}{2}.$$

$$P(\text{a head precedes a tail}) = P(HT) = \frac{1}{4}.$$

2. Two fair dice are thrown simultaneously. Find (i) the probability that the sum of the two scores is at most 8, (ii) the probability that the two scores differ by two, (iii) the probability that the two scores differ by at least two, (iv) the probability that the two scores differ by not more than two.

¶ The sample space consists of the following 36 equally likely outcomes.

(1,1)	(1,2)	(1,3)	(1,4)	(1,5)	(1,6)
(2,1)	(2,2)	(2,3)	(2,4)	(2,5)	(2,6)
(3,1)	(3,2)	(3,3)	(3,4)	(3,5)	(3,6)
(4,1)	(4,2)	(4,3)	(4,4)	(4,5)	(4,6)
(5,1)	(5,2)	(5,3)	(5,4)	(5,5)	(5,6)
(6,1)	(6,2)	(6,3)	(6,4)	(6,5)	(6,6)

By the equally likely principle

$$P(\text{sum at most 8}) = \frac{\text{no. of outcomes whose sum is at most 8}}{36}$$

$$= \frac{26}{36} \qquad \text{by enumeration.}$$

Similarly $P(\text{scores differ by two}) = \frac{8}{36}$,

$$P(\text{scores differ by at least two}) = \frac{20}{36},$$

and $P(\text{scores differ by at most two}) = \frac{24}{36}.$

Note that constant sums and constant differences correspond to lines on the above diagram parallel to the main diagonals.

3. Two fair dice are thrown simultaneously. Find the probabilities that the smaller of the two scores is equal to 1,2,3,4,5 and 6 respectively. Hence find the most likely value of the smaller score.

¶ Let SS be the smaller score. Using the sample space in question 2 above, it follows by enumeration that

$$P(SS=1) = \frac{11}{36}, \quad P(SS=2) = \frac{9}{36}, \quad P(SS=3) = \frac{7}{36}, \quad P(SS=4) = \frac{5}{36},$$

$$P(SS=5) = \frac{3}{36}, \quad P(SS=6) = \frac{1}{36}.$$

The most likely value of SS is 1 since this corresponds to the maximum probability above.

4. A hat contains five tickets numbered consecutively from 1 to 5. Two tickets are drawn out together at random. Find the probability that (i) the larger number drawn is 3, (ii) the sum of the numbers on the two tickets is a prime number.

¶ We can take the sample space to be
{(1,2), (1,3), (1,4), (1,5), (2,3), (2,4), (2,5), (3,4), (3,5), (4,5)}
and all ten outcomes are equally likely. By enumeration, therefore, P(larger number drawn is 3) = 2/10 as two outcomes, (1,3), (2,3), correspond to the event.
Similarly, P(sum is prime) = P(sum is 3,5 or 7) = 5/10.

5. Two letters are selected together at random from the letters of the word TOOK. Calculate the probability that the two letters selected are T and O.

¶ We can take the sample space to be {TO, TO, TK, OO, OK, OK}. These are not all distinct but have been listed because they are equally likely. Thus P(T and O selected) = 2/6, as two outcomes result in T and O being chosen.

6. A box contains three balls numbered 1, 2 and 3. Three balls are drawn at random so that after a ball has been chosen it is replaced before the next is drawn. Find the probability that the smallest number drawn is equal to 2 or more.

¶ The sample space is

(1,1,1), (1,1,2), (1,2,1), (2,1,1), (1,1,3), (1,3,1), (3,1,1),

(1,2,2), (2,1,2), (2,2,1), (1,3,3), (3,1,3), (3,3,1), (1,2,3),

(1,3,2), (2,1,3), (2,3,1), (3,1,2), (3,2,1), <u>(2,2,2)</u>, <u>(2,2,3)</u>,

<u>(2,3,2)</u>, <u>(3,2,2)</u>, <u>(3,2,3)</u>, <u>(3,3,2)</u>, <u>(2,3,3)</u>, <u>(3,3,3)</u>.

There are eight outcomes (underlined) corresponding to the event that the smallest number is at least 2, and so the required probability is 8/27.

7. Six balls numbered 1,2,3,4,5 and 6 are placed in a bag and three are drawn out together at random. Calculate the probabilities that
(i)   the sum of the numbers on the three balls is equal to 10,
(ii)   the ball numbered 6 is one of the chosen balls,
(iii) the product of the numbers is even.

¶ The 20 equally likely outcomes which make up the sample space are

(1,2,3), (1,2,4), (1,2,5), <u>(1,2,6)</u>, (1,3,4), (1,3,5), <u>(1,3,6)</u>,

(1,4,5), <u>(1,4,6)</u>, <u>(1,5,6)</u>, (2,3,4), (2,3,5), <u>(2,3,6)</u>, (2,4,5),

<u>(2,4,6)</u>, <u>(2,5,6)</u>, (3,4,5), <u>(3,4,6)</u>, <u>(3,5,6)</u>, <u>(4,5,6)</u>.

(i) P(Sum is 10) = 3/20 as outcomes (1,3,6), (2,3,5), (1,4,5) lead to a sum of 10.

(ii) P(6 is chosen) = 10/20, corresponding to the triples underlined.

(iii) P(Product is even) = 19/20 as all outcomes except (1,3,5) lead to an even product.

8. A botanist uses 6 similar plants in an experiment. The plants are divided at random into two groups of 3. One group is to be treated with a chemical, but the other is to be left untreated to act as a 'control'. The plants all have slightly different total leaf areas. Find the probability that the plants in the control group are the ones with the smallest total leaf areas. What would this probability have been if the botanist had used 8 plants, dividing them into two groups of 4?

¶ Let the plants be numbered 1,2,3,4,5 and 6 in increasing order of leaf area. The possibilities for the control plants are the twenty outcomes listed in the solution to Question 7 above. The outcome (1,2,3) corresponds to the event that the control group contains

the three with smallest leaf areas and so has probability 1/20.
If there are eight plants, numbered 1 to 8, we can list all
selections of four from eight. Lengthy enumeration shows that
there are 70 possibilities so that the required probability is 1/70.
[The answer can be obtained more quickly by the methods used in
 Section 2.4.]

9. In a certain game, the direction of movement of a counter is decided
   by selecting a disc at random from a bag containing four discs,
   marked respectively N,S,E,W. The letters indicate a movement of
   1 unit in a North, South, East, West direction. After the move,
   the disc is replaced before the next selection. Calculate the
   probability that the counter is (i) due North, (ii) North-east,
   (iii) due West of its original position, after (a) 1 move,
   (b) 2 moves.

¶   (a) After one move the counter must be due North, due East, due
       South or due West, each with equal probability.
       So P(due North) = 1/4, P(Northeast) = 0,
          P(due West) = 1/4.

    (b) The sample space for two moves can be written
        {NN,NE,NS,NW,EN,EE,ES,EW,SN,SE,SS,SW,WN,WE,WS,WW} and each
        outcome has probability 1/16.
        So P(due North) = P(NN) = 1/16,
           P(Northeast) = P(EN or NE) = 2/16,
           P(due West) = P(WW) = 1/16.

10. Two letters are selected simultaneously at random from the four
    letters LINK. Find the probability that
    (i) the letter N is not selected,
    (ii) the letters I and N are selected.
    Suppose instead that the selection is not simultaneous and that the
    first letter chosen can be selected again. Calculate the
    probabilities of the above events in this case.

¶   The sample space is {LI,LN,LK,IN,IK,NK}.
    Thus P(N not selected) = 3/6 by the equally likely principle as 3
    outcomes do not involve N.
    Similarly P(I and N selected) = 1/6.

If the selection is not simultaneous then the sample space is {LL,LI,LN,LK,IL,II,IN,IK,NL,NI,NN,NK,KL,KI,KN,KK}, where the first of the pair corresponds to the first choice and the second to the second choice. It is necessary to do this so that all outcomes are equally likely - two L's can be chosen in one way but an L and an I in two ways.

Therefore $P(\text{N not selected}) = \frac{9}{16}$,

$$P(\text{I and N selected}) = \frac{2}{16}.$$

11. Two fair dice are thrown simultaneously. The two events A,B are defined as follows:

A: the sum of the two scores is 6,7 or 8,

B: the scores differ by at most 2.

Find the following probabilities by enumeration.
(i) $P(A)$, (ii) $P(B)$, (iii) $P(A \cap B)$, (iv) $P(A \cup B)$, (v) $P(A \cap B')$, (vi) $P(A' \cup B)$, (vii) $P(A' \cup B')$, (viii) $P(A' \cap B')$.

¶ The sample space is

(1,1)*	(1,2)*	(1,3)*	(1,4)	(1,5)	(1,6)
(2,1)*	(2,2)*	(2,3)*	(2,4)*	(2,5)	(2,6)
(3,1)*	(3,2)*	(3,3)*	(3,4)*	(3,5)*	(3,6)
(4,1)	(4,2)*	(4,3)*	(4,4)*	(4,5)*	(4,6)*
(5,1)	(5,2)	(5,3)*	(5,4)*	(5,5)*	(5,6)*
(6,1)	(6,2)	(6,3)	(6,4)*	(6,5)*	(6,6)*

Pairs corresponding to A are underlined and those corresponding to B are starred.

By enumeration,
(i) $P(A) = \frac{16}{36}$, (ii) $P(B) = \frac{24}{36}$, (iii) $P(A \cap B) = \frac{8}{36}$,

(iv) $P(A \cup B) = \frac{32}{36}$, (v) $P(A \cap B') = \frac{8}{36}$, (vi) $P(A' \cup B) = \frac{28}{36}$,

(vii) $P(A' \cup B') = \frac{28}{36}$, (viii) $P(A' \cap B') = \frac{4}{36}$.

12. Three married couples are waiting for a bus. When it arrives there is room for only three passengers. In order to decide who gets on, the six names are put into a hat and three are drawn out at random. Enumerate the sample space and deduce the probabilities that
(i) the three people chosen to travel are all of the same sex,
(ii) a married couple travels on the bus.

¶ The sample space is

$$\underline{(M_1M_2M_3)} \qquad (M_1M_2F_1)* \qquad (M_1M_2F_2)* \qquad (M_1M_2F_3)$$
$$(M_1M_3F_1)* \qquad (M_1M_3F_2) \qquad (M_1M_3F_3)* \qquad (M_1F_1F_2)*$$
$$(M_1F_1F_3)* \qquad (M_1F_2F_3) \qquad (M_2M_3F_1) \qquad (M_2M_3F_2)*$$
$$(M_2M_3F_3)* \qquad (M_2F_1F_2)* \qquad (M_2F_1F_3) \qquad (M_2F_2F_3)*$$
$$(M_3F_1F_2) \qquad (M_3F_1F_3)* \qquad (M_3F_2F_3)* \qquad \underline{(F_1F_2F_3)}$$

where (M_1F_1), (M_2F_2), (M_3F_3) denote the three married couples.

(i) $P(3 \text{ of same sex}) = \frac{2}{20}$ (corresponding to the underlined triples).

(ii) $P(\text{a married couple on bus}) = \frac{12}{20}$ (corresponding to the starred triples).

Exercises 2.3 Rules of Probability

1. Two fair dice are thrown simultaneously. The two events A,B are defined as follows:

   A: the sum of the two scores is 6, 7 or 8,

   B: the scores differ by at most 2.

   Find the values of $P(A)$, $P(B)$, $P(A \cap B)$ by enumeration and use the rules of probability to deduce the values of

   (i) $P(A \cup B)$, (ii) $P(A \cap B')$, (iii) $P(A' \cup B)$, (iv) $P(A' \cup B')$, (v) $P(A' \cap B')$.

   [See also Question 11 of Section 2.2.]

¶ As in Question 11 of Section 2.2

$$P(A) = \frac{16}{36}, \quad P(B) = \frac{24}{36}, \quad P(A \cap B) = \frac{8}{36}.$$

Then

(i) $P(A \cup B) = P(A) + P(B) - P(A \cap B) = \frac{16}{36} + \frac{24}{36} - \frac{8}{36} = \frac{32}{36}$,

(ii) $P(A \cap B') = P(A) - P(A \cap B) = \frac{16}{36} - \frac{8}{36} = \frac{8}{36}$,

(iii) $P(A' \cup B) = 1 - P(A \cap B') = 1 - \frac{8}{36} = \frac{28}{36}$ [since $A' \cup B = (A \cap B')'$],

(iv) $P(A' \cup B') = 1 - P(A \cap B) = 1 - \frac{8}{36} = \frac{28}{36}$ [since $A' \cup B' = (A \cap B)'$],

(v) $P(A' \cap B') = 1 - P(A \cup B) = 1 - \frac{32}{36} = \frac{4}{36}$ [since $A' \cap B' = (A \cup B)'$].

2. A man is selected at random from a large population of males in which 60% are taller than 1.75m and 40% weigh more than 75kg. What is wrong with the calculation that the probability he is taller than 1.75m or weighs more than 75kg (or both) equals 0.6+0.4 = 1?

¶ Define events

        A: the man is taller than 1.75m,

        B: the man weighs more than 75 kg.

Then $P(A \cup B) = P(A) + P(B) - P(A \cap B)$.

The statement ignores the last term and will be incorrect unless it is impossible for a man to be taller than 1.75m and weigh more than 75kg.

3. In a large city 80% of families own a colour television set, 30% own a black and white television set and 15% own both kinds of set. If a family is selected at random what is the probability that it will be found not to possess a television set?

¶ Let BW, C denote respectively the events that a family possesses a black and white set and a colour set.

$$P(\text{no TV}) = 1 - P(BW \cup C)$$
$$= 1 - (P(BW) + P(C) - P(BW \cap C))$$
$$= 1 - (0.3 + 0.8 - 0.15)$$
$$= 0.05.$$

This is illustrated in the Venn diagram.

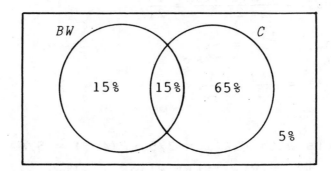

4. In a certain Scandinavian city 50% of females have blue eyes, 55% have blonde hair but 25% have neither characteristic. Find the probability that a randomly selected female will be a blue-eyed blonde.

¶ Let BE be the event that a randomly selected female has blue eyes and BH that she has blonde hair.

    We have $P(BE) = 0.5$, $P(BH) = 0.55$.

Now $P(\text{neither characteristic}) = 1 - P(BE \cup BH)$

so that $P(BE \cup BH) = 1 - 0.25 = 0.75$.

Therefore $P(BE \cap BH) = P(BE) + P(BH) - P(BE \cup BH)$
$$= 0.5 + 0.55 - 0.75 = 0.3.$$

5. A die is weighted so that the probability of a number appearing when the die is tossed is proportional to the given number. Let $A = \{1,2,3\}$, $B = \{2,4,5\}$ and $C = \{1,3,5\}$.

(i) Find the probability of each possible outcome when the die is tossed.

(ii) Find $P(A)$, $P(B)$ and $P(C)$.

(iii) Find the probability that (a) B or C (or both) occurs, (b) A and C both occur, (c) A occurs but not B.

¶ (i) We are given that $P(N=r) = kr$ $(r = 1,2,3,4,5,6)$, where N is the number showing and k some constant. Since the probabilities sum to 1,

$$21k = 1$$
$$\text{or} \qquad k = 1/21.$$

Hence $\qquad P(N=r) = r/21$, $(r = 1,2,3,4,5,6)$.

(ii) $$P(A) = \frac{1+2+3}{21} = \frac{6}{21},$$

$$P(B) = \frac{2+4+5}{21} = \frac{11}{21},$$

$$P(C) = \frac{1+3+5}{21} = \frac{9}{21}.$$

(iii) $$P(B \cup C) = \frac{1+2+3+4+5}{21} = \frac{15}{21},$$

$$P(A \cap C) = \frac{1+3}{21} = \frac{4}{21},$$

$$P(A \cap B') = \frac{1+3}{21} = \frac{4}{21}.$$

6. If A,B are events with $P(A') = 3/5$, $P(A \cup B) = 5/6$ and $P(A \cap B) = 1/5$, find (i) $P(A)$, (ii) $P(B)$, (iii) $P(A \cap B')$, (iv) $P(A' \cap B)$.

¶ (i) $$P(A) = 1 - P(A') = 1 - \frac{3}{5} = \frac{2}{5}.$$

(ii) Since $P(A \cup B) = P(A) + P(B) - P(A \cap B)$, it follows that

$$P(B) = P(A \cup B) + P(A \cap B) - P(A)$$
$$= \frac{5}{6} + \frac{1}{5} - \frac{2}{5} = \frac{19}{30}.$$

(iii) Since $\quad P(A) = P(A \cap B) + P(A \cap B')$, it follows that

$$P(A \cap B') = P(A) - P(A \cap B)$$
$$= \frac{2}{5} - \frac{1}{5} = \frac{1}{5}.$$

(iv) Similarly, $P(A' \cap B) = P(B) - P(A \cap B)$

$$= \frac{19}{30} - \frac{1}{5} = \frac{13}{30}.$$

An alternative method is to construct the following array:

	A	A'
B	$\frac{1}{5}$	$\frac{13}{30}$
B'	$\frac{1}{5}$	$\frac{1}{6}$

This can be completed as follows.

$$P(A \cap B) = 1/5 \text{ (given)}.$$

The two entries below A must add up to $P(A)$; this corresponds to the relationship

$$P(A \cap B) + P(A \cap B') = P(A).$$

Since $P(A) = 1 - P(A') = 2/5$, this gives $P(A \cap B') = 1/5$ as before. Since $A' \cap B' = (A \cup B)'$, it follows that

$$P(A' \cap B') = 1 - P(A \cup B)$$

$$= 1 - \frac{5}{6} = \frac{1}{6}.$$

Since all the entries add up to 1,

$$P(A' \cap B) = 1 - (\frac{1}{5} + \frac{1}{5} + \frac{1}{6}) = \frac{13}{30}.$$

7. Events A and B are such that $P(A) = P(B) = p$, $P(A \cap B) = 1/2$ and $P(A' \cap B') = 1/3$. Calculate p.

¶ $$P(A \cup B) = P(A) + P(B) - P(A \cap B) = 2p - \frac{1}{2}.$$

But $$P(A \cup B) = 1 - P(A' \cap B') = 1 - \frac{1}{3} = \frac{2}{3}.$$

Hence $$2p - \frac{1}{2} = \frac{2}{3} \text{ and } p = \frac{7}{12}.$$

This could also be found using the 'table method' described in question 6 above.

8. If $P(A) = 0.6$ and $P(A \cup B) = 0.9$, between what limits must $P(B)$ lie?

¶ $$P(B) = P(A \cup B) - P(A) + P(A \cap B)$$
$$= 0.3 + P(A \cap B).$$

Now $$0 \leqslant P(A \cap B) \leqslant \text{Min}\{P(A), P(B)\} \leqslant P(A),$$
whence $$0 \leqslant P(A \cap B) \leqslant 0.6. \quad \text{Thus } 0.3 \leqslant P(B) \leqslant 0.9.$$

9. The events A and B are such that $P(A) = 1/2$, $P(B) = 1/6$.
   Find $P(A-B)$ in the following cases:
   (i) A and B are mutually exclusive, (ii) $P(A \cap B) = 1/12$, (iii) $B \subseteq A$.

¶ We have $P(A-B) = P(A \cap B') = P(A) - P(A \cap B)$.
   (i) If A and B are mutually exclusive, $P(A \cap B) = 0$ and
   $$P(A-B) = P(A) = 1/2.$$

   (ii) $$P(A-B) = P(A) - P(A \cap B) = \frac{1}{2} - \frac{1}{12} = \frac{5}{12}.$$

   (iii) If $B \subseteq A$, $A \cap B = B$. Thus $P(A-B) = P(A) - P(B) = \frac{1}{3}$.

10. (i) Prove that $P(A \cap B) \geqslant 1 - P(A') - P(B')$ for any events A,B.
    (ii) A woman is selected at random from a large population of
    females in which 95% are shorter than 1.5m and 80% weigh less
    than 70 kg. Show that there is at least a 75% chance that she
    will be shorter than 1.5m and weigh less than 70kg.

¶ (i) $$P(A \cap B) = P(A) + P(B) - P(A \cup B)$$
$$= 1 - P(A') + 1 - P(B') - P(A \cup B)$$
$$= 1 - P(A') - P(B') + (1 - P(A \cup B))$$
$$\geqslant 1 - P(A') - P(B').$$

   (ii) Define events A: she is shorter than 1.5m,
                      B: she weighs less than 70kg.
   Since $P(A') = 1 - 0.95 = 0.05$ and $P(B') = 1 - 0.8 = 0.2$,
   $P(A \cap B) \geqslant 1 - 0.05 - 0.2 = 0.75$, using (i).

11. Prove that $P(A \cup B) \leqslant P(A) + P(B)$ and deduce that
   $$P(A \cup B \cup C) \leqslant P(A) + P(B) + P(C).$$

¶ $$P(A \cup B) = P(A) + P(B) - P(A \cap B)$$
$$\leqslant P(A) + P(B).$$

   Hence $$P(A \cup (B \cup C)) \leqslant P(A) + P(B \cup C)$$
$$\leqslant P(A) + P(B) + P(C).$$

12. Prove that for any three events A,B and C,
   $$P(A \cup B \cup C) = P(A) + P(B) + P(C) - P(A \cap B) - P(A \cap C) - P(B \cap C) + P(A \cap B \cap C).$$

¶ $$P(A \cup (B \cup C)) = P(A) + P(B \cup C) - P(A \cap (B \cup C)). \qquad (1)$$

Now $\quad P(B \cup C) = P(B) + P(C) - P(B \cap C).$

Also $P(A \cap (B \cup C)) = P((A \cap B) \cup (A \cap C))$

$$= P(A \cap B) + P(A \cap C) - P((A \cap B) \cap (A \cap C))$$

$$= P(A \cap B) + P(A \cap C) - P(A \cap B \cap C).$$

Substitution in (1) gives the required result.

Exercises 2.4 Permutations and Combinations

1. Evaluate the following.

(i) $^{13}P_2$, (ii) $^{5}P_5$, (iii) $^{6}P_4$, (iv) $^{4}C_2$, (v) $^{10}C_8$, (vi) $^{56}C_{52}$.

¶ (i) $^{13}P_2 = \dfrac{13!}{11!} = 156.$ (ii) $^{5}P_5 = \dfrac{5!}{0!} = 120.$

(iii) $^{6}P_4 = \dfrac{6!}{2!} = 360.$ (iv) $^{4}C_2 = \dfrac{4!}{2!2!} = 6.$

(v) $^{10}C_8 = \dfrac{10!}{8!2!} = 45.$ (vi) $^{56}C_{52} = \dfrac{56!}{52!4!} = 367290.$

2. If repetition is allowed, how many distinct 5-letter words can be made from

(i) the letters a,c,e,k,r,t,

(ii) the letters a,c,e?

[A 'word' is defined as any arrangement of letters; it need not have any meaning.]

¶ (i) Since each letter can be chosen in 6 ways,

Number of words $= 6^5 = 7776.$

(ii) Since each letter can be chosen in 3 ways,

Number of words $= 3^5 = 243.$

3. In how many ways can five people arrange themselves in five seats at the back of a coach?

¶ We require the number of permutations of 5 from 5,

i.e. $^{5}P_5 = 120.$

4. In how many ways can 8 passengers arrange themselves in a 12-seater minibus?

¶ We require the number of permutations of 8 from 12,

i.e. $^{12}P_8 = \frac{12!}{4!} = 19,958,400.$

5. In how many ways can five people arrange themselves in five seats around a table, if only the cyclic order and not the actual positions is taken into account?

¶ We are interested only in the positions relative to one individual. He has 4 possibilities for one neighbour and 3 for the other. The remaining two people can be arranged in 2 ways.
Hence the number of possibilities is 4×3×2 = 24.

6. In how many ways can 3 boys and 3 girls sit in a row if
   (i)   the boys sit together and the girls sit together,
   (ii) just the girls sit together,
   (iii) no girl sits next to another girl,
   (iv) no girl sits next to another girl and no boy sits next to another boy?

¶ (i)   The possible arrangements are BBBGGG and GGGBBB.
        In each of these, both the boys and girls can be permuted in $^3P_3$, i.e. 6 ways. There are therefore 36 permutations corresponding to each arrangement. There are thus 72 ways in which the boys and girls sit together.
  (ii) The possible arrangements are BBGGGB and BGGGBB.
        As in (i), each arrangement corresponds to 36 permutations of the children, giving 72 permutations in all.
  (iii) The possible arrangements are BGBGBG, GBBGBG, GBGBBG, GBGBGB.
        Each arrangement corresponds to 36 permutations, giving 144 permutations in all.
  (iv) The possible arrangements are BGBGBG and GBGBGB.
        Each arrangement corresponds to 36 permutations, giving 72 permutations in all.

7. In how many ways can a rowing eight arrange itself if the three heaviest members must sit in positions 4, 5 and 6, any order being permitted?

¶ Number of permutations for the 3 heaviest members = $^3P_3$ = 6.

Number of permutations for the remaining 5 members = $^5P_5$ = 120.

Therefore number of permutation of rowers = 6×120 = 720.

8. (i) How many 3 digit numbers can be formed from the five digits 1,2,5,8,9 allowing repetitions?
   (ii) How many of these are less than 300?
   (iii) How many are even?
   (iv) How many are multiples of 5?
   (v) How many contain no repeated digits?

¶ (i) Since each digit can be chosen in 5 ways,
     Number of 3 digit numbers = 5^3 = 125.
   (ii) To obtain a number less than 300, we can choose the most significant digit in 2 ways (i.e. 1 or 2) and the other 2 in 5 ways. Number of numbers less than 300 = 2×5×5 = 50.
   (iii) Even numbers end in 2 or 8, i.e. 2 possible choices. Number of even numbers = 5×5×2 = 50.
   (iv) Multiples of 5 end in 5, i.e. 1 possible choice. Number of multiples of 5 = 5×5×1 = 25.
   (v) If repetitions are not allowed, the 3 digit number is a permutation of 3 digits from 5.
     Therefore number of numbers = $^5P_3$ = $\frac{5!}{2!}$ = 60.

9. How many distinct arrangements of the letters a,a,a,c,c,i are there?

¶ Here, we have 3 a's, 2 c's and 1 i. Thus, using the formula for permutations when some objects are identical,

   Number of permutations = $\frac{6!}{3!2!1!}$ = 60.

10. A class of 28 pupils is to be divided into 4 groups of 7. In how many ways can this be done?

¶ The first group can be chosen in $^{28}C_7$ ways, the second in $^{21}C_7$ ways, the third in $^{14}C_7$ ways and the fourth in $^7C_7$ (i.e. 1 since there is no choice at this stage) ways.

Therefore number of ways $= {}^{28}C_7 \times {}^{21}C_7 \times {}^{14}C_7 \times {}^7C_7$

$$= \frac{28!}{21!7!} \times \frac{21!}{14!7!} \times \frac{14!}{7!7!} \times \frac{7!}{7!0!}$$

$$= \frac{28!}{(7!)^4} \approx 4.725 \times 10^{14}.$$

11. In how many ways can 11 identical sweets be divided among 5 children if the eldest is to receive three sweets and each of the others only two sweets?

¶ The number of possible selections of sweets for the eldest child is $^{11}C_3$, and then $^8C_2$, $^6C_2$, $^4C_2$ and $^2C_2$ for the others.

Therefore number of ways $= {}^{11}C_3 \times {}^8C_2 \times {}^6C_2 \times {}^4C_2 \times {}^2C_2$

$$= \frac{11!}{8!3!} \times \frac{8!}{6!2!} \times \frac{6!}{4!2!} \times \frac{4!}{2!2!} \times \frac{2!}{2!0!}$$

$$= \frac{11!}{3!(2!)^4} = 415,800.$$

12. In how many different ways can 6 identical balls be distributed among 10 boxes if no box can hold more than one ball?

¶ We must select 6 boxes out of 10 to put the balls in.

Therefore, number of ways $= {}^{10}C_6 = \frac{10!}{6!4!} = 210.$

13. A bag contains 5 white balls and 3 black balls. How many distinct ways are there of selecting three balls, two of which are white?

¶ We have to select 2 white balls and 1 black ball. The 2 white balls can be selected in $^5C_2$ ways and the 1 black in $^3C_1$ ways.

Therefore number of ways $= {}^5C_2 \times {}^3C_1 = 30.$

14. How many ways are there of selecting a hand of 4 cards containing 2 pairs of different values from an ordinary pack of 52 playing cards?

¶   The values of the 2 pairs can be selected in $^{13}C_2$ ways, since there are 13 different values. Since there are 4 cards of each value, each pair can be selected in $^4C_2$ ways.

Therefore number of ways = $^{13}C_2 \times {}^4C_2 \times {}^4C_2 = 2808$.

15. If six letters are chosen at random from the set {a,c,e,k,r,t}, what is the probability they spell *racket*
   (a) when the choice is made with replacement,
   (b) when the choice is made without replacement?

¶   (a) Number of possible words = 6^6 since each of the 6 letters can be chosen in any one of 6 ways. Since only one of these selections spells *racket*,

$$P(\text{letters spell } racket) = \frac{1}{6^6} = \frac{1}{46656}.$$

   (b) Number of possible words = $^6P_6$ corresponding to the permutations of 6 letters from 6. Again, only one of these spells *racket*, so that $P(\text{letters spell } racket) = \dfrac{1}{{}^6P_6} = \dfrac{1}{720}$.

16. If a random choice of six letters is made without replacement from the set {a,c,e,i,k,o,r,t} what is the probability of obtaining
   (a) *racket*, (b) *troika* or *rocket*?

¶   (a) Number of possible words = $^8P_6$, corresponding to the permutations of 6 letters from 8. Since only one of these spells *racket*,
$$P(racket) = \frac{1}{{}^8P_6} = \frac{1}{20160}.$$

   (b) Since two of these permutations spell *troika* or *rocket*,
$$P(troika \text{ or } rocket) = \frac{2}{{}^8P_6} = \frac{1}{10080}.$$

17. If a random choice of six letters is made with replacement from the set {a,c,i} what is the probability of obtaining the word *acacia*?

¶   There are 3 possibilities for each letter and so the number of possible words is 3^6. As only one spells *acacia*,
$$P(acacia) = 1/3^6 = 1/729.$$

18. Six members of the Mini-Metro Drivers Club go for a drink after a meeting of the Club. They all have identical cars and, being a little unsure of themselves at closing-time, they each choose a car at random out of the six to drive home. Calculate the probability that they all drive their own cars home.

¶ The number of possible selections of cars by drivers is $^6P_6$, i.e. 720. Only one of these corresponds to all drivers taking their own cars.

Therefore, required probability = 1/720.

19. The letters a,a,a,c,c,i are arranged in random order. What is the probability they spell *acacia*?

¶ Using the result of Question 9, there are 60 different permutations of the letters, one of which spells *acacia*.

Therefore, P(letters spell *acacia*) = 1/60.

20. A hand of 7 cards is dealt from a pack of 52. Find the probability the hand contains:

(i) 4 spades and 3 hearts, (ii) 3 spades and 1 heart, (iii) 2 Aces, (iv) exactly one Ace and exactly one King of the same suit.

¶ There are $^{52}C_7$ different hands of 7 cards selected from 52; we consider combinations and not permutations since the order of dealing the cards is not important.

(i) The 4 spades can be chosen in $^{13}C_4$ ways and the 3 spades in $^{13}C_3$ ways.

Therefore, P(4 spades and 3 hearts) = $\dfrac{^{13}C_4 \times {}^{13}C_3}{^{52}C_7} \approx 0.00153$.

(ii) The 3 spades can be chosen in $^{13}C_3$ ways, the 1 heart in $^{13}C_1$ ways and the other 3 cards in $^{26}C_3$ ways.

Thus, P(3 spades and 1 heart) = $\dfrac{^{13}C_3 \times {}^{13}C_1 \times {}^{26}C_3}{^{52}C_7} \approx 0.07226$.

(iii) The 2 Aces can be chosen in $^4C_2$ ways and the other 5 cards in $^{48}C_5$ ways.

Thus, P(2 Aces) = $\dfrac{^4C_2 \times {}^{48}C_5}{^{52}C_7} \approx 0.07679$.

(iv)   The 1 Ace can be chosen in $^4C_1$ ways, the King in just 1 way since it is fixed by the suit of the Ace, and the remaining 5 cards in $^{44}C_5$ ways. Thus,

$$P(\text{1 Ace and King of same suit}) = \frac{^4C_1 \times {}^{44}C_5}{^{52}C_7} \approx 0.03247.$$

21. A hand of 5 cards is dealt from a pack of 52.   Find the probability the hand contains

(i)   4 cards of the same value,

(ii)   3 cards of one value and 2 of another value,

(iii) 5 cards of different values,

(iv)   2 pairs, where a pair is two cards of different suits with the same value.

¶   There are $^{52}C_5$ different unordered selections of 5 cards from 52.

(i)   The four cards of the same value can be chosen in 13 ways (since there are 13 values), and the remaining card in 48 ways.   Thus,

$$P(\text{4 cards of same value}) = \frac{13 \times 48}{^{52}C_5} = \frac{1}{4165} \approx 2.4 \times 10^{-4}.$$

(ii)   There are respectively $^4C_3$ and $^4C_2$ ways of choosing 3 and 2 cards of a given value but the two values can be chosen in $^{13}C_2$ ways and assigned to the 3 cards of one value and the 2 cards of the other value in 2 ways.

Therefore, $P(\text{3 cards of one value and 2 of another})$

$$= \frac{2 \times {}^{13}C_2 \times {}^4C_3 \times {}^4C_2}{^{52}C_5} \approx 0.00144.$$

(iii) The 5 different values can be chosen in $^{13}C_5$ ways and each card in 4 ways, corresponding to the 4 suits.

Thus, $P(\text{5 different values}) = \dfrac{^{13}C_5 \times 4^5}{^{52}C_5} \approx 0.50703.$

(iv)   The values of the 2 pairs can be selected in $^{13}C_2$ ways, each of the pairs in $^4C_2$ ways and the 5th card in 44 ways.

Thus, $P(\text{2 pairs}) = \dfrac{^{13}C_2 \times ({}^4C_2)^2 \times 44}{^{52}C_5} \approx 0.04754.$

22. A lake contains n fish; m are caught, marked and then returned to the lake. What is the probability that a further sample of k fish will contain r marked fish? (Assume that every sample of size k is equally likely.)

¶ After the first marking, the lake contains m marked fish and (n−m) unmarked fish. In the second sample, the r marked fish can be chosen in ^mC_r ways and the (k−r) unmarked fish in $^{(n-m)}C_{(k-r)}$ ways. Since the k fish in the second sample can be chosen in ^nC_k ways it follows that

$$P(r \text{ marked fish in 2nd sample}) = \frac{^mC_r \times ^{(n-m)}C_{(k-r)}}{^nC_k}.$$

[Note that we require $r \leqslant m$ and $k-r \leqslant n-m$.]

23. A bag contains 3 black balls, 3 white balls and 3 red balls. A random sample of two balls is drawn without replacement. Find the probability that the balls have different colours.

¶ There are $^9C_2$, i.e. 36, ways of choosing two balls from nine.

There are $^3C_2$, i.e. 3, ways of choosing two black balls. Similarly there are 3 ways of choosing two white balls and 3 ways of choosing two red balls.

$$\text{So } P(\text{balls same colour}) = \frac{3+3+3}{36} = \frac{1}{4}$$

$$\text{and } P(\text{different colours}) = 1 - \frac{1}{4} = \frac{3}{4}.$$

24. Two letters are selected from the word MISSISSIPPI. Find the probability that they are the same.

¶ The number of ways of choosing 2 letters is $^{11}C_2$, i.e. 55.

Two S's can be chosen in $^4C_2$ ways, two I's in $^4C_2$ ways and two P's in $^2C_2$ ways.

$$\text{Hence } P(\text{letters are the same}) = \frac{^4C_2 + ^4C_2 + ^2C_2}{55} = \frac{13}{55}.$$

25. A box contains 20 items of which 3 are defective. A random sample of size 3 is taken without replacement. Calculate the respective probabilities that the sample contains 0,1,2,3 defective items.

¶ There are $^{20}C_3$ possible unordered selections of items. Consider the probability that there are k defectives, where k = 0,1,2 or 3. The k defectives can be chosen in $^{3}C_k$ ways and the 3-k non-defectives in $^{17}C_{3-k}$ ways.

Hence $P(\text{k defective items}) = \dfrac{^{3}C_k \times {^{17}C_{3-k}}}{^{20}C_3}$.

So $P(\text{0 defective items}) = \dfrac{^{17}C_3}{^{20}C_3} = \dfrac{680}{1140}$,

$P(\text{1 defective item}) = \dfrac{^{3}C_1 \times {^{17}C_2}}{^{20}C_3} = \dfrac{408}{1140}$,

$P(\text{2 defective items}) = \dfrac{^{3}C_2 \times {^{17}C_1}}{^{20}C_3} = \dfrac{51}{1140}$,

$P(\text{3 defective items}) = \dfrac{^{3}C_3}{^{20}C_3} = \dfrac{1}{1140}$.

Exercises 2.5 Conditional Probability

1. A coin is tossed 3 times. Consider the events

A = {at least 2 heads appear},

B = {2, but not 3, consecutive tails appear},

C = {at least 1 tail appears}.

Evaluate the conditional probabilities (i) $P(B|A)$, (ii) $P(C|A)$, (iii) $P(B|C)$, (iv) $P(A|C)$.

¶ The sample space is {HHH, HHT, HTH, HTT, THH, THT, TTH, TTT}.
Also A = {HHH, HHT, HTH, THH}, B = {HTT, TTH},
C = {HHT, HTH, HTT, THH, THT, TTH, TTT},
$A \cap B$ = $\emptyset$, $A \cap C$ = {HHT, HTH, THH}, $B \cap C$ = {HTT, TTH}.

Thus (i) $P(B|A) = \dfrac{P(B \cap A)}{P(A)} = 0$.

(ii) $P(C|A) = \dfrac{P(C \cap A)}{P(A)} = \dfrac{3/8}{4/8} = \dfrac{3}{4}$.

(iii) $P(B|C) = \dfrac{P(B \cap C)}{P(C)} = \dfrac{2/8}{7/8} = \dfrac{2}{7}$.

(iv) $P(A|C) = \dfrac{P(A \cap C)}{P(C)} = \dfrac{3/8}{7/8} = \dfrac{3}{7}$.

2. A fair die is rolled twice and the outcomes noted. Consider the events   A: the total score is at least 9,

   B: at least 1 six appears,

   C: both numbers are even.

Evaluate the conditional probabilities (i) $P(B|A)$, (ii) $P(A|B')$, (iii) $P(A|C)$, (iv) $P(C|B)$.

¶   The sample space is

(1,1)	(1,2)	(1,3)	(1,4)	(1,5)	†(1,6)
(2,1)	(2,2)*	(2,3)	(2,4)*	(2,5)	†(2,6)*
(3,1)	(3,2)	(3,3)	(3,4)	(3,5)	†(3,6)
(4,1)	(4,2)*	(4,3)	(4,4)*	(4,5)	†(4,6)*
(5,1)	(5,2)	(5,3)	(5,4)	(5,5)	†(5,6)
†(6,1)	†(6,2)*	†(6,3)	†(6,4)*	†(6,5)	†(6,6)*

Underlined outcomes correspond to A, those with a † to B, and those with a * to C. By enumeration,

(i) $P(B|A) = \dfrac{P(B \cap A)}{P(A)} = \dfrac{7/36}{10/36} = \dfrac{7}{10}$,

(ii) $P(A|B') = \dfrac{P(A \cap B')}{P(B')} = \dfrac{3/36}{25/36} = \dfrac{3}{25}$,

(iii) $P(A|C) = \dfrac{P(A \cap C)}{P(C)} = \dfrac{3/36}{9/36} = \dfrac{1}{3}$,

(iv) $P(C|B) = \dfrac{P(C \cap B)}{P(B)} = \dfrac{5/36}{11/36} = \dfrac{5}{11}$.

3. Two fair dice are thrown. What is the probability that both scores are odd given that the total score is even?

¶ $P(\text{both odd} | \text{total score even}) = \dfrac{P(\text{both odd \& total score even})}{P(\text{total score even})}$

   $= \dfrac{P(\text{both odd})}{P(\text{total score even})} = \dfrac{9/36}{18/36} = \dfrac{1}{2}$

by enumeration, using the sample space of Question 2 above.

4. A pair of fair dice is thrown. Find the probability that the sum is at least 9 if (a) 6 appears on the first die, (b) 6 appears on at least one of the dice.

¶   (a) $P(\text{sum} \geq 9 | \text{1st die is 6}) = \dfrac{P(\text{sum} \geq 9 \text{ and 1st die is 6})}{P(\text{1st die is 6})}$

   $= \dfrac{4/36}{1/6} = \dfrac{2}{3}$,

since the numerator corresponds to the outcomes $(6,3)$, $(6,4)$, $(6,5)$

and (6,6).

(b) $P(\text{sum} \geqslant 9 \,|\, \text{at least one 6 appears})$

$$= \frac{P(\text{sum} \geq 9 \text{ and at least one 6 appears})}{P(\text{at least one 6 appears})}$$

$$= \frac{7/36}{11/36} = \frac{7}{11}$$

by enumeration, using the sample space of Question 2 above.

5. Let A and B be events with $P(A) = 2/3$, $P(B) = 1/3$ and $P(A \cap B) = 1/6$. Find (i) $P(A \cup B)$, (ii) $P(A \,|\, B)$, (iii) $P(A \,|\, B')$, (iv) $P(B \,|\, A)$, (v) $P(A' \,|\, B)$, (vi) $P(A' \,|\, B')$.

¶ (i) $P(A \cup B) = P(A) + P(B) - P(A \cap B) = \frac{2}{3} + \frac{1}{3} - \frac{1}{6} = \frac{5}{6}$.

(ii) $P(A \,|\, B) = \frac{P(A \cap B)}{P(B)} = \frac{1/6}{1/3} = \frac{1}{2}$.

(iii) $P(A \,|\, B') = \frac{P(A \cap B')}{P(B')} = \frac{P(A) - P(A \cap B)}{1 - P(B)} = \frac{2/3 - 1/6}{1 - 1/3} = \frac{3}{4}$.

(iv) $P(B \,|\, A) = \frac{P(B \cap A)}{P(A)} = \frac{1/6}{2/3} = \frac{1}{4}$.

(v) $P(A' \,|\, B) = \frac{P(A' \cap B)}{P(B)} = \frac{P(B) - P(A \cap B)}{P(B)} = \frac{1/3 - 1/6}{1/3} = \frac{1}{2}$.

(vi) $P(A' \,|\, B') = \frac{P(A' \cap B')}{P(B')} = \frac{1 - P(A \cup B)}{1 - P(B)}$ (since $A' \cap B' = (A \cup B)'$)

$$= \frac{1 - 5/6}{1 - 1/3} = \frac{1}{4}.$$

6. Prove, using the rules of probability, that if $P(B) \neq 0$ then
$$P(A \,|\, B) + P(A' \,|\, B) = 1.$$
Verify that this result holds in Question 5 above.

¶ $\quad P(A \,|\, B) + P(A' \,|\, B) = \frac{P(A \cap B)}{P(B)} + \frac{P(A' \cap B)}{P(B)}$

$$= \frac{P(A \cap B) + P(A' \cap B)}{P(B)}$$

$$= \frac{P(B)}{P(B)} = 1.$$

In Question 5 above,
$$P(A \,|\, B) + P(A' \,|\, B) = \frac{1}{2} + \frac{1}{2} = 1 \quad \text{as required.}$$

7. If A and B are events with $P(A) = 1/5$, $P(B) = 3/5$ and $P(A \cup B) = 7/10$, find $P(A \,|\, B)$ and $P(B \,|\, A)$.

¶

$$P(A \cap B) = P(A) + P(B) - P(A \cup B)$$

$$= \frac{1}{5} + \frac{3}{5} - \frac{7}{10} = \frac{1}{10}.$$

Thus $\quad P(A|B) = \dfrac{P(A \cap B)}{P(B)} = \dfrac{1/10}{3/5} = \dfrac{1}{6}$

and $\quad P(B|A) = \dfrac{P(B \cap A)}{P(A)} = \dfrac{1/10}{1/5} = \dfrac{1}{2}.$

8. Find $P(B|A)$ if (i) A is a subset of B, (ii) A and B are mutually exclusive.

¶ (i) $\qquad P(B|A) = \dfrac{P(B \cap A)}{P(A)} = 1 \quad$ as $B \cap A = A$ if A is a subset of B.

(ii) $\qquad P(B|A) = \dfrac{P(B \cap A)}{P(A)} = 0 \quad$ if $A \cap B = \emptyset.$

9. In a nationwide examination in English and Mathematics, 85% passed in at least one subject, 55% passed in Mathematics and 65% passed in English. Given that a randomly selected examinee passed in English, what is the probability that he passed in Mathematics?

¶ Define events

$\qquad\qquad E$: examinee passes in English,

$\qquad\qquad M$: examinee passes in Mathematics.

Then $\qquad P(M \cap E) = P(M) + P(E) - P(M \cup E)$

$$= 0.55 + 0.65 - 0.85 = 0.35.$$

Thus $\qquad P(M|E) = \dfrac{P(M \cap E)}{P(E)} = \dfrac{0.35}{0.65} = \dfrac{7}{13}.$

10. The probability that a female lives to the age of 40 is 0.95 and the probability that a female lives to the age of 65 is 0.7. Calculate the probability that a female aged 40 lives to the age of 65.

¶ Define events

$\qquad\qquad A$: a female lives to the age of 40,

$\qquad\qquad B$: a female lives to the age of 65.

We require $P(B|A) = \dfrac{P(B \cap A)}{P(A)} = \dfrac{P(B)}{P(A)}, \quad$ as $B \cap A = B.$

Hence $\qquad P(B|A) = \dfrac{0.7}{0.95} = \dfrac{14}{19}.$

11. A hand of 5 cards is dealt from a pack of 52 well shuffled cards. Calculate the following conditional probabilities.
    (i) P(at least 1 diamond in the last 3 cards dealt|first 2 cards dealt were diamonds),
    (ii) P(at least 2 Aces|1 Ace is contained in the first 3 cards),
    (iii) P(2 pairs|first 2 cards form a pair).

¶   (i)   If the first 2 cards are diamonds, then the pack contains 50 cards, with only 11 diamonds after this. Then
           P(no diamond in last 3|first 2 are diamonds)
                 = P(no diamonds in 3 from the 'modified' pack)

$$= \frac{^{11}C_0 \times {}^{39}C_3}{^{50}C_3} = 0.46628.$$

           Therefore P(at least 1 diamond in last 3|first two are diamonds) = 1 - 0.46628 = 0.53372.

    (ii)   Consider P(not more than 1 Ace|1 Ace in first 3)
                 = P(no Aces in 2 cards drawn from a pack of 49 with 1 Ace removed)

$$= \frac{^{46}C_2}{^{49}C_2} \quad \text{(since there are 46 'non-Aces' left)}$$

                 = 0.88010.

           Therefore P(at least 2 Aces|1 Ace in first 3)
                 = 1 - P(not more than 1 Ace|1 Ace in first 3)
                 = 0.1199.

    (iii) P(2 pairs|first 2 cards form a pair)
                 = P(last 3 cards contain a pair and another card whose value differs from the values of the 2 pairs).

           The second pair can be chosen in $12 \times {}^4C_2$ ways, as there are 12 values left, and the other card can be chosen in 44 ways. In all there are $^{50}C_3$ possibilities for the last 3 cards and so the required probability is

$$\frac{12 \times {}^4C_2 \times 44}{^{50}C_3} = 0.16163.$$

12. Show that for any events A, B, C
$$P(A \cap B \cap C) = P(A)P(B|A)P(C|A \cap B).$$

¶
$$P((A \cap B) \cap C) = P(C|A \cap B)P(A \cap B)$$
$$= P(C|A \cap B)P(B|A)P(A)$$

by a double application of the multiplication rule. Furthermore, for any events $A, B, C, \ldots, D, E$
$$P(A \cap B \cap C \cap \ldots \cap D \cap E) = P(A|B \cap C \cap \ldots \cap D \cap E)P(B|C \cap \ldots \cap D \cap E) \ldots P(D|E)P(E).$$

13. A class has 15 boys and 5 girls. If three students are selected at random from the class what is the probability (i) that they are all boys, (ii) that there are two boys and a girl?

¶ Using the rule proved in Question 12,

(i) $P(\text{all boys}) = \dfrac{15}{20} \times \dfrac{14}{19} \times \dfrac{13}{18} = \dfrac{91}{228}$,

(ii) $P(\text{2 boys and 1 girl}) = 3 \times \dfrac{15}{20} \times \dfrac{14}{19} \times \dfrac{5}{18} = \dfrac{35}{76}$.

(The 3 arises from the 3 possible orders BBG, BGB, GBB, each having the same probability.)

14. A bag contains 9 white balls, 6 blue balls and 5 green balls. If three balls are selected at random without replacement find the probability that
(i) all three balls are of different colours,
(ii) two balls are white and one is green,
(iii) the first ball drawn is white and the other two are not white.

¶ (i) The probability the first is white, the second blue and the third green is $\dfrac{9}{20} \times \dfrac{6}{19} \times \dfrac{5}{18}$ using the rule proved in Question 12.

There are 6 different orders in which the balls can be chosen, all leading to three different colours, namely WBG, WGB, BWG, BGW, GBW, GWB. Each has the same probability and so

$$P(\text{all of different colours}) = 6 \times \dfrac{9}{20} \times \dfrac{6}{19} \times \dfrac{5}{18} = \dfrac{9}{38}.$$

Alternatively, using combinations, the probability is

$$\dfrac{{}^9C_1 \times {}^6C_1 \times {}^5C_1}{{}^{20}C_3} = \dfrac{9}{38} \quad \text{again.}$$

(ii) P(first two white, third green) $= \frac{9}{20} \times \frac{8}{19} \times \frac{5}{18}$.

The sequences WWG, WGW and GWW all have the same probability and so

$$P(\text{two white, one green}) = 3 \times \frac{9}{20} \times \frac{8}{19} \times \frac{5}{18} = \frac{3}{19}.$$

Alternatively, the required probability equals

$$\frac{^9C_2 \times {}^5C_1}{^{20}C_3} = \frac{3}{19} \quad \text{again.}$$

(iii) P(first ball white and other two not white) $= \frac{9}{20} \times \frac{11}{19} \times \frac{10}{18}$

$$= \frac{11}{76}$$

since there are 11 'non-white' balls initially.

Exercises 2.6 Independence

1. A fair coin is tossed 3 times and the outcomes are recorded. Let A be the event that there is at least one head in the first two tosses and let B be the event that a head appears on the third toss. Use the definition of independence to show that A and B are independent events.

¶   The sample space is {HHH, HHT, HTH, THH, TTH, THT, HTT, TTT}, and each outcome has probability 1/8. By enumeration,

$$P(A) = \frac{6}{8}, \quad P(B) = \frac{1}{2}, \quad P(A \cap B) = \frac{3}{8}.$$

Since $P(A \cap B) = P(A)P(B)$ the events are independent.

2. A fair die is rolled twice and the scores are recorded. Let A be the event that the first score is 6 and B the event that the second score is 5. Use the equally likely principle to demonstrate that the events A and B are independent.

¶   Clearly $P(A) = P(B) = 1/6$. There are 36 possible outcomes for the two scores and only one, (6,5), corresponds to $A \cap B$.

Hence $P(A \cap B) = \frac{1}{36} = P(A)P(B)$ and A and B are independent.

3. A fair coin is tossed twice. Consider the events

A: the first toss results in a head,

B: the second toss results in a tail,

C: the two outcomes are the same.

Prove that the events A, B, C are pairwise independent. Are the events A, B, C totally independent?

¶ The sample space is {TT, TH, HT, HH}.

By enumeration, using the equally likely principle,

$$P(A) = \frac{2}{4}, \quad P(B) = \frac{2}{4}, \quad P(C) = \frac{2}{4}, \quad P(B \cap C) = \frac{1}{4}, \quad P(C \cap A) = \frac{1}{4},$$

$$P(A \cap B) = \frac{1}{4}.$$

Hence $P(A \cap B) = P(A)P(B)$, $P(B \cap C) = P(B)P(C)$, $P(C \cap A) = P(C)P(A)$, so that A, B, C are pairwise independent.

Furthermore, $P(A \cap B \cap C) = 0$ since A, B, C cannot all occur simultaneously. Thus $P(A \cap B \cap C) \neq P(A)P(B)P(C)$ so that A, B, C are not totally independent.

4. A rifleman has probability 0.5 of hitting the target. Calculate the probability that in 6 independent shots the target is hit exactly 4 times.

¶ Let H and M denote respectively a hit and a miss. Then one possible sequence resulting in 4 hits is HHHHMM. This sequence has probability

$$\frac{1}{2} \times \frac{1}{2} \times \frac{1}{2} \times \frac{1}{2} \times \frac{1}{2} \times \frac{1}{2} = \frac{1}{64}.$$

Now there are $^6C_4$, i.e. 15, different sequences containing 4 H's and 2 M's. Thus

$$\text{required probability} = \frac{15}{64}.$$

5. In a girls' school the probability that a randomly selected girl is blue-eyed is 0.5 and that she is blonde is 0.55. What is wrong with the calculation that the probability that she is a blue-eyed blonde is 0.5 × 0.55 = 0.275?

¶ The calculation would be correct only if the events 'blue-eyed' and 'blonde' were independent of each other but this information is not given. See Question 4, page 27 for an example in which multiplying probabilities leads to the wrong answer.

6. Four tomato seeds are planted in a seed box. Each seed has probability 0.5 of germinating. Calculate
    (i)   the probability that all four seeds germinate,
    (ii)   the probability that no seeds germinate,
    (iii) the probability that at least one seed germinates.
    What assumption needs to be made to answer this question?

¶   (i) P(all seeds germinate) $= \frac{1}{2} \times \frac{1}{2} \times \frac{1}{2} \times \frac{1}{2} = \frac{1}{16}$.

    (ii) P(no seeds germinate) $= \frac{1}{2} \times \frac{1}{2} \times \frac{1}{2} \times \frac{1}{2} = \frac{1}{16}$.

    (iii) P(at least 1 germinates) $= 1 - P$(no seeds germinate)
$$= 1 - \frac{1}{16} = \frac{15}{16}.$$

We need to assume that the 4 seeds germinate independently of each other.

7. A bus route has 6 request stops. If the probability of stopping at each is p, determine the probability that the bus passes at least 3 stops in succession. What assumption needs to be made to answer this question?

¶   We assume that whether or not a bus passes a given stop is independent of its behaviour at other stops.
Now P(bus passes all stops) $= (1-p)^6$ as it passes each stop with probability $1-p$. Also P(passes 5 stops) $= 6p(1-p)^5$, since there are 6 possibilities for the stop at which it stops. In either of these cases it will pass at least 3 in succession.
The outcomes corresponding to passing 4 stops, including at least 3 in succession, are PPPPSS, SPPPPS, SSPPPP, PPPSSP, PPPSPS, SPPPSP, PSPPPS, PSSPPP, SPSPPP.
Each has probability $p^2(1-p)^4$ and so
$$P(\text{passes 4 stops and at least 3 in succession}) = 9p^2(1-p)^4.$$

Finally, P(passes 3 stops, all in succession)
$$= P(\{\text{PPPSSS, SPPPSS, SSPPPS, SSSPPP}\}) = 4p^3(1-p)^3.$$
Therefore the required probability $= (1-p)^6 + 6p(1-p)^5 + 9p^2(1-p)^4$
$$+ 4p^3(1-p)^3.$$

8. If A and B are independent events, prove that the pairs of events (A,B'), (A',B) and (A',B') are also independent.

¶
$$P(A \cap B') = P(A) - P(A \cap B)$$
$$= P(A) - P(A)P(B) \quad \text{(as } A,B \text{ are independent)}$$
$$= P(A)(1-P(B))$$
$$= P(A)P(B').$$

Hence A and B' are independent. The proof for A' and B follows by interchanging A and B.

$$P(A' \cap B') = P((A \cup B)') = 1 - P(A \cup B)$$
$$= 1 - P(A) - P(B) + P(A \cap B)$$
$$= 1 - P(A) - P(B) + P(A)P(B)$$
$$\text{(by independence)}$$
$$= (1-P(A))(1-P(B))$$
$$= P(A')P(B').$$

Again A' and B' are independent.

9. A and B are independent events such that $P(A \cup B) = 0.44$ and $P(A \cap B) = 0.06$. Find the possible values of $P(A)$ and $P(B)$.

¶ Let $P(A) = p$, $P(B) = q$.
$$P(A \cap B) = P(A)P(B) = pq = 0.06,$$
$$P(A \cup B) = P(A) + P(B) - P(A \cap B) = p+q-pq = 0.44.$$
Hence $p+q = 0.50$.

Then $p + \dfrac{0.06}{p} = 0.5$ and $100p^2-50p+6 = 0$,
$$\text{i.e.} \quad (10p-2)(10p-3) = 0.$$
Hence $p=0.2$ or 0.3 and $q=0.3$ or 0.2.
Therefore $P(A) = 0.2$, $P(B) = 0.3$ or vice versa.

10. Show that, in general, mutually exclusive events are not independent.

¶ Let A,B be mutually exclusive events.
Then $P(A \cap B) = 0 \neq P(A)P(B)$ unless either $P(A) = 0$ or $P(B) = 0$ (or both) which is not true in general.

11. Two people A,B take turns to play a game in which the first person to obtain a 6 when rolling a die wins. If A starts the game, what is the probability that B will win the game (a) on his 1st throw, (b) on his 2nd throw, (c) on his nth throw? Using these results, calculate the probability that B will win the game.

¶   Let A† denote the event that A obtains a six and A* the event that he does not, with B†, B* similarly defined.

(a) P(B wins on his first throw) = P(A*B†) = $\frac{5}{6} \times \frac{1}{6} = \frac{5}{36}$,

where A*B† denotes the event that A fails at his first attempt and then B succeeds at his first attempt.

(b) P(B wins on his second throw) = P(A*B*A*B†) = $(\frac{5}{6})^3 \times \frac{1}{6} = \frac{125}{1296}$.

(c) P(B wins on his nth throw) = $P(\underbrace{\text{A*B*....A*B*A*}}_{\text{2n-1 throws}}\text{B†})$

$$= (\frac{5}{6})^{2n-1} \times \frac{1}{6}.$$

So P(B wins game) = $\frac{1}{6}(\frac{5}{6} + (\frac{5}{6})^3 + (\frac{5}{6})^5 + ...)$

$$= \frac{1}{6} \cdot \frac{5/6}{1-(5/6)^2} \quad \text{(summing the geometric series)}$$

$$= \frac{5}{11}.$$

12. Two riflemen A,B have independent probabilities 0.7 and 0.3 respectively of hitting the target.

(i)   If each fires twice what is the probability that the target will be hit by at least one shot?

(ii) If B fires once only, how many times must A fire in order to make the probability of hitting the target at least 0.999?

¶   (i) P(target hit at least once) = $1 - P$(A and B both miss twice)
$$= 1 - (1-0.7)^2(1-0.3)^2 = 0.9559,$$

since A misses with probability 1-0.7 and B with probability 1-0.3.

(ii) Suppose B fires once and A fires n times.

P(all miss) = $(1-0.3) \times (1-0.7)^n = 0.7 \times 0.3^n$.

We require P(all miss) $\leqslant 0.001$ since P(at least 1 hit) must be at least 0.999 and the events are complementary.

So $0.7 \times 0.3^n \leqslant 0.001$.

Taking logs, $\log 0.7 + n \log 0.3 \leqslant \log 0.001$

and $n \geqslant \dfrac{\log 0.001 - \log 0.7}{\log 0.3}$

$$= 5.44.$$

(The inequality $\leqslant$ becomes $\geqslant$ on dividing by $\log 0.3$ which is a negative number.)

As n must be an integer we have $n \geqslant 6$.

Exercises 2.7 Bayes' Theorem

1. Two bags are filled with a mixture of black and white balls. One bag contains 7 white and 3 black balls whilst the other contains 4 white and 6 black balls. If a bag is selected at random and a ball is drawn from it at random, what is the probability that it is white?

¶ Let Bag I contain 7 white and 3 black balls and Bag II contain 4 white and 6 black balls. By the Law of Total Probability
P(white drawn) = P(white drawn|Bag I chosen)P(Bag I chosen)
$\qquad\qquad$ + P(white drawn|Bag II chosen)P(Bag II chosen)
$$= \frac{7}{10} \times \frac{1}{2} + \frac{4}{10} \times \frac{1}{2} = \frac{11}{20}.$$

2. Two fair coins and one double-headed coin are placed in a bag. A coin is selected at random and tossed. What is the probability that the result is a head?

¶ Using the Law of Total Probability
P(head) = P(head|fair coin)P(fair coin)
$\qquad\qquad$ + P(head|double-headed coin)P(double-headed coin)
$$= \frac{1}{2} \times \frac{2}{3} + 1 \times \frac{1}{3} = \frac{2}{3}.$$

3. In a mass-screening programme, a test indicates that a healthy person has a disease with probability 0.05. For a person with the disease there is a probability of 0.99 that the test will indicate its presence. If 5% of the population have the disease, what is the probability that the test will indicate the presence of the disease for a randomly selected person?

¶ Using the Law of Total Probability,
P(indicates disease)
$\quad$ = P(indicates disease|disease present)P(disease present)
$\quad$ + P(indicates disease|disease not present)P(disease not present)
$\quad$ = $0.99 \times 0.05 + 0.05 \times 0.95 = 0.097.$

4. Two boxes contain white and black balls in various proportions, the total number of balls in each box being equal to 10. If a box is

chosen at random and a ball is selected at random from it then the probability of that ball being white is 2/5. If one of the boxes contains 7 white balls what is the constitution of the other box?

¶ Suppose Box I contains 7 white and 3 black balls, while Box II contains x white and 10-x black.

P(white chosen) = P(white|Box I chosen)P(Box I chosen)
+ P(white|Box II chosen)P(Box II chosen)

$$= \frac{7}{10} \times \frac{1}{2} + \frac{x}{10} \times \frac{1}{2} = \frac{2}{5}.$$

Hence x = 1.

5. A bag contains 7 white balls, 2 red balls and 3 blue balls. Two balls are chosen at random without replacement. What is the probability that the second ball selected is blue?

¶ By the Law of Total Probability
P(second is blue) = P(second is blue|first is blue)P(first is blue)
+ P(second is blue|first is not blue)P(first is not blue)

$$= \frac{2}{11} \times \frac{3}{12} + \frac{3}{11} \times \frac{9}{12} = \frac{1}{4}.$$

Alternatively it could be argued that all 12 balls are equally likely to be chosen as the second, and 3 are blue; thus the required probability is 3/12.

6. Two bags contain white and black balls in various proportions. Bag 1 contains 6 white and 9 black balls whilst bag 2 contains 10 white and 5 black balls. A ball is selected at random from bag 1 and placed in bag 2. If two balls are now selected from bag 2, what is the probability that both balls are white?

¶ Define events A: the transferred ball is white,
B: the selected balls are white.
Then A' is the event that the transferred ball is black.
By the Law of Total Probability

$$P(B) = P(B|A)P(A) + P(B|A')P(A')$$

$$= \frac{11}{16} \times \frac{10}{15} \times \frac{6}{15} + \frac{10}{16} \times \frac{9}{15} \times \frac{9}{15} = \frac{49}{120}$$

since, for example, $P(B|A) = P$(two balls chosen are white when the bag contains 11 white and 5 black balls) $= \frac{11}{16} \times \frac{10}{15}$.

7. A double-headed coin and a fair coin are placed in a bag. A coin is selected at random and tossed, the outcome being a head. What is the probability that on a second toss a head will also appear?

¶ We first use Bayes' Theorem to find the probability that the selected coin is fair, given that a head occurs on the first toss. Define events F: the coin is fair,

DH: the coin is double-headed,

H_1: a head occurs on the first toss,

H_2: a head occurs on the second toss.

F and DH are mutually exclusive and exhaustive, so by Bayes' Theorem

$$P(F|H_1) = \frac{P(H_1|F)P(F)}{P(H_1|F)P(F) + P(H_1|DH)P(DH)}$$

$$= \frac{\frac{1}{2} \times \frac{1}{2}}{\frac{1}{2} \times \frac{1}{2} + 1 \times \frac{1}{2}} = \frac{1}{3}.$$

Hence $P(DH|H_1) = \frac{2}{3}$.

Thus after the first toss the probability that the coin is fair is 1/3 and that it is double-headed is 2/3.

Now by the Law of Total Probability

$$P(H_2) = P(H_2|F)P(F) + P(H_2|DH)P(DH)$$

$$= \frac{1}{2} \times \frac{1}{3} + 1 \times \frac{2}{3} = \frac{5}{6}.$$

8. In a multiple choice examination paper n answers are given for each question. Suppose a candidate knows the answer to a question with probability p. If he does not know it he guesses, choosing one of the answers at random. Show that if his answer is correct, the probability that he knew the answer is $\frac{np}{1+(n-1)p}$.

¶ Define events C: the answer is correct,

G: he guesses the answer,

K: he knew the answer,

so that G and K are complementary.

By Bayes' Theorem

$$P(K|C) = \frac{P(C|K)P(K)}{P(C|K)P(K) + P(C|G)P(G)}$$

$$= \frac{1 \times p}{1 \times p + \frac{1}{n} \times (1-p)} \qquad \text{as all n answers are equally likely if he guesses.}$$

$$= \frac{np}{1 + (n-1)p}.$$

9. Three urns A,B,C each contain a mixture of black and white balls. Urn A contains 5 black and 2 white, urn B contains 3 black and 6 white and urn C contains 4 black and 4 white balls. A ball is drawn at random from a randomly selected urn. If the ball is white, what is the probability it came from urn C?

¶ Let A,B,C denote the events that the urn chosen was A,B,C respectively. Let W be the event that the chosen ball was white. By Bayes' Theorem

$$P(C|W) = \frac{P(W|C)P(C)}{P(W|A)P(A) + P(W|B)P(B) + P(W|C)P(C)}$$

$$= \frac{\frac{4}{8}\times\frac{1}{3}}{\frac{2}{7}\times\frac{1}{3} + \frac{6}{9}\times\frac{1}{3} + \frac{4}{8}\times\frac{1}{3}} = \frac{21}{61}.$$

10. A chest has 3 drawers. The first contains two gold coins, the second contains a gold and silver coin and the third has two silver coins. A drawer is chosen at random and from it a coin is chosen at random. What is the probability that the coin still remaining in the chosen drawer is gold given that the coin chosen is silver?

¶ Define events GG: the chosen drawer has 2 gold coins,
GS: the chosen drawer has 1 gold and 1 silver coin,
SS: the chosen drawer has 2 silver coins,
S: the coin chosen is silver.

We require $P(GS|S)$. By Bayes' Theorem

$$P(GS|S) = \frac{P(S|GS)P(GS)}{P(S|GG)P(GG) + P(S|GS)P(GS) + P(S|SS)P(SS)}$$

$$= \frac{\frac{1}{2}\times\frac{1}{3}}{0\times\frac{1}{3} + \frac{1}{2}\times\frac{1}{3} + 1\times\frac{1}{3}} = \frac{1}{3}.$$

11. Three factories A,B,C all produce identical items. The outputs of the factories are in the ratios 2:1:1 respectively. The proportion of defective items produced by factory A is 0.02 whilst those of B and C are 0.03 and 0.04 respectively. If the outputs of the three factories are pooled what is the probability that an item selected at random is defective?

¶   Define events A: the item is produced at factory A,

B: the item is produced at factory B,

C: the item is produced at factory C,

D: the item is defective.

Since the outputs are in the ratios 2:1:1

$$P(A) = \frac{1}{2}, \quad P(B) = \frac{1}{4}, \quad P(C) = \frac{1}{4}.$$

By the Law of Total Probability

$$P(D) = P(D|A)P(A) + P(D|B)P(B) + P(D|C)P(C)$$

$$= 0.02 \times \frac{1}{2} + 0.03 \times \frac{1}{4} + 0.04 \times \frac{1}{4}$$

$$= \frac{11}{400}.$$

12. Factories A,B and C produce identical items. The outputs of these factories are in the ratios 3:4:5 respectively. The probability of producing a defective item is proportional to the output of the factory. If an item, selected at random from the pooled output of the three factories, is found to be defective what is the probability that it came from factory C?

¶   Using the notation defined in Question 11 above,

$$P(A) = 3k, \quad P(B) = 4k, \quad P(C) = 5k$$

for some k. Since they must sum to 1, k = 1/12.

By Bayes' Theorem

$$P(C|D) = \frac{P(D|C)P(C)}{P(D|A)P(A) + P(D|B)P(B) + P(D|C)P(C)}$$

The probability that an item is defective is proportional to the output of the factory where it is produced. Hence

$$P(D|A) = 3\alpha, \quad P(D|B) = 4\alpha, \quad P(D|C) = 5\alpha$$

for some constant α.

Therefore

$$P(C|D) = \frac{5\alpha \times \frac{5}{12}}{3\alpha \times \frac{3}{12} + 4\alpha \times \frac{4}{12} + 5\alpha \times \frac{5}{12}} = \frac{1}{2}.$$

Miscellaneous Problems

1. The probability that Jane can solve a certain problem is 0.4 and that Alice can solve it is 0.3. If they both try independently what is the probability that it is solved?

¶ P(problem not solved) = P(Jane fails and Alice fails)

$\quad\quad\quad\quad\quad$ = P(Jane fails)P(Alice fails)$\quad$ (by independence)

$\quad\quad\quad\quad\quad$ = $(1-0.4)(1-0.3)$

$\quad\quad\quad\quad\quad$ = 0.42.

Hence P(problem solved) = 0.58.

2. Consider a family with two children. If each child is as likely to be a boy as a girl what is the probability that both children are boys

(i) given that the older child is a boy,

(ii) given that at least one of the children is a boy?

¶ We assume that the sexes of the children are independent.

(i) $\quad P$(both boys|older is a boy) $= \dfrac{P(\text{both boys and older is a boy})}{P(\text{older is a boy})}$

$\quad\quad\quad = \dfrac{P(\text{both boys})}{P(\text{older is a boy})} \quad = \dfrac{1/4}{1/2} = \dfrac{1}{2}.$

(ii) P(both boys|at least 1 boy) $= \dfrac{P(\text{both boys and at least 1 boy})}{P(\text{at least 1 boy})}$

$\quad\quad\quad = \dfrac{P(\text{both boys})}{1 - P(\text{both girls})} \quad = \dfrac{1/4}{1 - 1/4} = \dfrac{1}{3}.$

3. A box of twelve items contains 3 defective ones. A sample of 4 items is chosen at random without replacement. Find the probability the sample contains (i) 1 defective item, (ii) no defective items, (iii) at least 1 defective item.

¶ The sample of 4 items can be chosen in $^{12}C_4 = 495$ ways.

(i) Since there are 3 defective and 9 non-defective items,

$\quad\quad$ number of ways of selecting 1 defective = $^{3}C_1 = 3$,

$\quad\quad$ number of ways of selecting 3 non-defectives = $^{9}C_3 = 84$.

$\quad$ Hence P(1 defective) $= \dfrac{3 \times 84}{495} = \dfrac{28}{55}.$

(ii) 4 non-defective items can be selected in $^{9}C_4 = 126$ ways.

$\quad$ Hence P(no defective) $= \dfrac{126}{495} = \dfrac{14}{55}.$

(iii) P(at least 1 defective) = $1 - P$(no defectives)

$\quad\quad\quad\quad = \dfrac{41}{55}.$

4. A system consists of two components, A and B. Suppose that $P(A$ fails$) = 0.2$, $P(A$ and B both fail$) = 0.15$ and $P(B$ fails alone$) = 0.15$. Find $P(A$ fails$|B$ has failed$)$ and $P(A$ fails alone$)$.

¶ $P(A$ fails$|B$ has failed$) = \dfrac{P(A \text{ fails and B fails})}{P(B \text{ fails})}$

Now $P(B$ fails$) = P(B$ fails alone$) + P(A$ and B both fail$)$
$$= 0.15 + 0.15 = 0.3.$$
Hence $P(A$ fails$|B$ has failed$) = \dfrac{0.15}{0.3} = \dfrac{1}{2}.$

$P(A$ fails alone$) = P(A$ fails$) - P(A$ and B both fail$)$
$$= 0.2 - 0.15 = 0.05.$$

5. If 1% of items in a large batch are defective how large must a random sample be if the probability it contains at least one defective item is to exceed 0.9?

¶ Let the sample contain n items.
Then P(at least 1 defective)$ = 1 - P(0$ defectives$)$
$$= 1 - 0.99^n$$
as P(item defective)$ = 0.01$.
We require $1 - 0.99^n > 0.9$, i.e. $0.99^n < 0.1$.
Taking logs, $n \log 0.99 < \log 0.1$

$$n > \frac{\log 0.1}{\log 0.99} = 229.1$$

(The inequality changes direction as $\log 0.99$ is negative.)
Since n must be an integer, the minimum value is 230.

6. A bag contains n black balls and n white balls. A random sample of two balls is drawn without replacement. Find the probability that the pair will consist of one black and one white ball.

¶ P(one black and one white)$ = \dfrac{{}^n C_1 \times {}^n C_1}{{}^{2n} C_2} = \dfrac{n}{2n-1}$

as there are ${}^{2n} C_2$ ways of choosing the balls, ${}^n C_1$ ways of choosing a black and ${}^n C_1$ ways of choosing a white.

7. Prove that if $P(A \cup B) = P(A \cap B)$ then $P(A) = P(B)$.

¶   Let $P(A \cap B) = P(A \cup B) = p$.

As $A \cap B \subseteq A \subseteq A \cup B$, $P(A \cap B) \leqslant P(A) \leqslant P(A \cup B)$,

i.e. $p \leqslant P(A) \leqslant p$, and so $P(A) = p$.

Similarly $P(B) = p$. Therefore $P(A) = P(B)$.

8. Let A be the event that a family has children of both sexes and let B be the event that the family has at most 1 girl. If the family has n children find the value of n for which A and B are independent. (Assume that each child is equilikely to be male or female, independently of all other children.)

¶
$$P(A) = 1 - P(\text{all girls or all boys})$$
$$= 1 - P(\text{all girls}) - P(\text{all boys})$$
$$= 1 - (\tfrac{1}{2})^n - (\tfrac{1}{2})^n$$
$$= 1 - (\tfrac{1}{2})^{n-1}.$$

$$P(B) = P(0 \text{ girls}) + P(1 \text{ girl}).$$

Now $P(1 \text{ girl}) = n(\tfrac{1}{2})^n$ since the probability of a given sequence of n-1 boys and 1 girl is $(\tfrac{1}{2})^n$ and there are n such sequences, corresponding to the n possibilities for the position of the girl.

$$\text{Thus } P(B) = (\tfrac{1}{2})^n + n(\tfrac{1}{2})^n = \frac{n+1}{2^n}.$$

Also $P(A \cap B) = P(\text{children of both sexes and at least 1 girl})$
$$= P(1 \text{ girl})$$
$$= \frac{n}{2^n} \quad \text{as above.}$$

A and B are independent if $P(A \cap B) = P(A)P(B)$, i.e. if
$$\frac{n}{2^n} = \frac{n+1}{2^n}(1 - \frac{1}{2^{n-1}}).$$

Simplifying, this becomes $n+1 = 2^{n-1}$ and the only solution is n=3.

9. 10% of the boys in a school are left-handed. Of those who are left-handed, 80% are left-footed; of those who are right-handed, 15% are left-footed. If a boy, selected at random, is left-footed, use Bayes' Theorem to calculate the probability that he is left-handed.

¶   In the obvious notation

$$P(LH|LF) = \frac{P(LF|LH)P(LH)}{P(LF|LH)P(LH) + P(LF|RH)P(RH)}$$

$$= \frac{0.8 \times 0.1}{0.8 \times 0.1 + 0.15 \times 0.9} = \frac{16}{43}.$$

10. Use the following method to solve Question 9. Assume that there are 1000 boys in the school, and calculate the number of boys who are (i) left-handed and left-footed, (ii) right-handed and left-footed. Hence use the equally likely principle to find the required probability.

¶   Number of left-handers = 1000×0.1 = 100.

Number of left-handers who are left-footed = 100×0.8 = 80.

Number of right-handers = 1000-100 = 900.

Number of right-handers who are left-footed = 900×0.15 = 135.

There are therefore 135+80 = 215 left-footers in the school, 80 of whom are left-footed.

Thus, required probability = $\frac{80}{215} = \frac{16}{43}$.

11. Two schools I, II allow selected pupils to sit O-level Mathematics at the end of their fourth year. Past records show that in School I, 40% of these pupils obtain Grade A, 35% obtain Grade B and 25% obtain Grade C. In School II, 55% obtain Grade A, 30% obtain Grade B and 15% obtain Grade C. In a particular year, 30 pupils from School I and 20 pupils from School II sit O-level Mathematics at the end of their fourth year. If 2 pupils are selected at random, one from each school, what is the probability that

(i)   they both obtain Grade A,

(ii)   they both obtain the same grade,

(iii) the pupil from School I obtains a better grade than the pupil from School II?

A pupil is selected at random from the 50 examinees in both schools. If he is found to have obtained a Grade A, what is the probability that he comes from School I?

¶   (i)   P(both obtain A)

= P(pupil from I obtains A)×P(pupil from II obtains A)

= 0.4×0.55   (by independence)

= 0.22

58

(ii) $P(\text{same grade}) = P(\text{both obtain A}) + P(\text{both obtain B})$
$$+ P(\text{both obtain C})$$
$$= 0.4 \times 0.55 + 0.35 \times 0.3 + 0.25 \times 0.15 \quad \text{(as above)}$$
$$= 0.3625$$

(iii) In the obvious notation

$P(\text{I better than II}) = P(\text{I gets A and II gets B or C})$
$$+ P(\text{I gets B and II gets C})$$
$$= 0.4 \times (0.3 + 0.15) + 0.35 \times 0.15$$
$$= 0.2325.$$

$$P(\text{from I}|\text{gets A}) = \frac{P(\text{gets A}|\text{from I})P(\text{from I})}{P(\text{gets A}|\text{from I})P(\text{from I})+P(\text{gets A}|\text{from II})P(\text{II})}$$

$$= \frac{0.4 \times 30/50}{0.4 \times 30/50 + 0.55 \times 20/50}$$

$$= \frac{12}{23}.$$

12. Let A, B, C be events such that $P(A) = 1/2$, $P(B') = 3/4$, $P(A|B) = 2/3$, $P(C) = 1/2$, $P(A \cap C' \cap B') = 1/4$ and $P(A|C) = 1/4$. Find (i) $P(A \cap B)$, (ii) $P(A \cup B)$, (iii) $P(A|B')$, (iv) $P(A \cap C)$, (v) $P(A \cap B \cap C)$.

¶   (i)
$$P(A \cap B) = P(A|B)P(B)$$
$$= P(A|B)(1 - P(B'))$$
$$= \frac{2}{3} \times \frac{1}{4} = \frac{1}{6}.$$

(ii)
$$P(A \cup B) = P(A) + P(B) - P(A \cap B)$$
$$= \frac{1}{2} + (1 - \frac{3}{4}) - \frac{1}{6}$$
$$= \frac{7}{12}.$$

(iii)
$$P(A|B') = \frac{P(A \cap B')}{P(B')}$$
$$= \frac{P(A) - P(A \cap B)}{P(B')}$$
$$= \frac{\frac{1}{2} - \frac{1}{6}}{\frac{3}{4}} = \frac{4}{9}.$$

(iv)
$$P(A \cap C) = P(A|C)P(C)$$
$$= \frac{1}{4} \times \frac{1}{2} = \frac{1}{8}.$$

(v)
$$P(A) = P(A \cap (B \cup C)) + P(A \cap (B \cup C)')$$
$$= P((A \cap B) \cup (A \cap C)) + P(A \cap B' \cap C')$$
$$= P(A \cap B) + P(A \cap C) - P(A \cap B \cap C) + P(A \cap B' \cap C').$$

Hence $\qquad \frac{1}{2} = \frac{1}{6} + \frac{1}{8} - P(A \cap B \cap C) + \frac{1}{4}$

and $\qquad\qquad P(A \cap B \cap C) = \frac{1}{24}.$

13. A bag contains ten balls of which seven are blue and three are white. Two balls are chosen at random, without replacement. What is the probability that they are both blue? What is the probability that one is blue and one is white? A third ball is now drawn at random from the remaining balls in the bag. Find the probability that it is blue.

¶ $P(\text{both blue}) = \frac{7}{10} \times \frac{6}{9} = \frac{21}{45}.$

$P(\text{one blue, one white}) = P(\text{first blue, second white})$
$$+ P(\text{first white, second blue})$$
$$= \frac{7}{10} \times \frac{3}{9} + \frac{3}{10} \times \frac{7}{9} = \frac{21}{45}$$

Also $P(\text{both white}) = \frac{3}{10} \times \frac{2}{9} = \frac{3}{45}.$

Let these events correspond to A_1, A_2, A_3 respectively. Then
$P(\text{third blue}) = P(\text{third blue}|A_1)P(A_1) + P(\text{third blue}|A_2)P(A_2)$
$$+ P(\text{third blue}|A_3)P(A_3)$$
$$= \frac{5}{8} \times \frac{21}{45} + \frac{6}{8} \times \frac{21}{45} + \frac{7}{8} \times \frac{3}{45} = \frac{7}{10}$$

since, for example, $P(\text{third blue}|A_1) = \frac{5}{8}$ as there are 5 blue balls out of 8 if the first two drawn were blue.

A simple intuitive argument is that all 10 balls have the same probability of being the third one drawn, and so the probability it is blue is 7/10.

14. A bag contains 3 white and 2 black balls. Two players A and B use this to play a game. A ball is drawn at random from the bag and then replaced. If the ball drawn is white A wins a point. If the ball is black, however, A loses all his accumulated points and B scores a point. The game is continued until one player reaches three points and wins. Show that the probability that B takes a lead of one point to nil is 98/125 and hence find the probability that A wins the game.

¶ Let W,B denote white and black respectively. The possible sequences of colours leading to B leading 1-0 are

$$B, \quad WB, \quad WWB.$$

So $P(\text{B leads } 1\text{-}0) = \frac{2}{5} + \frac{3}{5}\times\frac{2}{5} + \frac{3}{5}\times\frac{3}{5}\times\frac{2}{5} = \frac{98}{125}.$

B wins if this happens 3 times, and so

$$P(\text{B wins}) = (98/125)^3.$$

Hence
$$P(\text{A wins}) = 1 - \left(\frac{98}{125}\right)^3 = 0.5181.$$

15. Which is more likely - one six in 4 throws of a fair die or two sixes in 8 throws of a fair die?

¶ $P(1 \text{ six in } 4 \text{ throws}) = 4 \times \frac{1}{6} \times \left(\frac{5}{6}\right)^3 = 0.3858.$

since the probability of not getting a six is $\frac{5}{6}$. The 4 corresponds to the 4 possible positions of the six in the sequence of scores.

In a sequence of 8 scores, 2 sixes can occur in $^8C_2$ positions.

Hence $P(2 \text{ sixes in } 8 \text{ throws}) = {}^8C_2 \times \left(\frac{1}{6}\right)^2 \times \left(\frac{5}{6}\right)^6$

$$= 0.2605.$$

Hence the former is more likely.

16. If A and B are any events show that
    (i)   if $B \subseteq A$ then $P(A-B) = P(A) - P(B)$,
    (ii) $P(A \Delta B) = P(A) + P(B) - 2P(A \cap B)$, where Δ is the *symmetric difference* defined by
    $$A \Delta B = (A-B) \cup (B-A).$$

¶ (i)
$$P(A-B) = P(A \cap B')$$
$$= P(A) - P(A \cap B)$$
$$= P(A) - P(B) \quad \text{since } P(A \cap B) = P(B) \text{ if } B \subseteq A.$$

(ii)
$$P(A \Delta B) = P((A \cap B') \cup (A' \cap B))$$
$$= P(A \cap B') + P(A' \cap B)$$
(since $(A \cap B')$ and $(A' \cap B)$ are mutually exclusive)
$$= P(A) - P(A \cap B) + P(B) - P(A \cap B)$$
$$= P(A) + P(B) - 2P(A \cap B).$$

17. In a town of n+1 inhabitants a person tells a rumour to a second person who in turn repeats it to a third, etc. At each stage the

recipient of the rumour is chosen at random (i.e. with equal probability) from the n people available. Find the probability that if the rumour is told r times it will never be (i) told to the originator, (ii) told to any person more than once.

¶ (i) On the first telling the rumour can be told to any of n people but thereafter it can be told only to n-1 out of n if it is not to be told to the originator.

Therefore the required probability = $(\frac{n-1}{n})^{r-1}$.

(ii) The originator can of course tell the rumour to any of n inhabitants without telling it to someone who has already been told. The second person can also tell it to any of n people (including the originator) but thereafter the number of people to whom the rumour can be told decreases by one on each occasion if it is not to be told to any person more than once. If r < n+1 then, multiplying conditional probabilities, we have

P(Rumour not told to any person more than once)

$$= \frac{n}{n} \times \frac{n}{n} \times \frac{n-1}{n} \times \frac{n-2}{n} \times \ldots \times \frac{n-r+2}{n}$$

$$= \frac{n(n-1)\ldots(n-r+2)}{n^{r-1}}$$

$$= \frac{{}^{n}P_{r-1}}{n^{r-1}}$$

If r > n+1 then the required probability is zero.

N.B. It would be more realistic if at each stage the teller was not allowed to tell the rumour to the person who told the rumour to him or her. If this restriction were to be imposed then the required probabilities in (i) and (ii) would be

$$(\frac{n-2}{n-1})^{r-2} \quad \text{and} \quad \frac{{}^{n-1}P_{r-2}}{(n-1)^{r-2}} \quad \text{respectively.}$$

18. A packet containing six sweets of different colours is passed down a queue of six children, none of whom wants the green sweet. If each child draws one sweet at random from those remaining find the probability that the unlucky one will be (a) the first in the line, (b) the third in the line, (c) the last in the line.

¶ (a) P(first child chooses the green sweet) = $\frac{1}{6}$.

(b) If the third child chooses it, the first two must choose a different one. Thus the required probability is
$$\frac{5}{6} \times \frac{4}{5} \times \frac{1}{4} = \frac{1}{6}.$$

(c) Similarly

P(last child chooses the green sweet) = $\frac{5}{6} \times \frac{4}{5} \times \frac{3}{4} \times \frac{2}{3} \times \frac{1}{2} \times \frac{1}{1} = \frac{1}{6}$

as the first five must not choose it.

Alternatively we could argue that each child is equally likely to choose any one of the sweets and so the probability for each child is $\frac{1}{6}$.

19. A machine is used to detect the presence or absence of a certain phenomenon which is present with probability p. The machine gives a positive response (indicating its presence) with probability p_1 if the phenomenon is present. If it is not present the machine gives a positive response with probability p_2.

(i) Show that if a positive response is given, the phenomenon is present with probability $pp_1/(pp_1 + p_2(1-p))$.

(ii) Find the probability it is present if 3 independent tests give 2 positive responses and 1 negative response.

¶ (i) Let A be the event that the phenomenon is absent, so that A' is the event that it is present, and let B be the event of a positive response.

By Bayes' Theorem
$$P(A'|B) = \frac{P(B|A')P(A')}{P(B|A')P(A') + P(B|A)P(A)} = \frac{p_1 p}{p_1 p + p_2(1-p)}.$$

(ii) Let C be the event that the three tests lead to 2 positive responses and 1 negative response. Then
$$P(C|A') = 3p_1^2(1-p_1),$$
$$P(C|A) = 3p_2^2(1-p_2),$$

the 3 arising because there are 3 possibilities for the negative response.

Hence
$$P(A'|C) = \frac{P(C|A')P(A')}{P(C|A')P(A') + P(C|A)P(A)}$$
$$= \frac{3p_1^2(1-p_1)p}{3p_1^2(1-p_1)p + 3p_2^2(1-p_2)(1-p)}$$
$$= \frac{pp_1^2(1-p_1)}{pp_1^2(1-p_1) + p_2^2(1-p_2)(1-p)}.$$

20. A random sample of size nine is taken with replacement from the population {1,2,3}. Find (a) the probability that the sample contains three digits of each kind, (b) the probability that the sample contains exactly four of one kind and exactly three of another kind.

¶ (a) One possible sequence is 111222333. This has probability $(\frac{1}{3})^9$. The number of distinct arrangements of these numbers is

$$\frac{9!}{3!3!3!}.$$

Thus the required probability $= \frac{9!}{3!3!3!}(\frac{1}{3})^9$

$$= \frac{560}{6561}.$$

(b) One possible sequence is 111122233. This has probability $(\frac{1}{3})^9$. The number of arrangements is

$$\frac{9!}{4!3!2!}.$$

Furthermore, the digit occurring 4 times can be selected in 3 ways and the digit occurring 3 times can be selected in 2 ways. Thus

$$\text{Required probability} = 3 \times 2 \times \frac{9!}{4!3!2!}(\frac{1}{3})^9 = \frac{280}{729}.$$

21. In the first-round draw of a football cup competition there are n teams from the North and n from the South. Find the probability that the draw results in n North-South pairings.

¶ $P(\text{First pair is North-South}) = P(\text{North first, South second})$
$$+ P(\text{South first, North second})$$
$$= \frac{n}{2n}\times\frac{n}{2n-1} + \frac{n}{2n}\times\frac{n}{2n-1} = \frac{2n^2}{2n(2n-1)}$$

Similarly

$P(\text{Second pair is North-South}|\text{First pair is North-South})$

$$= \frac{2(n-1)^2}{(2n-2)(2n-3)},$$

$P(\text{Third pair is North-South}|\text{First and second pairs are North-South})$

$$= \frac{2(n-2)^2}{(2n-4)(2n-5)},$$

etc.

Hence the probability that all pairs are North-South is

$$\frac{2n^2}{2n(2n-1)} \times \frac{2(n-1)^2}{(2n-2)(2n-3)} \times \frac{2(n-2)^2}{(2n-4)(2n-5)} \times \cdots \times \frac{2.1^2}{2.1} = \frac{2^n(n!)^2}{(2n)!} = \frac{2^n}{{}_{2n}C_n}.$$

22. (i) Find the probability that all six faces will be obtained in only six throws of a fair die.

    (ii) A random sample of size six with replacement is taken from the population $\{0,1,2,\ldots,9\}$. Find the probability that the six digits are all different.

¶ (i) There are $6!$ permutations of $1,2,3,4,5,6$ each having probability $1/6^6$.
   Therefore $P(\text{all six faces obtained}) = \dfrac{6!}{6^6} = \dfrac{5}{324}$.

   (ii) The number of ways of choosing 6 digits without replacement is $^{10}P_6$. So there are $^{10}P_6$ sequences of 6 digits in which no digit appears more than once. Therefore, since each sequence has probability $1/10^6$,
   $$P(\text{digits are all different}) = \frac{^{10}P_6}{10^6} = 0.1512.$$

   In general, if r symbols are selected at random with replacement from n distinct symbols then the probability that the selection contains no symbol more than once equals
   $$\frac{^nP_r}{n^r}$$

   This formula yields some surprising results. For example, if 8 strangers enter a lift and if each of them is equally likely to get out at any one of 12 floors, then the probability that all 3 get out at different floors is only 0.0464.

23. A and B are events such that $P(A|B') = 3/5$, $P(B|A') = 1/2$ and $P(A \cap B) = 1/8$. Find $P(A)$ and $P(B)$.

¶ Let $P(A) = p$, $P(B) = q$.
   Now $P(A|B') = \dfrac{P(A \cap B')}{P(B')} = \dfrac{P(A) - P(A \cap B)}{1 - P(B)}$

   and so $\qquad \dfrac{3}{5} = \dfrac{p - 1/8}{1 - q}$,

   i.e. $\qquad 5p + 3q = \dfrac{29}{8}$. $\qquad\qquad\qquad (1)$

   Similarly $\qquad P(B|A') = \dfrac{P(B) - P(A \cap B)}{1 - P(A)}$

   and $\qquad \dfrac{1}{2} = \dfrac{q - 1/8}{1 - p}$,

   i.e. $\qquad p + 2q = \dfrac{5}{4}$. $\qquad\qquad\qquad (2)$

Solving (1) and (2) we find that $p = \frac{1}{2}$, $q = \frac{3}{8}$.

24. An island is inhabited by two tribes in equal numbers - the Thesno, who tell the truth always, and the Sarli, who tell the truth with probability 1/2, answers to different questions being independent. A visitor to the island is lost but he encounters a native at teatime. He asks the questions 'Is it morning or afternoon?' and 'Which way is the nearest village?'. The answer to the first question is 'afternoon'. What is the probability that the answer to the second question is correct?

¶   We know that the answer to the first question was correct and so we require P(second answer correct|first answer correct).
By Bayes' Theorem

P(Thesno|first answer correct)

$$= \frac{P(\text{first correct}|\text{Thesno})P(\text{Thesno})}{P(\text{first correct}|\text{Thesno})P(\text{Thesno})+P(\text{first correct}|\text{Sarli})P(\text{Sarli})}$$

$$= \frac{1 \times \frac{1}{2}}{1 \times \frac{1}{2} + \frac{1}{2} \times \frac{1}{2}} = \frac{2}{3}.$$

Hence after the first answer the probability the native is a Thesno is 2/3. Hence by the Law of Total Probability

P(second answer correct) $= P$(second correct|Thesno)P(Thesno)
$\qquad\qquad\qquad\qquad + P$(second correct|Sarli)$P$(Sarli)

$$= 1 \times \frac{2}{3} + \frac{1}{2} \times \frac{1}{3} = \frac{5}{6},$$

since the probability that the native is a Sarli is 1/3.

25. The letters of the word MISSISSIPPI are arranged in random order.
    (a) Find the probability that the four S's are consecutive.
    (b) Find the probability that the four S's and also the four I's are consecutive.

¶   (a) As there are 4 S's, 4 I's and 2 P's the number of distinct permutations of the letters is

$$\frac{11!}{4!4!2!}.$$

    If the S's are to be consecutive we could regard them as being a single symbol. There are then 8 letters, including 4 I's and

2 P's. The number of distinct permutations is then $\frac{8!}{4!2!}$. As this is the number in which the S's are consecutive,

$$P(4 \text{ S's consecutive}) = \frac{8!/4!2!}{11!/4!4!2!} = \frac{8!4!}{11!} = \frac{4}{165}.$$

(b) In a similar way we can regard the 4 S's as one symbol and the 4 I's as a different single symbol. The number of distinct permutations in which the S's are consecutive and the I's are consecutive is then $5!/2!$ as there are 5 symbols, including 2 P's. Hence the required probability is

$$\frac{5!/2!}{11!/4!4!2!} = \frac{5!4!4!}{11!} = \frac{2}{1155}.$$

26. Two men, A and B, have respective probabilities p and q of succeeding each time they attempt a certain task. They attempt it in the order A,B,A,B,A,...., successive attempts being indepedent. Find the probability that A succeeds before B. Show that the players have equal probabilities of succeeding first if $q=p/(1-p)$ and that then $p \leqslant 1/2$.

¶ Let p_A denote the probability that A succeeds before B. A will succeed before B if A succeeds on his first attempt, or A and B fail on their first attempts and A succeeds on his second attempt, or A and B fail on their first and second attempts and A succeeds on his third attempt, etc.

Therefore $p_A = p + (1-p)(1-q)p + (1-p)^2(1-q)^2p + \ldots$
$$= p(1 + (1-p)(1-q) + ((1-p)(1-q))^2 + \ldots)$$
$$= \frac{p}{1 - (1-p)(1-q)}.$$

An alternative argument which does not entail the summation of an infinite series goes as follows. A can succeed at his first attempt or he can fail. If he fails he will get another go only if B fails at his first attempt, but if this position is reached then the probability that he will succeed before B is the same as at the start. This gives us the following equation:

$$p_A = p + (1-p)(1-q)p_A.$$

Solving we obtain the expression for p_A given above.

The players have equal probabilities of succeeding first if

$$\frac{p}{1 - (1-p)(1-q)} = \frac{1}{2} \quad \text{which leads to} \quad q = \frac{p}{1-p}$$

Now $q \leqslant 1$ so that $1-p \geqslant p$ or $p \leqslant \frac{1}{2}$.

27. A mathematician carries one match box in his right pocket and another in his left. When he wants a match he selects a pocket at random and takes a match from the box in that pocket. If each matchbox initially contains N matches, show that, on the first occasion that he finds one box empty, the probability that the other box contains r matches is

$$^{2N-r}C_N \left(\tfrac{1}{2}\right)^{2N-r} \quad (r = 0,1,\ldots,N).$$

¶ Let the boxes be labelled I and II and consider the event that he seeks a match in Box II when it is empty and there are r matches in Box I. Of the first 2N-r matches chosen, N were from Box II. Now the probability of a given sequence of N Box II's and N-r Box I's is $\left(\tfrac{1}{2}\right)^{2N-r}$, as each has probability $\tfrac{1}{2}$ of being chosen. The number of such sequences is the number of ways of choosing N positions in the sequence for the N Box II's, i.e. $^{2N-r}C_N$.

Hence the probability of having N Box II's in the first 2N-r choices is

$$^{2N-r}C_N \left(\tfrac{1}{2}\right)^{2N-r}.$$

Since the probability that Box II is chosen next is $\tfrac{1}{2}$, the probability that Box II is chosen when empty and when Box I contains r matches is

$$^{2N-r}C_N \left(\tfrac{1}{2}\right)^{2N-r} \times \tfrac{1}{2}.$$

Clearly the probability that Box I is chosen when it is empty and when Box II contains r matches is the same. Hence the required probability is

$$2 \times {}^{2N-r}C_N \times \left(\tfrac{1}{2}\right)^{2N-r} \times \tfrac{1}{2} = {}^{2N-r}C_N \left(\tfrac{1}{2}\right)^{2N-r}.$$

28. Frank is leading John in a set of tennis by 5 games to 3. The probability that Frank wins a game on his service is 0.6 but on John's service it is 0.5, the outcomes of the games being independent of each other. It is Frank's service next. Find the probability that Frank wins the set (a) within 12 games, (b) with no restriction on the number of games. (Assume as in Davis Cup matches, that the winner of a set containing more than 12 games is the first player to obtain a lead of 2 games, i.e. no tie break.)

¶ (a) P(Frank wins the set within 12 games)

$= P$(Frank wins 6-3) $+ P$(Frank wins 6-4) $+ P$(Frank wins 7-5)

$= 0.6 + 0.4 \times 0.5 + 0.4 \times 0.5 \times 0.6 \times 0.5$

$= 0.86.$

(b) First of all note that if the set is not won by either player within 12 games then Frank will serve at 6-6.

Define the events F: Frank wins the set,

A: Frank serves at 6-6,

B: Frank serves at 7-7,

Then $F \cap A'$ is the event that Frank wins within 12 games.

Therefore $P(F) = P(F \cap A') + P(F \cap A) = 0.86 + P(A) \times P(F|A)$

$$= 0.86 + 0.1 \times P(F|A)$$

since $P(A) = 0.4 \times 0.5 \times (0.6 + 0.4) \times 0.5 = 0.1$.

Now if Frank is to win the set from the position 6-6 without having to serve at 7-7 he must win 8-6.

Therefore $P(F \cap B'|A) = 0.6 \times 0.5 = 0.3$

and $P(F|A) = 0.3 + P(F \cap B|A)$.

Also $P(F \cap B|A) = P(B|A)P(F|B \cap A)$

$$= P(B|A)P(F|B) \qquad \text{(since } B \cap A = B\text{)}$$

$$= (0.4 \times 0.5 + 0.6 \times 0.5)P(F|B)$$

$$= 0.5 \times P(F|B).$$

Therefore $P(F|A) = 0.3 + 0.5 \times P(F|B)$,

but $P(F|B) = P(F|A)$ since Frank has the same probability of winning the set from the position 7-7 as from 6-6.

Therefore $P(F|A) = \dfrac{0.3}{1-0.5} = 0.6$.

Therefore $P(F) = 0.86 + 0.1 \times 0.6 = 0.92$.

A more obvious method of solution is to sum the probabilities that Frank wins 8-6, 9-7, 10-8, etc. This entails summing the infinite series

$0.1 \times 0.3 + 0.1 \times 0.5 \times 0.3 + 0.1 \times 0.5^2 \times 0.3 + \ldots$

$$= 0.03 \times (1 + 0.5 + 0.5^2 + \ldots) = \frac{0.03}{1-0.5} = 0.06$$

and the required probability is $0.86 + 0.06 = 0.92$ as before.

29. Three students independently make visits to a cafe, the probabilities of going on a given morning being 1/2, 2/3 and 3/4. Find the probability that exactly k go on a given morning (k=0,1,2,3). Find the probability that in a five-day week the total number of attendances is exactly five.

¶ Let the 3 students be A,B,C and let p_k be the probability that k of them go on a particular morning. Then

$$p_0 = P\text{(None of them goes)}$$

$$= \frac{1}{2} \times \frac{1}{3} \times \frac{1}{4} = \frac{1}{24}.$$

$$p_1 = P\text{(A goes but not B or C)} + P\text{(B goes but not C or A)}$$
$$+ P\text{(C goes but not A or B)}$$

$$= (\frac{1}{2} \times \frac{1}{3} \times \frac{1}{4}) + (\frac{2}{3} \times \frac{1}{4} \times \frac{1}{2}) + (\frac{3}{4} \times \frac{1}{2} \times \frac{1}{3}) = \frac{6}{24}.$$

$$p_2 = P\text{(A and B go but not C)} + P\text{(B and C go but not A)}$$
$$+ P\text{(C and A go but not B)}$$

$$= (\frac{1}{2} \times \frac{2}{3} \times \frac{1}{4}) + (\frac{2}{3} \times \frac{3}{4} \times \frac{1}{2}) + (\frac{3}{4} \times \frac{1}{2} \times \frac{1}{3}) = \frac{11}{24}.$$

$$p_3 = P\text{(All of them go)}$$

$$= \frac{1}{2} \times \frac{2}{3} \times \frac{3}{4} = \frac{6}{24}.$$

The possible partitions of 5 visits over 5 days are

3	1	1	0	0	$5 \times {}^4C_2$ ways
3	2	0	0	0	5×4 ways
2	1	1	1	0	5×4 ways
2	2	1	0	0	$5 \times {}^4C_2$ ways
1	1	1	1	1	1 way.

The number of ways each partition can occur is given above, e.g. in the first row, the 3 can be placed in any one of 5 positions and the 2 1's in any one of ${}^4C_2$ ways. Using the probabilities obtained earlier,

$$P\text{(5 visits in 5 days)} = 5 \times {}^4C_2 \times \frac{6}{24} \times (\frac{6}{24})^2 \times (\frac{1}{24})^2 + 5 \times 4 \times \frac{6}{24} \frac{11}{24} \times (\frac{1}{24})^3$$

$$+ 5 \times 4 \times \frac{11}{24} \times (\frac{6}{24})^3 \times \frac{1}{24} + 5 \times {}^4C_2 \times (\frac{11}{24})^2 \times \frac{6}{24} \times (\frac{1}{24})^2 + (\frac{1}{24})^5$$

$$= 0.009683.$$

30. A ball is drawn at random from an urn containing n numbered balls $B_1, \ldots, B_n$. Two independent observers, X and Y, state which ball is drawn. Each tells the truth with probability 1/5 but if he lies he is equally likely to name any of the balls not drawn.

(i) If B_1 is drawn find the probability that X claims it was B_2.

(ii) Suppose both X and Y assert that the ball chosen was B_1. Show that the probability it was, in fact, B_1 is $\frac{(n-1)}{(n+15)}$.

¶   (i) $P(X$ claims $B_2|B_1$ chosen$)$ $= P(X$ lies and chooses $B_2)$

$$= P(X \text{ chooses } B_2|X \text{ lies})P(X \text{ lies})$$

$$= \frac{1}{n-1} \times \frac{4}{5}.$$

(ii) Let A be the event that X and Y both assert B_1 was chosen.

Now $P(A|B_1$ chosen$) = \frac{1}{5} \times \frac{1}{5}$

as X and Y behave independently and each tells the truth with probability 1/5.

Also $P(A|B_1$ not chosen$) = P(X$ claims $B_1|B_1$ not chosen$)\times$

$$P(Y \text{ claims } B_1|B_1 \text{ not chosen})$$

$$= (\frac{4}{5(n-1)})^2$$

from (i) as the result there applies whichever ball is chosen other than B_2.

By Bayes' Theorem

$P(B_1$ chosen$|A)$

$$= \frac{P(A|B_1 \text{ chosen})P(B_1 \text{ chosen})}{P(A|B_1 \text{ chosen})P(B_1 \text{ chosen})+P(A|B_1 \text{ not chosen})P(B_1 \text{ not chosen})}$$

$$= \frac{\frac{1}{25} \times \frac{1}{n}}{\frac{1}{25} \times \frac{1}{n} + (\frac{4}{5(n-1)})^2 \times \frac{n-1}{n}}$$

$$\doteq \frac{n-1}{n+15}.$$

31. A certain cell, when subjected to a particular treatment, dies with probability 1/4 or splits into two cells similar to the original with probability 3/4. Distinct cells react independently to the treatment. Let X_1 be the number of cells living after submitting a single cell to the treatment, X_2 be the number living after submitting each of the X_1 cells to the treatment, X_3 be the number living after submitting each of the X_2 cells to the treatment and so on. Find (i) $P(X_2=0)$, (ii) $P(X_3=0)$.

¶   (i) $P(X_2=0) = P(X_1=0) + P(X_1=2 \text{ and } X_2=0)$

$$= P(X_1=0) + P(X_2=0|X_1=2)P(X_1=2)$$

$$= \frac{1}{4} + (\frac{1}{4})^2 \cdot \frac{3}{4}$$

$$= \frac{19}{64}.$$

(ii) $P(X_3=0) = P(X_1=0) + P(X_1=2$ and $X_2=0)$
$$+ P(X_1=2, X_2=2, X_3=0) + P(X_1=2, X_2=4, X_3=0).$$

Now $P(X_1=2, X_2=2, X_3=0) = P(X_3=0|X_2=2, X_1=2)P(X_2=2|X_1=2)P(X_1=2)$
$$= (\tfrac{1}{4})^2 \times 2 \times \tfrac{3}{4} \times \tfrac{1}{4} \times \tfrac{3}{4} = \frac{9}{512}$$

as $P(X_2=2|X_1=2) = P(\text{one splits and one dies})$
$$= 2 \times \frac{3}{4} \times \frac{1}{4}$$

since the cell to split is one of two.

Also $P(X_3=0, X_2=4, X_1=2) = P(X_3=0|X_2=4, X_1=2)P(X_2=4|X_1=2)P(X_1=2)$
$$= (\tfrac{1}{4})^4 \times (\tfrac{3}{4})^2 \times \tfrac{3}{4}$$
$$= \frac{27}{16384}.$$

Thus $P(X_3=0) = \dfrac{19}{64} + \dfrac{9}{512} + \dfrac{27}{16384} = \dfrac{5179}{16384} = 0.3161.$

32. A 12-seat minibus service takes passengers from a village to a
nearby town. The probability that any seat is occupied is 1/2 and
the probability that any passenger will wish to get off at a request
stop on the journey is 1/12. Find the probability that a given seat
is occupied given that it is not vacated at the request stop.
Hence show that if r passengers get off at the request stop
$(0 \leqslant r \leqslant 12)$ the probability that the bus had been full is $(\tfrac{11}{23})^{12-r}$.
By considering the probability that the bus is full given that it
does not need to stop at the request stop, find the probability that
it need not stop.

¶ Define events NV: a seat is not vacated at the request stop,
O: a seat is occupied.

Then $P(O|NV) = \dfrac{P(NV|O)P(O)}{P(NV|O)P(O) + P(NV|O')P(O')}$

$$= \dfrac{\tfrac{11}{12} \times \tfrac{1}{2}}{\tfrac{11}{12} \times \tfrac{1}{2} + 1 \times \tfrac{1}{2}} = \dfrac{11}{23}$$

as $P(NV|O') = 1$, since if a seat is not occupied it cannot be
vacated.

Now $P(\text{bus full}|r \text{ get off})$
$$= P(\text{remaining } 12-r \text{ seats occupied} \mid \text{not vacated})$$
$$= (\tfrac{11}{23})^{12-r} \quad \text{by the first part.}$$

Setting r=0,

P(bus full | does not need to stop) $= (\frac{11}{23})^{12}$.

But P(bus full | does not need to stop)

$$= \frac{P(\text{bus full and does not need to stop})}{P(\text{does not need to stop})}$$

$$= \frac{P(\text{does not need to stop} | \text{bus full}) P(\text{bus full})}{P(\text{does not need to stop})}$$

Thus $(\frac{11}{23})^{12} = \dfrac{(\frac{11}{12})^{12} (\frac{1}{2})^{12}}{P(\text{does not need so stop})}$

and P(does not need to stop) $= (\frac{23}{24})^{12} = 0.6001$.

33. A dog is subjected to a series of trials, in each of which it is given the choice of going to a dish on its left or to one on its right. The one on its right has a tasty piece of food while the one on the left has food with an unpleasant taste. If it goes to the tasty one on any occasion, then it will do likewise next time with probability 0.6, while if it goes to the unpleasant one, it will do likewise next time with probability 0.3. At the first trial it chooses a dish at random. Let p_n denote the probability that on the nth trial it selects the tasty dish. Show that

$$p_n = 0.7 - 0.1 p_{n-1}$$

and deduce that p_n has a limiting value of 7/11 as n gets very large.

¶ For n = 1,2,.... let A_n be the event that on the nth trial it selects the tasty dish. By the Law of Total Probability

$$P(A_n) = P(A_n | A_{n-1}) P(A_{n-1}) + P(A_n | A'_{n-1}) P(A'_{n-1})$$

and so $p_n = 0.6 p_{n-1} + 0.7(1-p_{n-1})$

$$= 0.7 - 0.1 p_{n-1}.$$

Suppose p_n tends towards a limiting value π. As p_{n-1} would also tend to this, if n is large

$$\pi = 0.7 - 0.1\pi.$$

Hence $\pi = \frac{7}{11}$.

34. Three men A,B,C are imprisoned. They are told by their gaoler that two, having been chosen at random, are to be executed. A decides to question the gaoler. He asks for the name of one of the other two who is to be executed, pointing out that since at least one of

them must be executed the gaoler is not giving away information. The gaoler tells him that B is to be executed. A now reasons: "Since either C or myself is to be freed, I actually have a probability of 1/2, not 1/3, of being freed." Is his reasoning valid? (It may be assumed that if B and C are both to be executed, the gaoler chooses a name at random.)

¶   Define events   *AF*: A is to be freed,

$\quad\quad\quad\quad\quad\quad$ *BE*: B is to be executed,

$\quad\quad\quad\quad\quad\quad$ *GB*: Gaoler says B is to be executed.

Since A,B,C are equally likely to be freed when the original selection is made, $P(AF|BE) = 1/2$ but the relevant probability when the gaoler tells A that B is to be executed is $P(AF|GB)$.

By Bayes' Theorem

$$P(AF|GB) = \frac{P(GB|AF)P(AF)}{P(GB|AF)P(AF) + P(GB|AF')P(AF')}.$$

Now $P(AF) = \frac{1}{3}$ and $P(AF') = \frac{2}{3}$.

Also $P(GB|AF) = \frac{1}{2}$ since if B and C are to be executed then the gaoler chooses one of their names at random, and $P(GB|AF') = \frac{1}{2}$ since the gaoler must name B if he is to be executed along with A and this occurs with probability $\frac{1}{2}$.

Therefore $P(AF|GB) = \dfrac{\frac{1}{2}\times\frac{1}{3}}{\frac{1}{2}\times\frac{1}{3} + \frac{1}{2}\times\frac{2}{3}} = \frac{1}{3} \neq \frac{1}{2} = P(AF|BE)$.

So A's reasoning is invalid. The difference between $P(AF|BE)$ and $P(AF|GB)$ arises because the gaoler is not free to name A in any circumstance whereas in the original selection A is as likely to be selected as B and C.

Note that $P(AF|GB) = P(AF)$ so that the events *AF* and *GB* are independent. Thus A's contention that the gaoler's statement gives him no information about his own fate is correct.

35. *A,B,C* are independent events. The probability that only *A* occurs is a, the probability that only *B* occurs is b and the probability that only *C* occurs is c. Verify that

$$P(A) = \frac{a}{a+x}, \quad P(B) = \frac{b}{b+x}, \quad P(C) = \frac{c}{c+x},$$

where x satisfies the equation

$$(a+x)(b+x)(c+x) = x^2.$$

¶   Let $P(A) = p$, $P(B) = q$ and $P(C) = r$.

Now P(only A occurs)

$$= P(A \text{ occurs}) P(B \text{ does not occur}) P(C \text{ does not occur})$$

$$= p(1-q)(1-r) = a. \qquad \text{(by independence)} \qquad (1)$$

Similarly P(only B occurs) $= (1-p)q(1-r) = b$

and $\qquad P$(only C occurs) $= (1-p)(1-q)r = c$.

Let $x = (1-p)(1-q)(1-r)$.   Multiplying (1) by $(1-p)$ we obtain

$$px = a(1-p).$$

Similarly $\qquad qx = b(1-q),$

$$rx = c(1-r).$$

Hence $p = \dfrac{a}{a+x}$, $\quad q = \dfrac{b}{b+x}$, $\quad r = \dfrac{c}{c+x}$.

But since $\quad p(1-q)(1-r) = \dfrac{a}{a+x}\left(1 - \dfrac{b}{b+x}\right)\left(1 - \dfrac{c}{c+x}\right)$

$$= \frac{ax^2}{(a+x)(b+x)(c+x)}$$

$$= a \qquad \text{by (1)},$$

we have $\qquad x^2 = (a+x)(b+x)(c+x)$

as required.

3
Discrete Distributions

Exercises 3.1 Random Variables

1. The random variable X has the probability function
$$p_x = kx \quad \text{if } x = 1,2,3,4,5,$$
$$= 0 \quad \text{otherwise},$$
where k is a constant. Determine the value of k.

¶ Since $\sum_x p_x = 1,$ $k(1+2+3+4+5) = 1.$

Therefore $k = \dfrac{1}{15}.$

2. The random variables X,Y have probability functions p_x, q_y given by
$$p_x = k_1(1+x^2) \quad \text{if } x = 0,\pm1,\pm2,\pm3,$$
$$= 0 \quad\quad\quad \text{otherwise},$$
$$q_y = k_2(1+|y|) \quad \text{if } y = 0,\pm1,\pm2,\pm3,$$
$$= 0 \quad\quad\quad \text{otherwise},$$
where k_1, k_2 are constants.
(i) Determine the values of k_1 and k_2.
(ii) Which of X,Y is the more likely to take the value
     (a) 0, (b) 3?

¶ (i) Since $\sum_x p_x = \sum_y q_y = 1,$

$k_1(1+2+2+5+5+10+10) = k_2(1+2+2+3+3+4+4) = 1$

so that $k_1 = \dfrac{1}{35},$ $k_2 = \dfrac{1}{19}.$

(ii) (a) $P(X=0) = \dfrac{1}{35},$ $P(Y=0) = \dfrac{1}{19}.$
           Therefore Y is more likely to take the value 0.

(b) $P(X=3) = \dfrac{10}{35}$, $P(Y=3) = \dfrac{4}{19}$.

Therefore X is more likely to take the value 3.

3. The random variable X has the probability function
$$p_x = \frac{1}{5} \qquad \text{if } x = 0,1,2,3,4,$$
$$= 0 \qquad \text{otherwise.}$$

Find an expression for the cumulative distribution function F(x), and draw its graph.

¶ $F(x) = 0$ if $x < 0$,

$\qquad = \dfrac{1}{5}$ if $0 \leqslant x < 1$,

$\qquad = \dfrac{2}{5}$ if $1 \leqslant x < 2$,

$\qquad = \dfrac{3}{5}$ if $2 \leqslant x < 3$,

$\qquad = \dfrac{4}{5}$ if $3 \leqslant x < 4$,

$\qquad = 1$ if $x \geqslant 4$,

or, equivalently,

$F(x) = 0$ \qquad if $x < 0$,

$\qquad = \dfrac{1+[x]}{5}$ \quad if $0 \leqslant x < 4$,

$\qquad = 1$ \qquad if $x \geqslant 4$,

where $[x]$ denotes the integral part of x.

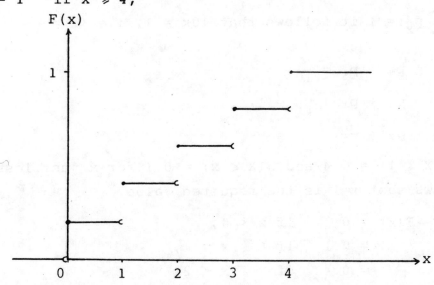

4. The random variable X has the cumulative distribution function
$$F(x) = 0 \qquad \text{if } x < 0,$$
$$= \frac{1}{3} \qquad \text{if } 0 \leqslant x < 2,$$
$$= \frac{1}{2} \qquad \text{if } 2 \leqslant x < 3,$$
$$= \frac{3}{4} \qquad \text{if } 3 \leqslant x < 6,$$
$$= 1 \qquad \text{if } x \geqslant 6.$$

Determine the probability function of X, giving your answer in the form of a probability table.

¶   The required probability table is

x	0	2	3	6
p_x	$\frac{1}{3}$	$\frac{1}{6}$	$\frac{1}{4}$	$\frac{1}{4}$

where the probabilities in the table equal the sizes of the 'jumps' in $F(x)$.

5. The random variable X has a probability function p_x of the following form, where k is an unknown constant:

$$\begin{aligned} p_x &= k && \text{if } x = 0, \\ &= 3k && \text{if } x = 1, \\ &= 6k && \text{if } x = 2, \\ &= 0 && \text{otherwise.} \end{aligned}$$

(a) Determine the value of k.

(b) Find $P(X < 2)$, $P(X \leqslant 2)$ and $P(X > 1)$.

(c) What is the smallest value of x for which $P(X \leqslant x) > 0.25$?

(d) Determine the cumulative distribution function of X.

¶   (a) Since $\sum_x p_x = 1$ it follows that $10k = 1$, i.e. $k = \frac{1}{10}$.

(b) $P(X < 2) = p_0 + p_1 = \frac{4}{10}$,

$P(X \leqslant 2) = p_0 + p_1 + p_2 = 1$,

$P(X > 1) = p_2 = \frac{6}{10}$.

(c) Since $P(X \leqslant 1) = 0.4$ and $P(X \leqslant x) = 0.1$ for x just less than 1, it follows that x=1 is the required value.

(d)
$$\begin{aligned} F(x) &= 0 && \text{if } x < 0, \\ &= 0.1 && \text{if } 0 \leqslant x < 1, \\ &= 0.4 && \text{if } 1 \leqslant x < 2, \\ &= 1 && \text{if } x \geqslant 2. \end{aligned}$$

6. A fair die is tossed twice. Let X equal the first score minus the second score. Determine (a) the probability function of X, (b) the cumulative distribution function of X and draw its graph.

¶ The sample space is

(1,1)	(1,2)	(1,3)	(1,4)	(1,5)	(1,6)
(2,1)	(2,2)	(2,3)	(2,4)	(2,5)	(2,6)
(3,1)	(3,2)	(3,3)	(3,4)	(3,5)	(3,6)
(4,1)	(4,2)	(4,3)	(4,4)	(4,5)	(4,6)
(5,1)	(5,2)	(5,3)	(5,4)	(5,5)	(5,6)
(6,1)	(6,2)	(6,3)	(6,4)	(6,5)	(6,6)

(a) Working along the diagonals we find by enumeration that X has the following probability function

x	-5	-4	-3	-2	-1	0	1	2	3	4	5
p_x	$\frac{1}{36}$	$\frac{2}{36}$	$\frac{3}{36}$	$\frac{4}{36}$	$\frac{5}{36}$	$\frac{6}{36}$	$\frac{5}{36}$	$\frac{4}{36}$	$\frac{3}{36}$	$\frac{2}{36}$	$\frac{1}{36}$

More concisely,

$$p_x = \frac{6-|x|}{36} \quad \text{if } x = 0, \pm1, \pm2, \pm3, \pm4, \pm5,$$
$$= 0 \quad \text{otherwise.}$$

(b)

$$F(x) = 0 \quad \text{if } x < -5,$$
$$= \frac{1}{36} \quad \text{if } -5 \leqslant x < -4,$$
$$= \frac{3}{36} \quad \text{if } -4 \leqslant x < -3, \quad \text{etc.}$$

Using the formula $\sum_{i=1}^{n} i = \frac{1}{2}n(n+1)$ we find that the cumulative distribution function $F(x)$ can be written concisely in the form

$$F(x) = 0 \quad \text{if } x < -5$$
$$= \frac{(6+[x])(7+[x])}{72} \quad \text{if } -5 \leqslant x < 0,$$
$$= \frac{21}{36} + \frac{[x](11-[x])}{72} \quad \text{if } 0 \leqslant x < 5,$$
$$= 1 \quad \text{if } x \geqslant 5,$$

where [x] denotes the integral part of x.

For example, $F(-3.5) = \frac{(6-4)(7-4)}{72} = \frac{3}{36}$,

$$F(3.5) = \frac{21}{36} + \frac{3(11-3)}{72} = \frac{33}{36}.$$

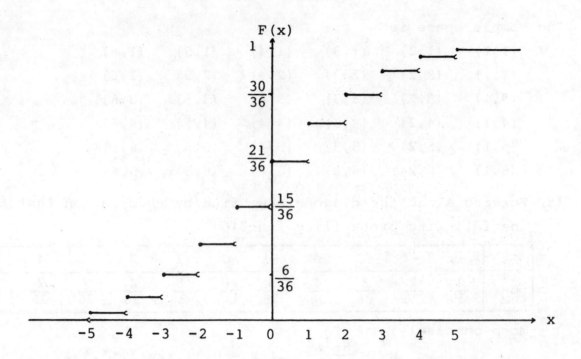

7. Two fair dice are tossed. Let X denote the smaller of the two scores obtained. Determine (a) the probability function of X, (b) the cumulative distribution function of X and draw its graph.

¶ (a) Using the sample space of Question 6, we find by enumeration that X has the probability function

x	1	2	3	4	5	6
p_x	$\dfrac{11}{36}$	$\dfrac{9}{36}$	$\dfrac{7}{36}$	$\dfrac{5}{36}$	$\dfrac{3}{36}$	$\dfrac{1}{36}$

or
$$p_x = \frac{13-2x}{36} \quad \text{if } x = 1,2,3,4,5,6,$$
$$= 0 \quad \text{otherwise.}$$

(b) The distribution function is given by

$$F(x) = 0 \qquad \text{if } x < 1,$$
$$= \frac{[x](12-[x])}{36} \qquad \text{if } 1 \leqslant x < 6,$$
$$= 1 \qquad \text{if } x \geqslant 6,$$

where [x] denotes the integral part of x.

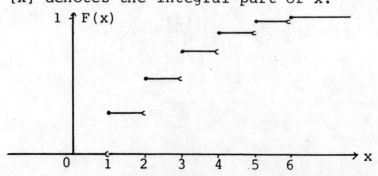

8. The cumulative distribution function of a random variable X is as
   follows.

$$F(x) = 0 \quad \text{if } x < -2,$$
$$= \frac{1}{4} \quad \text{if } -2 \leqslant x < 0,$$
$$= \frac{1}{2} \quad \text{if } 0 \leqslant x < 2,$$
$$= \frac{5}{6} \quad \text{if } 2 \leqslant x < 3,$$
$$= 1 \quad \text{if } x \geqslant 3.$$

(a) Draw the graph of F(x).

(b) Find $P(X \leqslant 1)$, $P(X < -3)$, $P(X < -2)$, $P(-1 < X \leqslant 2)$,
    $P(1 \leqslant X \leqslant 3)$, $P(X \leqslant 2.5)$, $P(X > 0)$ and $P(0 \leqslant X \leqslant 3)$.

(c) Construct a probability table showing the probability function
    of X.

¶   (a)

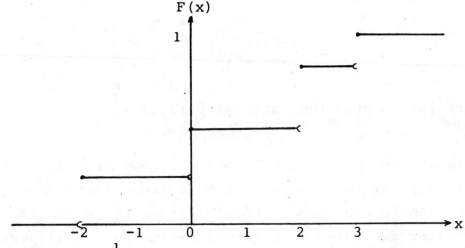

(b) $P(X \leqslant 1) = F(1) = \frac{1}{2}$,

    $P(X < -3) = F(-3-) = 0$,   N.B. x- denotes a value just

    $P(X < -2) = F(-2-) = 0$,   less than x.

    $P(-1 < X \leqslant 2) = F(2) - F(-1) = \frac{5}{6} - \frac{1}{4} = \frac{7}{12}$,

    $P(1 \leqslant X \leqslant 3) = F(3) - F(1-) = 1 - \frac{1}{2} = \frac{1}{2}$,

    $P(X \leqslant 2.5) = F(2.5) = \frac{5}{6}$,

    $P(X > 0) = 1 - P(X \leqslant 0) = 1 - F(0) = 1 - \frac{1}{2} = \frac{1}{2}$,

    $P(0 \leqslant X \leqslant 3) = F(3) - F(0-) = 1 - \frac{1}{4} = \frac{3}{4}$.

(c) The probability function of X can be constructed by evaluating
    the 'jumps' in F(x). This gives

x	-2	0	2	3
P_x	$\frac{1}{4}$	$\frac{1}{4}$	$\frac{1}{3}$	$\frac{1}{6}$

The random variable X has probability function

$$p_x = \frac{2x}{n(n+1)} \quad \text{if } x = 1,2,\ldots,n,$$

$$= 0 \quad \text{otherwise.}$$

Find an expression for the cumulative distribution function $F(x)$ when x is a positive integer between 1 and n. Hence find $F(x)$ for all x.

If x is a positive integer between 1 and n,

$$F(x) = \frac{2}{n(n+1)} \sum_{y=1}^{x} y$$

$$= \frac{2}{n(n+1)} \cdot \frac{x(x+1)}{2} = \frac{x(x+1)}{n(n+1)}.$$

Extending to all x,

$$F(x) = 0 \quad \text{if } x < 1,$$

$$= \frac{[x]([x]+1)}{n(n+1)} \quad \text{if } 1 \leqslant x \leqslant n,$$

$$= 1 \quad \text{if } x > n,$$

where [x] denotes the integral part of x.

10. There are three defectives in a lot of 7 articles. A sample of four articles is drawn at random (without replacement) from the lot. Let X denote the number of defectives in the sample.
    (a) Determine the probability function of X and construct a probability table.
    (b) Determine the cumulative distribution function of X and draw its graph.

¶ Total number of possible samples = $^{7}C_4$ = 35.

Number containing no defectives = $^{3}C_0 \times {}^{4}C_4$ = 1.

Number containing 1 defective = $^{3}C_1 \times {}^{4}C_3$ = 12.

Number containing 2 defectives = $^{3}C_2 \times {}^{4}C_2$ = 18.

Number containing 3 defectives = $^{3}C_3 \times {}^{4}C_1$ = 4.

It is not possible to have 4 defectives in the sample.

(a) The probability function of X is

x	0	1	2	3
p_x	1/35	12/35	18/35	4/35

(b) The cumulative distribution function of X is

$$F(x) = 0 \qquad \text{if } x < 0,$$
$$= \frac{1}{35} \qquad \text{if } 0 \leqslant x < 1,$$
$$= \frac{13}{35} \qquad \text{if } 1 \leqslant x < 2,$$
$$= \frac{31}{35} \qquad \text{if } 2 \leqslant x < 3,$$
$$F(x) = 1 \qquad \text{if } x \geqslant 3.$$

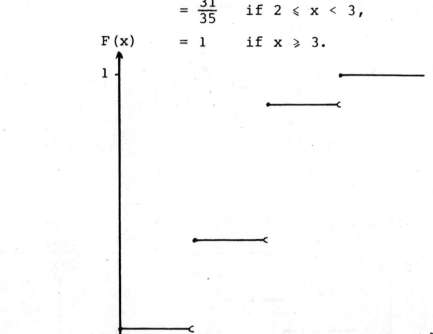

11. A coin is tossed three times. If X denotes the number of heads minus the number of tails, find the probability function of X and draw a graph of its cumulative distribution function when
    (a) the coin is fair,
    (b) the coin is biased so that $P(H) = \frac{3}{5}$ and $P(T) = \frac{2}{5}$.

¶ The possibilities are

Sequence	X	Prob. in (a)	Prob. in (b)
HHH	3	1/8	$(3/5)^3$
HHT	1	1/8	$(3/5)^2 (2/5)$
HTH	1	1/3	$(3/5)^2 (2/5)$
THH	1	1/8	$(3/5)^2 (2/5)$
HTT	-1	1/8	$(3/5)(2/5)^2$
THT	-1	1/8	$(3/5)(2/5)^2$
TTH	-1	1/8	$(3/5)(2/5)^2$
TTT	-3	1/8	$(2/5)^3$

The probability functions in the two cases are therefore

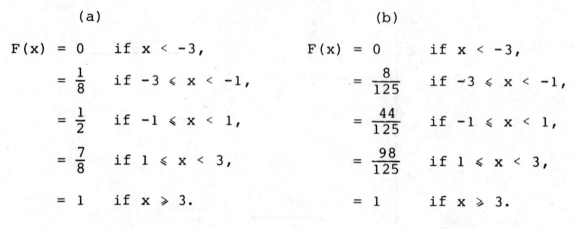

	(a)			
x	-3	-1	1	3
p_x	$\frac{1}{8}$	$\frac{3}{8}$	$\frac{3}{8}$	$\frac{1}{8}$

	(b)			
x	-3	-1	1	3
p_x	$\frac{8}{125}$	$\frac{36}{125}$	$\frac{54}{125}$	$\frac{27}{125}$

The cumulative distribution functions are

(a)

$$F(x) = 0 \quad \text{if } x < -3,$$
$$= \frac{1}{8} \quad \text{if } -3 \leqslant x < -1,$$
$$= \frac{1}{2} \quad \text{if } -1 \leqslant x < 1,$$
$$= \frac{7}{8} \quad \text{if } 1 \leqslant x < 3,$$
$$= 1 \quad \text{if } x \geqslant 3.$$

(b)

$$F(x) = 0 \quad \text{if } x < -3,$$
$$= \frac{8}{125} \quad \text{if } -3 \leqslant x < -1,$$
$$= \frac{44}{125} \quad \text{if } -1 \leqslant x < 1,$$
$$= \frac{98}{125} \quad \text{if } 1 \leqslant x < 3,$$
$$= 1 \quad \text{if } x \geqslant 3.$$

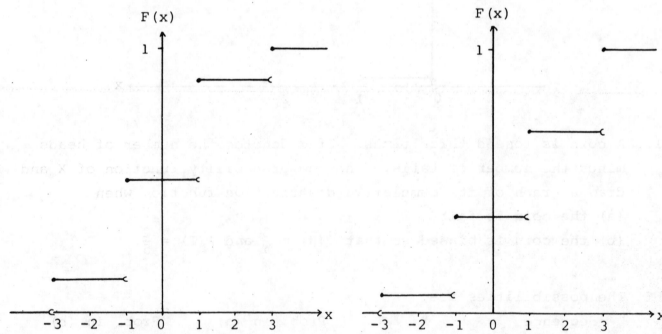

12. Let X denote the number of Aces in a hand drawn at random without replacement from an ordinary pack of 52 playing cards. Find the probability function of X when the hand consists of (a) 4 cards, (b) 13 cards, (c) 3 cards. Leave your answers in combinatorial form.

¶ (a) $$p_x = {}^4C_x \times {}^{48}C_{4-x} \bigg/ {}^{52}C_4 \quad \text{if } x = 0,1,2,3,4,$$
$$= 0 \quad \text{otherwise.}$$

(b) $\qquad p_x = {}^4C_x \times {}^{48}C_{13-x} \Big/ {}^{52}C_{13} \qquad$ if $x = 0,1,2,3,4,$

$\qquad\qquad = 0 \qquad\qquad\qquad\qquad$ otherwise.

(c) $\qquad p_x = {}^4C_x \times {}^{48}C_{3-x} \Big/ {}^{52}C_3 \qquad$ if $x = 0,1,2,3,$

$\qquad\qquad = 0 \qquad\qquad\qquad\qquad$ otherwise.

13. A gambler draws three balls at random without replacement from a bag containing 6 red, 2 white and 2 black balls. A red ball gains him nothing but he wins £10 for each white ball selected and loses £10 for each black ball selected. Find the probability function of his total winnings.

¶ Combination	Probability	Winnings
3 red	${}^6C_3 \Big/ {}^{10}C_3$	0
2 red, 1 white	${}^6C_2 \times {}^2C_1 \Big/ {}^{10}C_3$	10
2 red, 1 black	${}^6C_2 \times {}^2C_1 \Big/ {}^{10}C_3$	--10
1 red, 2 white	${}^6C_1 \times {}^2C_2 \Big/ {}^{10}C_3$	20
1 red, 1 white, 1 black	${}^6C_1 \times {}^2C_1 \times {}^2C_1 \Big/ {}^{10}C_3$	0
1 red, 2 black	${}^6C_1 \times {}^2C_2 \Big/ {}^{10}C_3$	-20
2 white, 1 black	${}^2C_2 \times {}^2C_1 \Big/ {}^{10}C_3$	10
1 white, 2 black	${}^2C_1 \times {}^2C_2 \Big/ {}^{10}C_3$	--10

The probability function of his winnings is therefore

x	-20	-10	0	10	20
p_x	$\dfrac{6}{120}$	$\dfrac{32}{120}$	$\dfrac{44}{120}$	$\dfrac{32}{120}$	$\dfrac{6}{120}$

14. The probability function of an integer valued random variable X is

$$p_x = \frac{1}{x(x+1)} \qquad \text{if } x = 1,2,3,\ldots\ldots,$$

$$\quad = 0 \qquad\qquad \text{otherwise.}$$

Show that for positive integral x the cumulative distribution function F(x) of X is such that

$$F(x) = 1 - \frac{1}{(x+1)}.$$

If m and n are positive integers (m < n) find expressions for
(i) $P(X > m)$, (ii) $P(m < X \leqslant n)$, (iii) $P(m \leqslant X \leqslant n)$.

¶ We can write

$$p_x = \frac{1}{x} - \frac{1}{(x+1)}$$

so that, for positive integral x,

$$F(x) = \sum_{r=1}^{x} p_r$$

$$= \sum_{r=1}^{x} (\frac{1}{r} - \frac{1}{r+1})$$

$$= (1 + \frac{1}{2} + \frac{1}{3} + \ldots + \frac{1}{x}) - (\frac{1}{2} + \frac{1}{3} + \ldots + \frac{1}{(x+1)})$$

$$= 1 - \frac{1}{(x+1)}.$$

(i) $P(X > m) = 1 - P(X \leqslant m)$

$$= 1 - F(m) = \frac{1}{m+1}.$$

(ii)   Since $P(X \leqslant m) + P(m < X \leqslant n) = P(X \leqslant n)$
       it follows that

$$P(m < X \leqslant n) = P(X \leqslant n) - P(X \leqslant m)$$
$$= F(n) - F(m)$$
$$= \frac{1}{(m+1)} - \frac{1}{(n+1)}.$$

(iii) $P(m \leqslant X \leqslant n) = P(m-1 < X \leqslant n)$

$$= \frac{1}{m} - \frac{1}{(n+1)} \quad \text{using (ii).}$$

15. A mother knows that her food cupboard contains 3 tins of beans,
    2 tins of dog food and 2 tins of rice pudding. She decides to
    give her son beans for tea but when she goes to her cupboard she
    finds that he has removed all the labels. Since all the tins are
    superficially identical, she decides to start opening the tins at
    random until she opens a tin of beans. Find the probability
    function of X, the number of tins that she opens.

¶ $P(X=1) = P(\text{1st tin is beans}) = \frac{3}{7}.$

$P(X=2) = P(\text{1st tin is not beans and 2nd tin is beans})$
$= P(\text{1st tin is not beans}) \times$
$\quad P(\text{2nd tin is beans}|\text{1st tin is not beans})$
$= \frac{4}{7} \times \frac{3}{6} = \frac{2}{7}.$

Similarly,

$P(X=3) = \frac{4}{7} \times \frac{3}{6} \times \frac{3}{5} = \frac{6}{35},$

$P(X=4) = \frac{4}{7} \times \frac{3}{6} \times \frac{2}{5} \times \frac{3}{4} = \frac{3}{35},$

$P(X=5) = \frac{4}{7} \times \frac{3}{6} \times \frac{2}{5} \times \frac{1}{4} \times \frac{3}{3} = \frac{1}{35}.$

Clearly X cannot exceed 5. The probability function of X is therefore

x	1	2	3	4	5
p_x	$\frac{15}{35}$	$\frac{10}{35}$	$\frac{6}{35}$	$\frac{3}{35}$	$\frac{1}{35}$

Exercises 3.2 Mean and Variance

1. The random variable X has probability function

$$p_x = \frac{1}{14}(1+x) \quad \text{if } x = 1,2,3,4,$$
$$= 0 \quad \text{otherwise.}$$

Find the mean and variance of X.

¶ $p_1 = \frac{2}{14}, \quad p_2 = \frac{3}{14}, \quad p_3 = \frac{4}{14}, \quad p_4 = \frac{5}{14}.$

$$E(X) = \sum_x x p_x$$
$$= 1\times\frac{2}{14} + 2\times\frac{3}{14} + 3\times\frac{4}{14} + 4\times\frac{5}{14} = \frac{20}{7}.$$
$$E(X^2) = 1\times\frac{2}{14} + 4\times\frac{3}{14} + 9\times\frac{4}{14} + 16\times\frac{5}{14} = \frac{65}{7}.$$

Therefore $Var(X) = E(X^2) - [E(X)]^2$
$$= \frac{65}{7} - \frac{400}{49} = \frac{55}{49}.$$

2. The random variable X has probability function
$$p_x = k[1+|x-3|] \quad \text{if } x = 1,2,3,4,5,$$
$$= 0 \quad \text{otherwise,}$$

where k is a constant. Calculate k and find the mean and variance of X.

¶ Since $\sum\limits_{x} p_x = 1$, $k(3+2+1+2+3) = 1$. Therefore $k = \frac{1}{11}$.

$$E(X) = \sum\limits_{x} x p_x$$

$$= 1 \times \frac{3}{11} + 2 \times \frac{2}{11} + 3 \times \frac{1}{11} + 4 \times \frac{2}{11} + 5 \times \frac{3}{11}$$

$$= 3. \quad \text{(This is obvious by symmetry.)}$$

$$Var(X) = E(X - E(X))^2$$

$$= \frac{3}{11}(1-3)^2 + \frac{2}{11}(2-3)^2 + \frac{1}{11}(3-3)^2 + \frac{2}{11}(4-3)^2 + \frac{3}{11}(5-3)^2$$

$$= \frac{28}{11}.$$

3. Let X denote the score when a fair die is thrown. Determine the probability function of X and find its mean and variance.

¶ . The probability function of X is

x	1	2	3	4	5	6
p_x	$\frac{1}{6}$	$\frac{1}{6}$	$\frac{1}{6}$	$\frac{1}{6}$	$\frac{1}{6}$	$\frac{1}{6}$

$$E(X) = \sum\limits_{x} x p_x$$

$$= \frac{1}{6} \times 1 + \frac{1}{6} \times 2 + \frac{1}{6} \times 3 + \frac{1}{6} \times 4 + \frac{1}{6} \times 5 + \frac{1}{6} \times 6$$

$$= \frac{7}{2}.$$

$$Var(X) = E(X^2) - [E(X)]^2$$

$$= \frac{1}{6} \times 1 + \frac{1}{6} \times 4 + \frac{1}{6} \times 9 + \frac{1}{6} \times 16 + \frac{1}{6} \times 25 + \frac{1}{6} \times 36 - (\frac{7}{2})^2$$

$$= \frac{35}{12}.$$

4. Two fair dice are tossed and X equals the larger of the two scores obtained. Find the probability function of X and determine E(X).

¶ Using the sample space for Question 6 on page 79, we find that X has probability function

x	1	2	3	4	5	6
p_x	$\frac{1}{36}$	$\frac{3}{36}$	$\frac{5}{36}$	$\frac{7}{36}$	$\frac{9}{36}$	$\frac{11}{36}$

$$E(X) = \frac{1}{36}\times1 + \frac{3}{36}\times2 + \frac{5}{36}\times3 + \frac{7}{36}\times4 + \frac{9}{36}\times5 + \frac{11}{36}\times6$$
$$= \frac{161}{36}.$$

5. A bag contains 2 white and 2 red balls. Balls are selected one at a time, without replacement, until a red one is drawn. If X denotes the number of balls drawn, determine E(X).

¶
$$P(X=1) = P(\text{1st ball } R) = \frac{2}{4}.$$

$$P(X=2) = P(\text{1st ball } W \text{ and 2nd ball } R) = \frac{2}{4} \times \frac{2}{3} = \frac{1}{3}.$$

Similarly
$$P(X=3) = \frac{2}{4} \times \frac{1}{3} \times \frac{2}{2} = \frac{1}{6}.$$

X cannot exceed 3. The probability function is therefore

x	1	2	3
p_x	$\frac{1}{2}$	$\frac{1}{3}$	$\frac{1}{6}$

Thus $\quad E(X) = \frac{1}{2}\times1 + \frac{1}{3}\times2 + \frac{1}{6}\times3 = \frac{5}{3}.$

6. In a certain country, 10% of letters posted arrive the following day, 50% take two days, 30% take three days and the remainder take four days. Find the mean and standard deviation of the delivery time of a letter.

¶ The distribution of the delivery time T is given by

t	1	2	3	4
p_t	0.1	0.5	0.3	0.1

Hence
$$E(T) = 0.1\times1 + 0.5\times2 + 0.3\times3 + 0.1\times4 = 2.4 \text{ days}.$$

$$Var(T) = E(T^2) - [E(T)]^2$$
$$= 0.1\times1 + 0.5\times4 + 0.3\times9 + 0.1\times16 - (2.4)^2 = 0.64.$$

Thus S.D. $= \sqrt{0.64}$

$= 0.8$ days.

7. Two fair dice are tossed. If X and Y denote the two scores, find the probability function of XY and calculate E(XY).

¶ Referring to the sample space given in Question 6 on page 79, we find by enumeration that $Z = XY$ has probability function

z	1	2	3	4	5	6	8	9	10	12	15	16	18	20	24	25	30	36
p_z	$\frac{1}{36}$	$\frac{2}{36}$	$\frac{2}{36}$	$\frac{3}{36}$	$\frac{2}{36}$	$\frac{4}{36}$	$\frac{2}{36}$	$\frac{1}{36}$	$\frac{2}{36}$	$\frac{4}{36}$	$\frac{2}{36}$	$\frac{1}{36}$	$\frac{2}{36}$	$\frac{2}{36}$	$\frac{2}{36}$	$\frac{1}{36}$	$\frac{2}{36}$	$\frac{1}{36}$

$$E(Z) = \frac{1}{36}\times 1 + \frac{2}{36}\times 2 + \frac{2}{36}\times 3 + \frac{3}{36}\times 4 + \ldots + \frac{1}{36}\times 36$$

$$= \frac{49}{4}.$$

8. When is $E(X^2) = [E(X)]^2$?

¶ Since $\text{Var}(X) = E(X^2) - [E(X)]^2$, $E(X^2) = [E(X)]^2$ implies that $\text{Var}(X) = 0$.
This in turn implies that X takes some fixed value with probability 1.

9. A thousand tickets are sold in a lottery in which there is one top prize of £200, four prizes of £50, and ten prizes of £10. A ticket costs £1. If X is the net gain from one ticket, find E(X).

¶ The probability function of X is

x	199	49	9	-1
p_x	$\frac{1}{1000}$	$\frac{4}{1000}$	$\frac{10}{1000}$	$\frac{985}{1000}$

Thus

$$E(X) = \frac{1}{1000}\times 199 + \frac{4}{1000}\times 49 + \frac{10}{1000}\times 9 - \frac{985}{1000}\times 1$$

$$= -0.5, \text{ i.e. } -50\text{p}.$$

10. The random variable X has probability function
$$p_x = k(1+\alpha x) \quad \text{if } x = 0,1,2,3,$$
$$= 0 \quad \text{otherwise,}$$
where k, α are constants. Obtain k and $E(X)$ in terms of α. Hence find numerical values for k and α given that $E(X)$ is (a) 2, (b) 1.

¶ Since $\displaystyle\sum_x p_x = 1$, $k(1+1+\alpha+1+2\alpha+1+3\alpha) = 1$.

Therefore $k = \dfrac{1}{(4+6\alpha)}$.

$$E(X) = \sum_x x p_x$$
$$= 1 \times \left(\frac{1+\alpha}{4+6\alpha}\right) + 2 \times \left(\frac{1+2\alpha}{4+6\alpha}\right) + 3 \times \left(\frac{1+3\alpha}{4+6\alpha}\right)$$
$$= \frac{6+14\alpha}{4+6\alpha}.$$

(a) If $E(X) = 2$,
$$2 = \frac{6+14\alpha}{4+6\alpha}.$$
Therefore $\alpha = 1$, $k = \dfrac{1}{10}$.

(b) If $E(X) = 1$,
$$1 = \frac{6+14\alpha}{4+6\alpha}.$$
Therefore $\alpha = -\dfrac{1}{4}$, $k = \dfrac{2}{5}$.

11. The random variable X is uniformly distributed on the integers $0, \pm 1, \pm 2, \ldots, \pm n$. i.e.
$$p_x = \frac{1}{2n+1} \quad \text{if } x = 0, \pm 1, \pm 2, \ldots, \pm n,$$
$$= 0 \quad \text{otherwise.}$$
Obtain expressions for the mean and variance in terms of n. Given that the variance is 10, find n.

¶
$$E(X) = \sum_x x p_x = \frac{1}{2n+1} \sum_{x=-n}^{n} x = 0.$$

$$E(X^2) = \sum_x x^2 p_x = \frac{1}{2n+1} \sum_{x=-n}^{n} x^2$$

$$= \frac{2}{(2n+1)} \frac{n(n+1)(2n+1)}{6} = \frac{n(n+1)}{3}.$$

Therefore $\text{Var}(X) = E(X^2) - [E(X)]^2 = \dfrac{n(n+1)}{3}$.

If $\text{Var}(X) = 10$,

then $\dfrac{n(n+1)}{3} = 10$

$n^2 + n - 30 = 0$.

Therefore $n = 5$ (rejecting -6).

12. Let X be a random variable with mean μ and standard deviation σ. Express the mean and standard deviation of Z in terms of μ and σ when (a) $Z = 10X-5$, (b) $Z = (X-6)/3$, (c) $Z = (X-\mu)/\sigma$.

¶ (a) $E(Z) = E(10X-5) = 10E(X)-5 = 10\mu-5$.

$\text{Var}(Z) = \text{Var}(10X-5) = 100\text{Var}(X) = 100\sigma^2$.

Therefore S.D.$(Z) = 10\sigma$.

(b) $E(Z) = E[\dfrac{X}{3} - 2] = \dfrac{1}{3}E(X) - 2 = \dfrac{1}{3}\mu - 2$.

$\text{Var}(Z) = \text{Var}[\dfrac{X}{3} - 2] = \dfrac{1}{9}\text{Var}(X) = \dfrac{1}{9}\sigma^2$.

Therefore S.D.$(Z) = \dfrac{1}{3}\sigma$.

(c) $E(Z) = E[\dfrac{X}{\sigma} - \dfrac{\mu}{\sigma}] = \dfrac{E(X)}{\sigma} - \dfrac{\mu}{\sigma} = \dfrac{\mu}{\sigma} - \dfrac{\mu}{\sigma} = 0$.

$\text{Var}(Z) = \text{Var}[\dfrac{X}{\sigma} - \dfrac{\mu}{\sigma}] = \dfrac{1}{\sigma^2}\text{Var}(X) = \dfrac{1}{\sigma^2}\sigma^2 = 1$.

Therefore S.D.$(Z) = 1$.

13. The random variable X has a probability function p_X such that $p_1 = p_3 = \alpha$, $p_2 = 1-2\alpha$, where $0 < \alpha < \dfrac{1}{2}$, and $p_X = 0$ if $x \neq 1,2,3$. Find (a) $E(X)$, (b) $E(\dfrac{1}{X})$ and find the condition under which

$$E(\dfrac{1}{X}) = \dfrac{1}{E(X)}.$$

Use your result to show that in general $E(\dfrac{1}{X}) \neq \dfrac{1}{E(X)}$.

¶ (a) $E(X) = \displaystyle\sum_{x=1}^{3} xp_X$

$= 1.\alpha + 2(1-2\alpha) + 3\alpha$

$= 2$.

(b)

$$E\left(\tfrac{1}{X}\right) = \sum_{x=1}^{3} \tfrac{1}{x}\, p_x$$

$$= 1.\alpha + \tfrac{1}{2}(1-2\alpha) + \tfrac{1}{3}\alpha$$

$$= \tfrac{\alpha}{3} + \tfrac{1}{2}.$$

Thus $E\left(\tfrac{1}{X}\right) = \dfrac{1}{E(X)}$ if $\tfrac{\alpha}{3} + \tfrac{1}{2} = \tfrac{1}{2}$, i.e. if $\alpha = 0$.

For $\alpha \neq 0$, $E\left(\tfrac{1}{X}\right) \neq \dfrac{1}{E(X)}$.

14. Find $E(X)$ and $Var(X)$ in the following cases.

(a) $p_x = p$ if $x = 1$,   (b) $p_x = p$ if $x = 1$,
      $= 1-p$ if $x = 0$, $= 1-p$ if $x = -1$,
      $= 0$ otherwise. $= 0$ otherwise.

¶ (a)

$$E(X) = p.1 + (1-p).0 = p,$$
$$E(X^2) = p.1^2 + (1-p).0^2 = p,$$

so that $Var(X) = E(X^2) - [E(X)]^2 = p - p^2 = p(1-p).$

(b)

$$E(X) = p.1 + (1-p).(-1) = 2p-1,$$
$$E(X^2) = p.1^2 + (1-p).(-1)^2 = 1,$$

so that $Var(X) = E(X^2) - [E(X)]^2$
$$= 1 - (2p-1)^2 = 4p(1-p).$$

15. Find $E(X)$ and $Var(X)$ when $p_x = \dfrac{2x}{n(n+1)}$ if $x = 1,\ldots,n,$

$$= 0 \qquad \text{otherwise.}$$

¶

$$E(X) = \frac{2}{n(n+1)} \sum_{x=1}^{n} x^2 = \frac{2}{n(n+1)} \frac{n(n+1)(2n+1)}{6}$$

$$= \frac{(2n+1)}{3}.$$

$$E(X^2) = \frac{2}{n(n+1)} \sum_{x=1}^{n} x^3 = \frac{2}{n(n+1)} \frac{n^2(n+1)^2}{4} = \frac{n(n+1)}{2},$$

so that $Var(X) = E(X^2) - [E(X)]^2$

$$= \frac{n(n+1)}{2} - \frac{(2n+1)^2}{9}$$

$$= \frac{(n+2)(n-1)}{18}.$$

Exercises 3.3 The Binomial Distribution

1. The random variable X is binomially distributed with parameters n,p. Use tables to find (a) $P(X \leqslant 3)$, (b) $P(X = 3)$, (c) $P(X \geqslant 2)$, in the following cases: (i) n=6, p=0.4, (ii) n=8, p=0.3, (iii) n=10, p=0.475 (use linear interpolation).

¶ Using tables of the binomial cumulative distribution function $F(x;n,p)$,

(i)   (a) $P(X \leqslant 3) = F(3;6,0.4) = 0.82080,$

      (b) $P(X = 3) = P(X \leqslant 3) - P(X \leqslant 2)$

                          $= F(3;6,0.4) - F(2;6,0.4)$

                          $= 0.82080 - 0.54432$

                          $= 0.27648,$

      (c) $P(X \geqslant 2) = 1 - P(X \leqslant 1)$

                          $= 1 - F(1;6,0.4)$

                          $= 1 - 0.23328$

                          $= 0.76672.$

(ii)   (a) $P(X \leqslant 3) = F(3;8,0.3) = 0.80590,$

      (b) $P(X = 3) = P(X \leqslant 3) - P(X \leqslant 2)$

                          $= F(3;8,0.3) - F(2;8,0.3)$

                          $= 0.80590 - 0.55177$

                          $= 0.25413,$

      (c) $P(X \geqslant 2) = 1 - P(X \leqslant 1)$

                          $= 1 - F(1;8,0.3)$

                          $= 1 - 0.25530$

                          $= 0.74470.$

(iii)   (a) $P(X \leqslant 3) = F(3;10,0.475) \approx \frac{1}{2}(0.26604 + 0.17188)$

                          $= 0.21896,$

      (b) $P(X = 3) = P(X \leqslant 3) - P(X \leqslant 2)$

                          $= F(3;10,0.475) - F(2;10,0.475)$

                          $\approx 0.21896 - \frac{1}{2}(0.09956 + 0.05469)$

                          $= 0.14184,$

      (c) $P(X \geqslant 2) = 1 - P(X \leqslant 1)$

                          $= 1 - F(1;10,0.475)$

                          $\approx 1 - \frac{1}{2}(0.02326 + 0.01074)$

                          $= 0.98300.$

2. The random variable X is binomially distributed with parameters n,p. Use the formula for $P(X = x)$ to find (a) $P(X \leqslant 3)$, (b) $P(X = 3)$, (c) $P(X \geqslant 2)$, in the following cases: (i) n=6, p=0.4, (ii) n=8, p=0.3, (iii) n=10, p=0.475 and compare your results with Question 1 above.

¶ (i) (a) $P(X \leqslant 3) = {}^6C_0(0.4)^0(0.6)^6 + {}^6C_1(0.4)^1(0.6)^5$

$$+ {}^6C_2(0.4)^2(0.6)^4 + {}^6C_3(0.4)^3(0.6)^3$$

$$= 0.82080,$$

(b) $P(X = 3) = {}^6C_3(0.4)^3(0.6)^3 = 0.27648,$

(c) $P(X \geqslant 2) = 1 - P(X \leqslant 1)$

$$= 1 - ({}^6C_0(0.4)^0(0.6)^6 + {}^6C_1(0.4)^1(0.6)^5)$$

$$= 0.76672.$$

(ii) (a) $P(X \leqslant 3) = {}^8C_0(0.3)^0(0.7)^8 + {}^8C_1(0.3)^1(0.7)^7$

$$+ {}^8C_2(0.3)^2(0.7)^6 + {}^8C_3(0.3)^3(0.7)^5$$

$$= 0.80590,$$

(b) $P(X = 3) = {}^8C_3(0.3)^3(0.7)^5 = 0.25413,$

(c) $P(X \geqslant 2) = 1 - P(X \leqslant 1)$

$$= 1 - ({}^8C_0(0.3)^0(0.7)^8 + {}^8C_1(0.3)^1(0.7)^7)$$

$$= 0.74470.$$

(iii) (a) $P(X \leqslant 3) = {}^{10}C_0(0.475)^0(0.525)^{10} + {}^{10}C_1(0.475)^1(0.525)^9$

$$+ {}^{10}C_2(0.475)^2(0.525)^8 + {}^{10}C_3(0.475)^3(0.525)^7$$

$$= 0.21596,$$

(b) $P(X = 3) = {}^{10}C_3(0.475)^3(0.525)^7 = 0.14138,$

(c) $P(X \geqslant 2) = 1 - P(X \leqslant 1)$

$$= 1 - ({}^{10}C_0(0.475)^0(0.525)^{10}$$

$$+ {}^{10}C_1(0.475)^1(0.525)^9)$$

$$= 0.98402.$$

3. The random variable X is binomially distributed with parameters n,p. Use tables to find (a) $P(X \leqslant 19)$, (b) $P(X = 23)$, (c) $P(X \geqslant 21)$, in the following cases: (i) n=30, p=0.6, (ii) n=35, p=0.55, (iii) n=25, p=0.875 (use linear interpolation).

¶ (i)   (a) $P(X \leqslant 19) = F(19;30,0.6)$
$$= 1 - F(10;30,0.4)$$
$$= 1 - 0.29147$$
$$= 0.70853,$$

(b) $P(X = 23) = F(23;30,0.6) - F(22;30,0.6)$
$$= 1 - F(6;30,0.4) - (1 - F(7;30,0.4))$$
$$= F(7;30,0.4) - F(6;30,0.4)$$
$$= 0.04352 - 0.01718$$
$$= 0.02634,$$

(c) $P(X \geqslant 21) = 1 - P(X \leqslant 20)$
$$= 1 - F(20;30,0.6)$$
$$= 1 - (1 - F(9;30,0.4))$$
$$= F(9;30,0.4)$$
$$= 0.17629.$$

(ii)   (a) $P(X \leqslant 19) = F(19;35,0.55)$
$$= 1 - F(15;35,0.45)$$
$$= 1 - 0.46850$$
$$= 0.53150,$$

(b) $P(X = 23) = F(23;35,0.55) - F(22;35,0.55)$
$$= F(12;35,0.45) - F(11;35,0.45)$$
$$= 0.13436 - 0.07294$$
$$= 0.06142,$$

(c) $P(X \geqslant 21) = 1 - P(X \leqslant 20)$
$$= 1 - F(20;35,0.55)$$
$$= F(14;35,0.45)$$
$$= 0.33757.$$

(iii) (a) $P(X \leqslant 19) = F(19;25,0.875)$
$$= 1 - F(5;25,0.125)$$
$$\approx 1 - \frac{1}{2}(0.96660 + 0.83848)$$
$$= 0.09746,$$

(b) $\quad P(X = 23) = F(23;25,0.875) - F(22;25,0.875)$

$$= F(2;25,0.125) - F(1;25,0.125)$$

$$\approx \frac{1}{2}(0.53709 + 0.25374) - \frac{1}{2}(0.27121 + 0.09307)$$

$$= 0.21328,$$

(c) $\quad P(X \geqslant 21) = 1 - P(X \leqslant 20)$

$$= 1 - F(20;25,0.875)$$

$$= F(4;25,0.125)$$

$$\approx \frac{1}{2}(0.90201 + 0.68211)$$

$$= 0.79206.$$

4. A fair coin is spun 10 times. What are the probabilities of getting (i) exactly 2 heads, (ii) less than 2 heads, (iii) more than 2 heads, (iv) at most 2 heads, (v) at least 2 heads?

¶ Let X be the number of heads obtained. Then X is $B(10,\frac{1}{2})$.
Using tables of the binomial cumulative distribution function,

(i) $\quad P(X = 2) = F(2;10,\frac{1}{2}) - F(1;10,\frac{1}{2})$

$$= 0.05469 - 0.01074$$

$$= 0.04395,$$

(ii) $\quad P(X < 2) = F(1;10,\frac{1}{2}) = 0.01074,$

(iii) $\quad P(X > 2) = 1 - F(2;10,\frac{1}{2}) = 0.94531,$

(iv) $\quad P(X \leqslant 2) = F(2;10,\frac{1}{2}) = 0.05469,$

(v) $\quad P(X \geqslant 2) = 1 - F(1;10,\frac{1}{2}) = 1 - 0.01074 = 0.98926.$

5. A pair of fair dice is tossed six times. What is the probability of getting a total of 7 (i) twice, (ii) at least once, (iii) more than three times?

¶ Let X be the number of times a total of 7 is obtained.
Then X is $B(n,p)$ with $n=6$ and $p = 6/36 = 1/6$.
Using tables and interpolating,

(i) $\quad P(X = 2) = F(2;6,\frac{1}{6}) - F(1;6,\frac{1}{6})$

$$\approx 0.93548 - 0.73611$$

$$= 0.19937,$$

(ii) $P(X \geqslant 1) = 1 - P(X = 0)$

$= 1 - F(0;6,\frac{1}{6})$

$\approx 1 - 0.33881$

$= 0.66119,$

(iii) $P(X > 3) = 1 - P(X \leqslant 3)$

$= 1 - F(3;6,\frac{1}{6})$

$\approx 1 - 0.99042$

$= 0.00958.$

6. The probability of a defective item being produced on a production line is 0.1. Are you more likely to find (i) no defectives among ten items, or (ii) at most 1 defective among 20 items? What would the probability of a defective be if the above two probabilities were equal?

¶ Assuming independence we find, using tables, that

(i) P(no defectives in 10) $= F(0;10,0.1) = 0.34868,$

(ii) P(at most 1 defective in 20) $= F(1;20,0.1) = 0.39175.$

If the probabilities in (i) and (ii) are equal then p, the probability that an item is defective, must satisfy the equation

$$(1-p)^{10} = (1-p)^{20} + 20p(1-p)^{19}$$

i.e. $(1-p)^9(1+19p) = 1.$

We know from the above calculations that p=0.1 is an approximate root and, using this as a starting point, trial and error shows that p = 0.128 to 3 decimal places.

7. The probability of having no King in a bridge hand is 0.304. What is the probability that a person who plays 10 hands of bridge will never receive a King?

¶ P(no King in 10 hands) $= (0.304)^{10} = 6.7 \times 10^{-6}.$

Note that this probability cannot be calculated accurately using 5-figure tables of the binomial cumulative distribution function.

8. The random variable X has a binomial distribution with mean 1.5 and variance 1.275. Find the probability that X is at most 3.

¶ We are given that np=1.5 and npq=1.275.
Therefore q = 1-p = 0.85, p=0.15, n=10.
Using tables, $P(X \leqslant 3) = 0.95003$.

9. A man tries his luck at a coconut shy. He buys 6 throws for £1, and he wins £2 for every coconut he hits. If he has a probability 0.2 of hitting a coconut with each throw, determine an expression for the probability function of his profit and calculate his expected profit.

¶ Let X be the number of hits and Y his profit.
Then Y = 2X-1. Assuming independence, X is B(6,0.2) and therefore
$$P(Y = y) = P(2X-1 = y)$$
$$= P(X = \tfrac{1}{2}(y+1))$$
$$= {}^{6}C_{(y+1)/2}(0.2)^{(y+1)/2}(0.3)^{(11-y)/2}$$
for the values -1,1,3,5,7,9,11 of y; $P(Y = y) = 0$ for all other values of y.

Now
$$E(Y) = E(2X-1)$$
$$= 2E(X) - 1$$
$$= 2 \times 6 \times 0.2 - 1$$
$$= 1.4,$$
so his expected profit is £1.40.
N.B. The methods of Chapter 5 show that the expected profit is £1.40 even if successive throws are not independent.

10. Suppose that n independent trials are carried out, each having a probability p of success and q = 1-p of failure. Let Z = X-Y where X and Y denote respectively the number of successes and failures obtained in these trials. Find the probability distribution of Z and show that
$$E(Z) = n(2p-1).$$

¶ Since Y = n-X, Z = X - (n-X)
$$= 2X-n.$$
The possible values for X are 0,1,2,...,n. So for values -n,-n+2,

-n+4,...,n-2,n of z

$$P(Z = z) = P(2X-n=z)$$
$$= P(X = \tfrac{1}{2}(n+z))$$
$$= {}^{n}C_{(n+z)/2}\, p^{(n+z)/2}\, q^{(n-z)/2}.$$

$$P(Z = z) = 0 \text{ for all other values.}$$

Finally

$$E(Z) = E(2X-n)$$
$$= 2E(X)-n$$
$$= 2np-n$$
$$= n(2p-1).$$

11. A clairvoyant attempts to predict whether a coin will fall 'heads' or 'tails' and makes 30 correct predictions in 50 attempts. What is the probability that this result or a better one would be obtained if the predictions were mere guesswork?

¶ Let X be the number of correct predictions. Then X is $B(50,\tfrac{1}{2})$ if the predictions are mere guesswork. Using tables,

$$P(X \geqslant 30) = 1 - P(X \leqslant 29)$$
$$= 1 - 0.89868$$
$$= 0.10132.$$

12. A gambler bets on one of the integers from 1 to 6. Three fair dice are rolled and if the gambler's number appears k times (k=1,2,3), then he wins £k but if his number fails to appear he loses £1. Calculate the gambler's expected winnings.

¶ Let W be the gambler's winnings and let X be the number of times his number appears. Then X is $B(3,\tfrac{1}{6})$ and

$$P(W = -1) = P(X = 0) = (\tfrac{5}{6})^3 = \tfrac{125}{216},$$

$$P(W = 1) = P(X = 1) = {}^{3}C_{1}\,(\tfrac{1}{6})\,(\tfrac{5}{6})^2 = \tfrac{75}{216},$$

$$P(W = 2) = P(X = 2) = {}^{3}C_{2}\,(\tfrac{1}{6})^2\,(\tfrac{5}{6}) = \tfrac{15}{216},$$

$$P(W = 3) = P(X = 3) = (\tfrac{1}{6})^3 = \tfrac{1}{216}.$$

Therefore $E(W) = -1\times\tfrac{125}{216} + 1\times\tfrac{75}{216} + 2\times\tfrac{15}{216} + 3\times\tfrac{1}{216} = -\tfrac{17}{216}.$

So in the long run the gambler loses nearly 8 pence per game on average.

13. If the probability of success is 0.05 what is the minimum number of Bernoulli trials which must be performed in order that the probability of at least one success is at least 0.75?

¶ In n trials,

$$P(\text{at least 1 success}) = 1 - P(\text{no successes})$$

$$= 1 - 0.95^n.$$

We require

$$1 - 0.95^n \geqslant 0.75,$$

$$0.95^n \leqslant 0.25,$$

$$n \geqslant \frac{\log 0.25}{\log 0.95} = 27.03.$$

The required minimum number of trials is 28.

14. In a certain district of a city the proportion of people who vote Conservative is 0.30. Let a random sample of 100 voters be selected from the district.

   (i) Calculate the mean and variance of the number of people in the sample who vote Conservative.

   (ii) If X denotes the number in the sample who vote Conservative and μ and σ are the mean and standard deviation respectively as calculated in (i), evaluate (a) $P(\mu-\sigma \leqslant X \leqslant \mu+\sigma)$, (b) $P(\mu-2\sigma \leqslant X \leqslant \mu+2\sigma)$.

¶ If the number of voters in the district is much larger than 100, then X may be taken to be B(100,0.3) even though sampling is without replacement, since the proportion of Conservative voters will hardly change.

   (i) $E(X) = 100 \times 0.3 = 30.$

   $\text{Var}(X) = 100 \times 0.3 \times 0.7 = 21.$

   (ii) We must therefore calculate

   (a) $P(30-\sqrt{21} \leqslant X \leqslant 30+\sqrt{21})$ or $P(26 \leqslant X \leqslant 34)$, since X can take only integral values, and

   (b) $P(30-2\sqrt{21} \leqslant X \leqslant 30+2\sqrt{21})$ or $P(21 \leqslant X \leqslant 39)$.

Using tables of the binomial cumulative distribution function,

   (a) $P(26 \leqslant X \leqslant 34) = 0.83714 - 0.16313$

   $= 0.67401.$

   (b) $P(21 \leqslant X \leqslant 39) = 0.97901 - 0.01646$

   $= 0.96255.$

15. An electrical device contains 2n identical components connected in parallel. Whenever the device is switched on each component fails with probability p independently of the other components but the device continues to function unless n or more of the components fail simultaneously. What is the probability that the device functions when it is switched on?

Similar devices are produced by two rival companies A and B but company A uses 6 components in parallel whereas B uses only 4 components in its product. Show that if the two companies use components of identical quality than A's product is more reliable than B's if $p < \frac{3}{5}$.

¶ Let X be the number of components which fail. Then
$$P(\text{Device functions}) = P(X \leqslant n-1)$$
$$= \sum_{x=0}^{n-1} {}^{2n}C_x p^x (1-p)^{2n-x}.$$

A's product is more reliable than B's if and only if
$$\sum_{x=0}^{2} {}^{6}C_x p^x (1-p)^{6-x} > \sum_{x=0}^{1} {}^{4}C_x p^x (1-p)^{4-x}.$$

This condition reduces to $6p^2 - 10p^3 > 0$ or $p < \frac{6}{10}$.

Exercises 3.4 The Poisson Distribution

1. The random variable X has a Poisson distribution with parameter $\lambda = 3$. Find the following probabilities.
(i) $P(X \leqslant 2)$, (ii) $P(2 < X \leqslant 5)$, (iii) $P(X \geqslant 4)$.

¶ Using tables of the Poisson cumulative distribution function $F(x,\lambda)$,
(i) $\quad\quad P(X \leqslant 2) = F(2,3) = 0.42319.$

(ii) $\quad P(2 < X \leqslant 5) = F(5,3) - F(2,3)$
$$= 0.91608 - 0.42319$$
$$= 0.49289.$$

(iii) $\quad\quad P(X \geqslant 4) = 1 - P(X \leqslant 3)$
$$= 1 - F(3,3)$$
$$= 1 - 0.64723$$
$$= 0.35277.$$

2. If X is Poisson distributed with mean λ, find an expression for $P(X \geqslant 3)$.

   (i) Evaluate this for $\lambda=2$.

   (ii) Given that $P(X \geqslant 3) = 0.3$, find λ correct to 1 decimal place.

¶
$$P(X \geqslant 3) = 1 - P(X \leqslant 2)$$
$$= 1 - [e^{-\lambda} + \lambda e^{-\lambda} + \frac{\lambda^2}{2}e^{-\lambda}]$$
$$= 1 - e^{-\lambda}(1 + \lambda + \lambda^2/2).$$

   (i) If $\lambda=2$,
$$P(X \geqslant 3) = 1 - e^{-2}(1+2+2)$$
$$= 0.32332.$$

   (ii) This could be done by solving (by trial and error) the equation
$$1 - e^{-\lambda}(1 + \lambda + \lambda^2/2) = 0.3.$$
It is, however, much easier to use tables. We require
$$1 - F(2,\lambda) = 0.3$$
$$\text{or} \qquad F(2,\lambda) = 0.7.$$
Running along the x=2 line in the Poisson tables, it is clear that $\lambda=1.9$ is the required value.

3. The random variable X is binomially distributed with parameters n=50 and p=0.05. Evaluate the following probabilities using (a) the binomial distribution, (b) the Poisson approximation.
   (i) $P(X \leqslant 0)$, (ii) $P(X \leqslant 1)$, (iii) $P(X = 1)$, (iv) $P(X \leqslant 2)$, (v) $P(X = 2)$, (vi) $P(X \leqslant 3)$, (vii) $P(X = 3)$.

¶ The Poisson approximation has $\lambda = np = 2.5$. Using tables of the binomial and Poisson cumulative distribution functions we obtain

   (i)   (a) $P(X \leqslant 0) = 0.07694$,

          (b) $P(X \leqslant 0) \approx 0.08208$,

   (ii)   (a) $P(X \leqslant 1) = 0.27943$,

          (b) $P(X \leqslant 1) \approx 0.28730$,

   (iii) (a) $P(X = 1) = P(X \leqslant 1) - P(X \leqslant 0)$
$$= 0.27943 - 0.07694$$
$$= 0.20249,$$

          (b) $P(X = 1) = P(X \leqslant 1) - P(X \leqslant 0)$
$$\approx 0.28730 - 0.08208$$
$$= 0.20522,$$

(iv) (a) $P(X \leqslant 2) = 0.54053$,

      (b) $P(X \leqslant 2) \approx 0.54381$,

(v)   (a) $P(X = 2) = 0.54053 - 0.27943 = 0.26110$,

      (b) $P(X = 2) \approx 0.54381 - 0.28730 = 0.25651$,

(vi) (a) $P(X \leqslant 3) = 0.76041$,

      (b) $P(X \leqslant 3) \approx 0.75758$,

(vii) (a) $P(X = 3) = 0.76041 - 0.54053 = 0.21988$,

      (b) $P(X = 3) \approx 0.75758 - 0.54381 = 0.21377$.

4. The random variable X has a Poisson distribution with parameter λ. If $P(X = 0) = P(X = 1)$, calculate λ and hence find the probability that X is at least 2.

¶   If $P(X = 0) = P(X = 1)$ then $e^{-\lambda} = \lambda e^{-\lambda}$

so that $\lambda = 1$,

and $P(X \geqslant 2) = 1 - P(X \leqslant 1) = 1 - 0.73576 = 0.26424$.

5. The probability of being dealt a Royal Flush at poker is $1/649740$. How many times must a gambler play poker to make it more likely than not that he will be dealt a Royal Flush at least once? [Hint: use the Poisson approximation.]

¶   Let him play n times. Using the Poisson approximation with

$$\lambda = np = \frac{n}{649740}$$

$$P(\text{At least 1 Royal Flush}) = 1 - P(\text{No Royal Flush})$$

$$= 1 - e^{-n/649740}.$$

We require $1 - e^{-n/649740} > 0.5$

or $n > 649740 \ln 2 = 450365.45$.

So the gambler is more likely than not to receive at least one Royal Flush if he plays at least 450366 games of poker.

6. In a litre of fluid it is known that there are 10^{15} molecules. 10^5 tracer molecules are added and the resulting fluid is mixed thoroughly. A sample of 10^{-6} litres is withdrawn and the number of tracer molecules in the sample is counted. Using the Poisson approximation, calculate the probability that there is exactly 1 tracer molecule in the sample.

¶ Assume that the molecules do not interact. When the tracer molecules are added the resulting change in volume is negligible as is the change in the total number of particles. So take the volume of the mixture to be 1 litre and the total number of molecules to be 10^{15}. The probability that a molecule selected at random will be a tracer molecule is $10^5 \times 10^{-15} = 10^{-10}$. Also, the sample contains $10^{-6} \times 10^{15} = 10^9$ molecules. It follows that the number of tracer molecules in the sample is approximately $B(10^9, 10^{-10})$ and so is approximately Poisson with mean $10^9 \times 10^{-10} = 0.1$.

Therefore $P(1 \text{ tracer molecule}) \approx e^{-0.1} \times 0.1 = 0.09048.$

Alternatively we can argue that the probability that a particular tracer molecule will be contained in the sample is 10^{-6} so that the number of tracer molecules in the sample is approximately Poisson with mean $10^5 \times 10^{-6} = 0.1$.

7. Let X have a Poisson distribution with mean 1 and let

$$Y = X \quad \text{if } X \leq 3,$$
$$Y = 3 \quad \text{if } X > 3.$$

Find the probability function of Y and calculate its mean.

¶ If $y = 0, 1$ or 2, $P(Y=y) = P(X=y) = \dfrac{e^{-1}}{y!}$.

Furthermore, $\quad P(Y=3) = P(X \geq 3)$

$$= 1 - P(X \leq 2)$$
$$= 1 - e^{-1}[1 + 1 + \tfrac{1}{2}]$$
$$= 0.0803.$$

Therefore $\quad E(Y) = 1 \times e^{-1} + 2 \times \dfrac{e^{-1}}{2} + 3 \times 0.0803$

$$= 0.9767.$$

8. The performance of a computer is studied over a period of time during which it makes 10^{15} computations. If the probability that a particular computation is incorrect equals 10^{-14}, independent of other computations, write down an expression for the probability that fewer than 10 errors occur and calculate an approximation to its value.

¶ Let X be the number of errors made. Then X is binomially distributed with $n = 10^{15}$ and $p = 10^{-14}$.

Thus

$$P(X \leqslant 9) = \sum_{x=0}^{9} 10^{15}C_x (10^{-14})^x (1-10^{-14})^{10^{15}-x}.$$

Using the Poisson approximation with $\lambda = np = 10$,

$$P(X \leqslant 9) \approx \sum_{x=0}^{9} e^{-10} \cdot \frac{10^x}{x!} = F(9,10) = 0.45793.$$

9. A firm has 3 concrete mixers for hire. The hire charge for these machines is £7 per day. The overheads are £2 per mixer per day, whether they are hired or not. If the daily demand for these machines is Poisson distributed with mean 2, what is the expected daily profit? Repeat this exercise in the case of 4 concrete mixers. Would you advise the firm to increase the number of machines for hire from 3 to 4?

¶ Let X be the demand and Y the number of machines actually hired in a day. Then

$$Y = X \quad \text{if } X \leqslant 3,$$
$$= 3 \quad \text{if } X > 3.$$

Now

$$P(Y = 1) = P(X = 1) = 2e^{-2} = 0.27067,$$
$$P(Y = 2) = P(X = 2) = 2e^{-2} = 0.27067,$$
$$P(Y = 3) = P(X \geqslant 3) = 0.32332.$$

Therefore

$$E(Y) = 1 \times 0.27067 + 2 \times 0.27067 + 3 \times 0.32332$$
$$= 1.782.$$

If P denotes the daily profit in pounds, then

$$P = 7Y - 6$$

Therefore

$$E(P) = 7E(Y) - 6 = 7 \times 1.782 - 6 = 6.474.$$

Now suppose the firm has 4 machines. Then

$$Y = X \quad \text{if } X \leqslant 4,$$
$$= 4 \quad \text{if } X > 4,$$

and

$$E(Y) = 1 \times 0.27067 + 2 \times 0.27067 + 3 \times 0.18044 + 4 \times 0.14288$$
$$= 1.925$$

since $P(Y=1) = P(Y=2) = 0.27067$, $P(Y=3) = 0.18044$ and $P(Y=4) = P(X \geqslant 4) = 0.14288.$

This time

$$P = 7Y - 8$$

so that

$$E(P) = 7E(Y) - 8 = 7 \times 1.925 - 8 = 5.474.$$

The firm should not increase from 3 to 4 mixers.

10. The number of letters delivered to a certain house on a weekday is Poisson distributed with mean λ. If the postman is seen walking up the drive one morning, what is the probability that he delivers r letters $(r \geqslant 1)$?

¶ Let X be the number of letters delivered on a particular day. Since the postman is seen walking up the drive, we can assume that $X \geqslant 1$. Thus, for $r \geqslant 1$,

$$P(X = r \mid X \geqslant 1) = \frac{P(X = r \text{ and } X \geqslant 1)}{P(X \geqslant 1)}$$

$$= \frac{P(X = r)}{1 - P(X = 0)}$$

$$= \frac{e^{-\lambda} \frac{\lambda^r}{r!}}{1 - e^{-\lambda}}$$

This gives the required probability.

11. The number of spectators who turn up to watch a local cricket team is known to be Poisson distributed with mean 10. If the admission charge is £3, find the probability distribution of the amount of money taken at the gate. If the gateman is paid £16 for collecting the admission money, find
(i) the expected profit on admission charges,
(ii) the probability of making a loss.

¶ Let X be the number of spectators and Y the gate money collected. Then $Y = 3X$ and for $y = 0, 3, 6, 9, \ldots$

$$P(Y = y) = P(3X = y)$$
$$= P(X = \tfrac{1}{3}y)$$

$$= e^{-10} \frac{10^{y/3}}{(\tfrac{1}{3}y)!}$$

(i) If P is the profit, in pounds, then
$$P = 3X - 16$$
and $E(P) = 3E(X) - 16 = 3 \times 10 - 16 = 14.$

(ii) A loss will be made if at most 5 spectators turn up. Using tables, we find that
$$P(X \leqslant 5) = 0.06709.$$

12. Starting with the series for e^θ, show that

$$\theta + \frac{\theta^3}{3!} + \frac{\theta^5}{5!} + \frac{\theta^7}{7!} + \ldots = \frac{e^\theta - e^{-\theta}}{2}.$$

Hence find an expression for the probability that X, a Poisson random variable with mean λ, takes a value that is odd. Show that this probability is approximately 1/2 for large λ.

¶

$$e^\theta = 1 + \theta + \frac{\theta^2}{2!} + \frac{\theta^3}{3!} + \frac{\theta^4}{4!} + \frac{\theta^5}{5!} + \frac{\theta^6}{6!} + \frac{\theta^7}{7!} + \ldots$$

$$e^{-\theta} = 1 - \theta + \frac{\theta^2}{2!} - \frac{\theta^3}{3!} + \frac{\theta^4}{4!} - \frac{\theta^5}{5!} + \frac{\theta^6}{6!} - \frac{\theta^7}{7!} + \ldots$$

By subtraction $\frac{1}{2}(e^\theta - e^{-\theta}) = \theta + \frac{\theta^3}{3!} + \frac{\theta^5}{5!} + \frac{\theta^7}{7!} + \ldots$

$$P(\text{X is odd}) = P(X=1) + P(X=3) + P(X=5) + P(X=7) + \ldots$$

$$= e^{-\lambda} + e^{-\lambda}\frac{\lambda^3}{3!} + e^{-\lambda}\frac{\lambda^5}{5!} + e^{-\lambda}\frac{\lambda^7}{7!} + \ldots$$

$$= e^{-\lambda}\left(1 + \frac{\lambda^3}{3!} + \frac{\lambda^5}{5!} + \frac{\lambda^7}{7!} + \ldots\right)$$

$$= \frac{e^{-\lambda}}{2}(e^\lambda - e^{-\lambda})$$

$$= \frac{(1 - e^{-2\lambda})}{2}.$$

When λ is large, $e^{-2\lambda}$ is near zero and $P(\text{X is odd}) \approx \frac{1}{2}$.

13. The daily demand for a certain grocery product can be assumed to have a Poisson distribution. Grocer A claims the mean demand is 6 while grocer B claims it is 9. They agree to resolve the disagreement by observing the demand on one particular day. B accepts A's claim if the observed demand is 7 or less; otherwise B's claim is accepted. Calculate (i) the probability that A's claim is accepted given that B is correct, (ii) the probability that B's claim is accepted given that A is correct. Do you think the grocers' procedure is a reasonable one?

¶ Let X be the demand on the day in question.

(i) P(A's claim accepted if B is correct)

$= P(X \leqslant 7$ if X is Poisson with mean 9) $= 0.32390$.

(ii) P(B's claim accepted if A is correct)

$= P(X \geqslant 8$ if X is Poisson with mean 6)

$= 1 - 0.74398 = 0.25602$.

Perhaps at first sight the procedure appears to be fair to both parties but B might well be less happy about it than A if he were to consider the above error probabilities. If A is correct then he has a 74% chance of having his claim accepted whereas B has only a 68% chance if he is correct. On the other hand, consider any procedure of the form "accept A's claim if and only if X < k" where k is a fixed integer. Using tables, we find that there is no value of k for which the two error probabilities are equal but that they are most nearly equal when k=7. So the agreed procedure is most reasonable in the sense that it comes nearest to balancing the error probabilities.

N.B. Both error probabilities are rather high and they could be greatly reduced by observing $\bar{X}$, the average daily demand over a number of days. Assuming independence, if the mean daily demand were μ then $n\bar{X}$, the total demand over n days, would be Poisson with mean $n\mu$ - Question 35, page 243. Thus, for example,

$$P(\bar{X} \leqslant 7) = P(n\bar{X} \leqslant 7n) = \sum_{r=0}^{7n} e^{-n\mu} \frac{(n\mu)^r}{r!}.$$

The normal approximation to the Poisson distribution could be used to evaluate the error probabilities.

14. The number of incoming calls at a switchboard in one hour is Poisson distributed with mean $\lambda = 8$. The numbers arriving in non-overlapping time intervals are statistically independent. Find the probability that in 10 non-overlapping one hour periods at least 2 of the periods have at least 15 calls.

¶ Let X be the number of calls arriving in an hour and let $P(X \geqslant 15)=p$. Then Y, the number of times out of 10 that $X \geqslant 15$, is $B(n,p)$ with n=10 and p = 1 - 0.98274 = 0.01726.

Therefore $P(Y \geqslant 2) = 1 - P(Y \leqslant 1)$
$$= 1 - ((0.98274)^{10} + 10(0.01726)(0.98274)^9).$$
$$= 0.01223.$$

15. The random variable X is Poisson distributed with mean λ. If $p_x = P(X = x)$ prove that

$$\frac{p_x}{p_{x-1}} = \frac{\lambda}{x}, \quad x \geqslant 1.$$

Hence find the most likely value or values of X if λ is (a) not an integer, (b) an integer.

¶   When $x \geqslant 1$,

$$\frac{P_x}{P_{x-1}} = e^{-\lambda} \frac{\lambda^x}{x} \cdot e^{\lambda} \frac{(x-1)!}{\lambda^{x-1}} = \frac{\lambda}{x}.$$

(a) If λ is not an integer then for $r \geqslant 0$, setting $x = [\lambda]-r$,

$$P_{[\lambda]-r-1} = \frac{[\lambda]-r}{\lambda} P_{[\lambda]-r} < \frac{\lambda-r}{\lambda} P_{[\lambda]-r} \leqslant P_{[\lambda]-r}$$

and, setting $x = [\lambda]+r+1$,

$$P_{[\lambda]+r+1} = \frac{\lambda}{[\lambda]+r+1} P_{[\lambda]+r} < \frac{[\lambda]+1}{[\lambda]+r+1} P_{[\lambda]+r} \leqslant P_{[\lambda]+r}.$$

It follows that

$$P_{[\lambda]} > P_{[\lambda]-1} > P_{[\lambda]-2} > \cdots$$

and

$$P_{[\lambda]} > P_{[\lambda]+1} > P_{[\lambda]+2} > \cdots$$

Therefore $[\lambda]$ is the most likely (or most probable) value of X. (N.B. $[\lambda]$ denotes the integral part of λ.)

(b) If λ is an integer then

$$\frac{P_\lambda}{P_{\lambda-1}} = \frac{\lambda}{\lambda} = 1.$$

Also, for $r \geqslant 1$,

$$P_{\lambda-r-1} = (1 - \frac{r}{\lambda})P_{\lambda-r} < P_{\lambda-r}$$

and

$$P_{\lambda+r} = \frac{\lambda}{\lambda+r}P_{\lambda+r-1} < P_{\lambda+r-1}.$$

Therefore

$$\cdots < P_{\lambda-3} < P_{\lambda-2} < P_{\lambda-1} = P_\lambda > P_{\lambda+1} > P_{\lambda+2} > \cdots$$

So there are two most likely (or most probable) values in this case, λ and $\lambda-1$.

Miscellaneous Problems

1. A meter reader knows from long experience that when he makes a call someone will be home with constant probability p regardless of his success with other calls. If the probability that the next four houses are occupied is 16/625, what is the probability that at least two will be occupied when he calls?

¶   Let p be the probability of being at home.

Then $(1-p)^4 = \dfrac{16}{625}$ so that $1-p = \dfrac{2}{5}$ and $p = \dfrac{3}{5} = 0.6$.

If X is the number of occupied houses in the next four, then X is B(4,0.6) and

$$P(X \geqslant 2) = 1 - F(1;4,0.6)$$
$$= F(2;4,0.4)$$
$$= 0.82080$$

where F(x;n,p) denotes the binomial cumulative distribution function.

2. A match manufacturer produces boxes of matches which should contain 40 matches.   The probability distribution of the number of matches is as shown below.

Number of matches in a box	38	39	40	41	42
Probability	0.1	0.2	0.4	0.2	0.1

If two boxes are chosen at random and the matches are counted what is the probability that there are at least 80 matches in total?

¶   Let the two boxes be labelled A and B and let Z denote the total number of matches.

$P(Z = 84) = P(42 \text{ in both}) = 0.1 \times 0.1 = 0.01,$

$P(Z = 83) = 2P(41 \text{ in A and 42 in B}) = 2 \times 0.2 \times 0.1 = 0.04,$
$\quad$ since $P(42 \text{ in A and 41 in B}) = P(41 \text{ in A and 42 in B}),$

$P(Z = 82) = 2P(40 \text{ in A and 42 in B}) + P(41 \text{ in both})$
$\quad\quad\quad = 2 \times 0.4 \times 0.1 + 0.2 \times 0.2 = 0.12,$

$P(Z = 81) = 2P(39 \text{ in A and 42 in B}) + 2P(40 \text{ in A and 41 in B})$
$\quad\quad\quad = 2 \times 0.2 \times 0.1 + 2 \times 0.4 \times 0.2 = 0.20,$

$P(Z = 80) = 2P(38 \text{ in A and 42 in B}) + 2P(39 \text{ in A and 41 in B})$
$\quad\quad\quad\quad + P(40 \text{ in both})$
$\quad\quad\quad = 2 \times 0.1 \times 0.1 + 2 \times 0.2 \times 0.2 + 0.4 \times 0.4 = 0.26.$

Therefore $P(Z \geqslant 80) = 0.01 + 0.04 + 0.12 + 0.20 + 0.26 = 0.63$.

Note that the probability function of Z is symmetrical about the value 80 and so can be written down without any additional calculation as follows:

z	76	77	78	79	80	81	82	83	84
p_z	0.01	0.04	0.12	0.20	0.26	0.20	0.12	0.04	0.01

3. The cumulative distribution function of a discrete random variable X is given by

$$F(x) = 0 \quad \text{if } x < 0,$$
$$= 0.1 \quad \text{if } 0 \leqslant x < 1,$$
$$= 0.5 \quad \text{if } 1 \leqslant x < 2,$$
$$= 0.8 \quad \text{if } 2 \leqslant x < 3,$$
$$= 1 \quad \text{if } x \geqslant 3.$$

Find the probability function of X. Using the cumulative distribution function find (i) $P(X < 2)$, (ii) $P(X \geqslant 1)$, (iii) $P(X^2 > 5)$.

¶ The probability function p_x of X is as follows

x	0	1	2	3
p_x	0.1	0.4	0.3	0.2

(i) $\qquad P(X < 2) = F(1.99) = 0.5.$

(ii) $\qquad P(X \geqslant 1) = 1 - P(X < 1) = 1 - F(0.99) = 1 - 0.1 = 0.9.$

(iii) $\qquad P(X^2 > 5) = P(X < -\sqrt{5}) + P(X > \sqrt{5})$
$$= 0 + (1 - P(X \leqslant \sqrt{5}))$$
$$= 1 - F(\sqrt{5})$$
$$= 1 - 0.8$$
$$= 0.2$$

$\qquad$ as $P(X < -\sqrt{5}) \leqslant P(X \leqslant -2) = F(-2) = 0.$

4. Five coins are tossed, and those which fall 'heads' are tossed again. Find the probability function, and hence the mean, of the number of coins which fall 'heads' on the second tossing.

¶ Let Y be the number of 'heads' on the second tossing.
The probability that x and y 'heads' are obtained on the first and second tossings respectively equals

$$^5C_x \left(\tfrac{1}{2}\right)^5 \times {}^xC_y \left(\tfrac{1}{2}\right)^x.$$

If Y=y then at least y 'heads' must have been obtained on the first tossing. Therefore

$$P(Y = y) = \sum_{x=y}^{5} {}^5C_x {}^xC_y \left(\tfrac{1}{2}\right)^{5+x}$$

and the probability function of Y in tabular form is

y	0	1	2	3	4	5
p_y	$\dfrac{243}{1024}$	$\dfrac{405}{1024}$	$\dfrac{270}{1024}$	$\dfrac{90}{1024}$	$\dfrac{15}{1024}$	$\dfrac{1}{1024}$

For example

$$P_3 = \sum_{x=3}^{5} {}^5C_x \, {}^xC_3 \, (\tfrac{1}{2})^{5+x}$$

$$= {}^5C_3 \, {}^3C_3 \, (\tfrac{1}{2})^8 + {}^5C_4 \, {}^4C_3 \, (\tfrac{1}{2})^9 + {}^5C_5 \, {}^5C_3 \, (\tfrac{1}{2})^{10}$$

$$= (10\times2^2 + 5\times4\times2 + 10)(\tfrac{1}{2})^{10}$$

$$= \frac{90}{1024}.$$

Finally

$$E(Y) = (405 + 2\times270 + 3\times90 + 4\times15 + 5)/1024 = 1.25.$$

5. An event A occurs with constant probability p whenever a certain experiment is carried out. Suppose independent repetitions of the experiment are made until either A occurs or n experiments have been performed. If X denotes the total number of experiments, find its probability function p_x and check your answer by evaluating $\sum_x p_x$. Find also $E(X)$.

¶ If $x = 1, 2, \ldots, n-1$ then $X = x$ if and only if A does not occur in the first x-1 trials but does occur at the x'th trial and so

$$P(X = x) = p(1-p)^{x-1}.$$

X takes the value n if and only if A does not occur in the first n-1 trials so that

$$P(X = n) = (1-p)^{n-1}.$$

Therefore

$$p_x = p(1-p)^{x-1} \qquad \text{if } x = 1, 2, \ldots, n-1,$$
$$= (1-p)^{n-1} \qquad \text{if } x = n,$$
$$= 0 \qquad\qquad \text{otherwise.}$$

Consider

$$\sum_x p_x = \sum_{x=1}^{n-1} p(1-p)^{x-1} + (1-p)^{n-1}$$

$$= \frac{p(1 - (1-p)^{n-1})}{1 - (1-p)} + (1-p)^{n-1}$$

$$= 1 \quad \text{as required.}$$

$$E(X) = \sum_{x=1}^{n-1} xp(1-p)^{x-1} + n(1-p)^{n-1}$$

$$= \frac{1 - (1-p)^{n-1}}{p} - (n-1)(1-p)^{n-1} + n(1-p)^{n-1}$$

113

$$= \frac{1 - (1-p)^{n-1}}{p} + (1-p)^{n-1}.$$

6. Suppose that the probability distribution of family size in a certain country is as shown below.

Number of children	0	1	2	3	4	5
Probability	0.4	0.2	0.15	0.1	0.1	0.05

(a) Let X denote the number of children in a family selected at random. Find μ_X and σ_X, the mean and standard deviation of X.

(b) A child is selected at random from the population of all children and asked how many children there are in his or her family. If Y denotes this random variable, calculate μ_Y and σ_Y.

(c) Which of μ_X and μ_Y is a better measure of the 'average' family size?

¶ (a)
$$\mu_X = 0.2 + 2\times0.15 + 3\times0.1 + 4\times0.1 + 5\times0.05$$
$$= 1.45$$
$$\sigma_X^2 = 0.2 + 2^2\times0.15 + 3^2\times0.1 + 4^2\times0.1 + 5^2\times0.05 - 1.45^2$$
$$= 2.4475.$$

Therefore $\sigma_X = 1.564$.

(b) Suppose that there are N families in all. Then the population of all children will contain 0.2N children who have no brothers or sisters, $2\times0.15N = 0.3N$ children who have only one brother or sister and so on. Thus we obtain the following frequency distribution.

Number of children in a child's family	Frequency
1	0.20N
2	0.30N
3	0.30N
4	0.40N
5	0.25N
	1.45N

Thus if a child is selected at random from the population of all children, the probability that he or she is an only child is 20/145 by the equally likely principle. The probability that he or she has only one brother or sister is 30/145 and so on. Y therefore has the following probability distribution.

y	1	2	3	4	5
p_y	$\dfrac{20}{145}$	$\dfrac{30}{145}$	$\dfrac{30}{145}$	$\dfrac{40}{145}$	$\dfrac{25}{145}$

Hence

$$\mu_Y = \frac{455}{145} = 3.138$$

and $\qquad \sigma_Y = \sqrt{1.706} = 1.306.$

(c) μ_Y is an unsatisfactory measure of average family size. The method of asking a child how many children there are in his or her family necessarily excludes childless families. Furthermore, the mean number of children per family when childless families are excluded is

$$(0.2 + 0.2\times0.15 + 3\times0.1 + 4\times0.1 + 5\times0.05)/0.6 = 2.417$$

whereas $\mu_Y = 3.138$. The reason that μ_Y exceeds 2.417 is that the procedure of choosing a family by selecting a child at random is biased in favour of the larger families. For example, a family of 4 children is twice as likely to be selected as one with only one child when this method is used even though there are twice as many single-child families as 4-child families.

7. A test consists of 3 multiple-choice questions, each with a choice of 4 answers. Let X be the number of correct answers. If a student guesses the answers find

   (i)   the probability distribution of X,

   (ii) the mean and variance of X.

   (iii) If the teacher rescaled the marks using the formula Y=aX+b, what would be the values of a and b if $E(Y) = 0$ and $Var(Y)=1$?

¶ (i)   X is binomially distributed with parameters $n=3$, $p=\frac{1}{4}$.

(ii) $\qquad\qquad E(X) = np = \frac{3}{4}, \quad Var(X) = npq = \frac{9}{16}.$

(iii) $\qquad\qquad E(Y) = aE(X) + b = \frac{3}{4}a + b = 0$

$$Var(Y) = a^2 Var(X) = \frac{9}{16}a^2 = 1$$

whence, rejecting the negative square root,

$$a = \frac{4}{3} \quad \text{and} \quad b = -1.$$

8. Suppose player A persuades player B to play the following game. A fair coin is tossed until the first head appears, but the game ends if no heads appear in the first 10 tosses. Player B agrees to pay player A 4p if a head turns up on the first toss, 4^2p if the first head appears on the second toss,...., 4^{10}p if the first head appears on the 10th toss. A receives nothing if a head does not appear after 10 tosses. What fee must player A pay player B if A's expected profit is to be zero?

¶ The probability that a head first appears on the xth toss is

$$(\tfrac{1}{2})^{x-1} \times \tfrac{1}{2} = (\tfrac{1}{2})^x ,$$

since x-1 tails are followed by a head. With no fee, A's expected profit is

$$\sum_{x=1}^{10} (\tfrac{1}{2})^x 4^x = \sum_{x=1}^{10} 2^x = \frac{2(1-2^{10})}{1-2} = 2046.$$

So A must pay B £20.46 if his expected profit is to be zero.

9. Let X denote a discrete random variable with mean μ and variance σ^2. If c is any real number prove that
$$E((X-c)^2) = \sigma^2 + (c-\mu)^2 .$$
Deduce that $E((X-c)^2)$ is minimised if $c = \mu$.

¶ $E((X-c)^2) = E(((X-\mu) + (\mu-c))^2) = E[(X-\mu)^2] + 2(\mu-c)E(X-\mu) + (\mu-c)^2$
$$= E[(X-\mu)^2] + (c-\mu)^2$$

     since $E(X-\mu) = \mu - \mu = 0$.
It follows that
$$E[(X-c)^2] \geqslant E[(X-\mu)^2]$$
with equality if $c = \mu$. This shows that $E[(X-c)^2]$ is minimised when $c = \mu$.

10. Three similar factories (1,2 and 3) produce identical items. The outputs of these factories are in the ratio 3:4:5 respectively. From past records it is reasonable to assume that a defective item is produced with probability proportional to the output of the factory. If an item produced is found to be defective, what is the probability that it came from factory 3? All defective items are returned to a consumer protection unit. What is the probability that of the first 4 defective items returned at least 2 of them are from factory 3?

¶ Let the probabilities that an item is defective be 3k, 4k and 5k respectively for the three factories, where k is a constant. Define the events A_i : Item comes from factory i (i=1,2,3),

$$D: \text{Item is defective.}$$

Using Bayes' Theorem

$$P(A_3|D) = \frac{P(D|A_3)P(A_3)}{\sum_{i=1}^{3} P(D|A_i)P(A_i)}$$

$$= \frac{5k \times \frac{5}{12}}{3k \times \frac{3}{12} + 4k \times \frac{4}{12} + 5k \times \frac{5}{12}}$$

$$= \frac{1}{2},$$

since $P(A_1) = \frac{3}{12}$, $P(A_2) = \frac{4}{12}$ and $P(A_3) = \frac{5}{12}$.

Let X be the number of defectives out of 4 which come from factory 3. Assuming independence, X is $B(4,\frac{1}{2})$ and

$$P(X \geqslant 2) = 1 - P(X \leqslant 1) = 1 - 0.31250 = 0.68750.$$

11. Three balls are drawn at random without replacement from a bag containing four white and eight red balls. Can you guess the expected number of white balls among the three? Check your answer by computing the exact value.

¶ The fact that one third of the balls are white suggests that the expected number of white balls is 1. Let X be the number of white balls drawn. Sampling is without replacement so that

$$P(X = 1) = P(2 \text{ red and } 1 \text{ white})$$

$$= 3 \times \frac{8}{12} \times \frac{7}{11} \times \frac{4}{10} \quad \text{(as there are three orders}$$

$$= \frac{672}{1320}, \qquad \qquad \text{in which the balls can be chosen)}$$

$$P(X = 2) = P(2 \text{ white and } 1 \text{ red})$$

$$= 3 \times \frac{4}{12} \times \frac{3}{11} \times \frac{8}{10}$$

$$= \frac{288}{1320},$$

$$P(X = 3) = P(\text{all white})$$

$$= \frac{4}{12} \times \frac{3}{11} \times \frac{2}{10}$$

$$= \frac{24}{1320}.$$

Therefore $E(X) = \dfrac{672}{1320} + 2 \times \dfrac{288}{1320} + 3 \times \dfrac{24}{1320} = 1.$

12. A boy has 12 matches of unit length. He selects X of them
$(1 \leqslant X \leqslant 5)$ and constructs a rectangle having adjacent sides X and
6-X. If X is a random variable which is uniformly distributed on
the integers 1,2,3,4,5, i.e. it has probability function
$$P(X = x) = \frac{1}{5} \quad \text{for } x = 1,2,3,4,5,$$
$$= 0 \quad \text{otherwise,}$$
determine the probability function of A, the area of the rectangle.
Also find E(A) and Var(A).

¶ If A is the area of the rectangle,
$$A = X(6-X),$$
that is

X	1	2	3	4	5
A	5	8	9	8	5

The probability function of A is therefore

a	5	8	9
p_a	$\frac{2}{5}$	$\frac{2}{5}$	$\frac{1}{5}$

Hence $E(A) = 5 \times \dfrac{2}{5} + 8 \times \dfrac{2}{5} + 9 \times \dfrac{1}{5} = 7.$

$Var(A) = (-2)^2 \times \dfrac{2}{5} + 1^2 \times \dfrac{2}{5} + 2^2 \times \dfrac{1}{5} = \dfrac{14}{5}.$

13. A particle, initially at the point O, moves once per second. Each
move is either 1 unit to the East with probability 1/2 or 1 unit to
the North with probability 1/2. If D_n denotes the distance of the
particle from O after n moves, find the probability function of D_n
for $n = 1,2,3,4$ and find $E(D_n)$ for these values of n.

¶ $D_1 = 1$ irrespective of whether the particle moves due North or due
East at its first step. Thus
$$P(D_1 = 1) = 1 \text{ and } E(D_1) = 1.$$
The possible values of D_2 are 2 (arising from NN or EE) and $\sqrt{2}$
(arising from NE or EN). Thus
$$P(D_2 = 2) = P(D_2 = \sqrt{2}) = \frac{2}{4}$$
and $E(D_2) = 2 \times \dfrac{2}{4} + \sqrt{2} \times \dfrac{2}{4} = 1 + \dfrac{1}{\sqrt{2}}.$

The possible values of D are 3 (NNN or EEE) and $\sqrt{5}$ (NNE,NEN,ENN,NEE, ENE or EEN). Thus

$$P(D_3 = 3) = \frac{2}{8}, \quad P(D_3 = \sqrt{5}) = \frac{6}{8}$$

and

$$E(D_3) = 3 \times \frac{2}{8} + \sqrt{5} \times \frac{6}{8} = \frac{3}{4}(1 + \sqrt{5}).$$

The possible values of D_4 are 4 (NNNN or EEEE), $\sqrt{10}$ (arising from three moves North and one move East or three moves East and one move North in any order) and $\sqrt{8}$ (arising from 2 moves North and 2 moves East in any order). Thus

$$P(D_4 = 4) = \frac{2}{16}, \quad P(D_4 = \sqrt{10}) = \frac{8}{16}, \quad P(D_4 = \sqrt{8}) = \frac{6}{16}$$

and

$$E(D_4) = 4 \times \frac{2}{16} + \sqrt{10} \times \frac{8}{16} + \sqrt{8} \times \frac{6}{16} = \frac{1}{2}(1 + \sqrt{10} + \frac{3}{\sqrt{2}}).$$

14. The number X of passengers wishing to travel on a late night bus has the following probability function

x	0	1	2	3	4	5
p_x	0.2	0.3	0.25	0.15	0.08	0.02

Find the mean and variance of X.

The bus does not run if there are no passengers. If Y is the number of passengers travelling on the bus given that it actually runs, find the probability function of Y and determine E(Y) and Var(Y).

¶ $E(X) = 1.67$, $E(X^2) = 4.43$, $Var(X) = 4.43 - 1.67^2 = 1.6411$.

If $y = 1,2,3,4,5$

$$P(Y = y) = P(X = y | X > 0)$$
$$= \frac{P(X = y \text{ and } X > 0)}{P(X > 0)}$$
$$= \frac{P(X = y)}{P(X > 0)} \qquad \text{as } y > 0$$
$$= \frac{P(X = y)}{0.8}.$$

Thus Y has the probability function

y	1	2	3	4	5
p_y	0.375	0.3125	0.1875	0.1	0.025

so that

$$E(Y) = 2.0875, \quad E(Y^2) = 5.5375, \quad Var(Y) = 5.5375 - 2.0875^2$$
$$= 1.1798.$$

15. Part of an electrical circuit between the points A and B contains four 100 ohm resistors in parallel. Each one of the resistors has a probability of 1/4 (independently of all others) of failing within 200 hours. Resistors which fail can be assumed to be disconnected, and, if all the resistors fail, a safety device operates which places a 100 ohm resistance between A and B. Find the probability function of R, the resistance between A and B after 200 hours, and deduce the values of E(R) and E(1/R). The points A,B are disconnected from the remainder of the circuit after 200 hours, and a 25 volt battery is connected across AB. Find the probability function of the resulting current I and determine E(I). Verify that

$$E(I) = 25E\left(\frac{1}{R}\right)$$

but $\qquad E(I) \neq \dfrac{25}{E(R)}.$

[N.B. The combined resistance R of n resistors R_1, R_2,...,R_n in parallel is given by

$$\frac{1}{R} = \frac{1}{R_1} + \frac{1}{R_2} + \dots + \frac{1}{R_n}$$

and the current I which flows through a resistance R across which a voltage V is connected is given by

$$I = \frac{V}{R}.]$$

¶ Let X of the resistors fail within 200 hours. Then X is binomially distributed with parameters n=4, p=0.25. The probability function of X is therefore

x	0	1	2	3	4
p_x	$\dfrac{81}{256}$	$\dfrac{108}{256}$	$\dfrac{54}{256}$	$\dfrac{12}{256}$	$\dfrac{1}{256}$

Using the rule for combining parallel resistors,

$$R = 25 \quad \text{if } X=0,$$
$$R = 33\tfrac{1}{3} \quad \text{if } X=1,$$
$$R = 50 \quad \text{if } X=2,$$
$$R = 100 \quad \text{if } X=3,$$
$$\text{and} \quad R = 100 \quad \text{if } X=4 \quad \text{because of the safety device.}$$

The probability function of R is therefore

r	25	$33\tfrac{1}{3}$	50	100
p_r	$\dfrac{81}{256}$	$\dfrac{108}{256}$	$\dfrac{54}{256}$	$\dfrac{13}{256}$

We find that

$$E(R) = \frac{9625}{256}$$

while

$$E\left(\frac{1}{R}\right) = \frac{1}{25}\times\frac{81}{256} + \frac{3}{100}\times\frac{108}{256} + \frac{1}{50}\times\frac{54}{256} + \frac{1}{100}\times\frac{13}{256}$$

$$= \frac{769}{25600}.$$

Now

$$I = \frac{V}{R} = \frac{25}{R}$$

so that

$$I = 1 \quad \text{if } R=25,$$

$$I = \frac{3}{4} \quad \text{if } R=33\tfrac{1}{3},$$

$$I = \frac{1}{2} \quad \text{if } R=50,$$

$$I = \frac{1}{4} \quad \text{if } R=100.$$

The probability function of I is

i	$\frac{1}{4}$	$\frac{1}{2}$	$\frac{3}{4}$	1
p_i	$\frac{13}{256}$	$\frac{54}{256}$	$\frac{108}{256}$	$\frac{81}{256}$

whence

$$E(I) = \frac{769}{1024}.$$

It follows that

$$\frac{E(I)}{E\left(\frac{1}{R}\right)} = \frac{769}{1024}\times\frac{25600}{769} = 25$$

but

$$E(I)E(R) = \frac{769}{1024}\times\frac{9625}{256} \neq 25.$$

16. Three coins are drawn at random from a large heap of equal numbers of 1p, 2p and 5p coins. Write down the probability functions of (i) X, the total value of the three coins, (ii) Y, the number of 5p coins drawn. Find the mean and variance of X and Y.

¶ Ten different unordered selections of three coins are possible. For example, 1,5,5 i.e. one 1p and two 5p coins, which has probability 3/27. (This assumes that the coins are drawn with replacement but the change in the probability caused by selecting the coins without replacement is negligible if the total number of coins is very large.)

Selection	X	Y	Prob.
1,1,1	3	0	$\frac{1}{27}$
1,1,2	4	0	$\frac{3}{27}$
1,1,5	7	1	$\frac{3}{27}$
1,2,2	5	0	$\frac{3}{27}$
1,2,5	8	1	$\frac{6}{27}$
1,5,5	11	2	$\frac{3}{27}$
2,2,2	6	0	$\frac{1}{27}$
2,2,5	9	1	$\frac{3}{27}$
2,5,5	12	2	$\frac{3}{27}$
5,5,5	15	3	$\frac{1}{27}$

The probability function of X is

x	3	4	5	6	7	8	9	11	12	15
p_x	$\frac{1}{27}$	$\frac{3}{27}$	$\frac{3}{27}$	$\frac{1}{27}$	$\frac{3}{27}$	$\frac{6}{27}$	$\frac{3}{27}$	$\frac{3}{27}$	$\frac{3}{27}$	$\frac{1}{27}$

and $E(X) = 8$, $Var(X) = \frac{25}{27} + \frac{48}{27} + \ldots + \frac{49}{27} = \frac{234}{27} = \frac{26}{3}$.

From above the probability function of Y is

y	0	1	2	3
p_y	$\frac{8}{27}$	$\frac{12}{27}$	$\frac{6}{27}$	$\frac{1}{27}$

but this could have been obtained by observing that Y is $B(3,\frac{1}{3})$.

Hence $E(Y) = 1$, $Var(Y) = \frac{2}{3}$.

17. Let X be a discrete random variable with sample space $\{0,1,2,\ldots,n\}$ and probability function $p_i = P(X=i)$, $i = 0,1,2,\ldots,n$. The function $G(\theta)$ defined by

$$G(\theta) = \sum_{i=0}^{n} \theta^i p_i$$

is called the *probability generating function* of X. Prove the following results.

$$\left. \frac{dG(\theta)}{d\theta} \right]_{\theta=1} = E(X), \quad \left. \frac{d^2 G(\theta)}{d\theta^2} \right]_{\theta=1} = E(X^2) - E(X).$$

If X has a binomial distribution with parameters n and p show that $G(\theta) = (q+p\theta)^n$, where $q = 1-p$, and deduce the mean and variance of X.

¶
$$G(\theta) = \sum_{i=0}^{n} \theta^i p_i$$

and
$$\frac{dG(\theta)}{d\theta} = \sum_{i=0}^{n} i\theta^{i-1} p_i.$$

Thus
$$\frac{dG(\theta)}{d\theta}\bigg]_{\theta=1} = \sum_{i=0}^{n} ip_i = E(X).$$

Also
$$\frac{d^2G(\theta)}{d\theta^2} = \sum_{i=0}^{n} i(i-1)\theta^{i-2} p_i$$

and
$$\frac{d^2G(\theta)}{d\theta^2}\bigg]_{\theta=1} = \sum_{i=0}^{n} i(i-1) p_i$$
$$= E[X(X-1)] = E(X^2) - E(X).$$

For the binomial distribution,
$$G(\theta) = \sum_{i=0}^{n} \theta^i \, ^nC_i p^i (1-q)^{n-i}$$

$$= \sum_{i=0}^{n} \, ^nC_i (p\theta)^i (1-q)^{n-i}$$

$$= (p\theta+q)^n \quad \text{by the binomial theorem.}$$

Thus
$$\frac{dG(\theta)}{d\theta} = np(p\theta+q)^{n-1}$$

so that
$$E(X) = \frac{dG(\theta)}{d\theta}\bigg]_{\theta=1} = np.$$

$$\frac{d^2G(\theta)}{d\theta^2} = n(n-1)p^2(p\theta+q)^{n-2}$$

and
$$E(X^2) - E(X) = \frac{d^2G(\theta)}{d\theta^2}\bigg]_{\theta=1} = n(n-1)p^2$$

Therefore $E(X^2) = n(n-1)p^2 + E(X) = n(n-1)p^2 + np.$

It follows that
$$Var(X) = E(X^2) - [E(X)]^2$$
$$= n(n-1)p^2 + np - n^2p^2$$
$$= np(1-p)$$
$$= npq.$$

18. Let X be a random variable which is Poisson distributed with mean λ. Obtain an expression for the probability generating function of X and hence find the mean and variance of X.

¶ If $G(\theta)$ is the probability generating function of X,

$$G(\theta) = \sum_{x=0}^{\infty} \theta^x e^{-\lambda} \frac{\lambda^x}{x!}$$

$$= e^{-\lambda} \sum_{x=0}^{\infty} \frac{(\theta\lambda)^x}{x!} = e^{-\lambda} e^{\theta\lambda} = e^{\lambda(\theta-1)}.$$

Thus $\dfrac{dG(\theta)}{d\theta} = \lambda e^{\lambda(\theta-1)}$,

$$\frac{d^2 G(\theta)}{d\theta^2} = \lambda^2 e^{\lambda(\theta-1)}.$$

Then $E(X) = \dfrac{dG(\theta)}{d\theta}\bigg]_{\theta=1} = \lambda$,

$$E(X^2) - E(X) = \frac{d^2 G(\theta)}{d\theta^2}\bigg]_{\theta=1} = \lambda^2,$$

Thus $E(X^2) = \lambda^2 + E(X) = \lambda^2 + \lambda$.

Finally, $Var(X) = E(X^2) - [E(X)]^2$

$$= \lambda^2 + \lambda - \lambda^2 = \lambda.$$

19. An event occurs at a given trial with constant probability p $(0 < p < 1)$. If the trials are independent and X is the number of successive trials until the event occurs for the first time show that X has the *geometric* probability function

$$p_x = p(1-p)^{x-1} \quad (x = 1,2,\ldots.)$$

and find its mean and variance. Obtain an expression for the cumulative distribution function of X and show that

$$P(X \leqslant x+k \,|\, X > x) = P(X \leqslant k) \quad (k = 1,2,\ldots.).$$

¶ X takes the value x if the event does not occur in the first x-1 trials but does occur at trial x. Thus

$$P(X = x) = p(1-p)^{x-1} \quad (x = 1,2,\ldots.).$$

If $G(\theta)$ is the probability generating function of X,

$$G(\theta) = \sum_{x=1}^{\infty} \theta^x p q^{x-1} = \frac{p}{q} \sum_{x=1}^{\infty} (\theta q)^x = \frac{p}{q} \frac{\theta q}{1-\theta q} = \frac{p\theta}{1-\theta q}.$$

Hence $\dfrac{dG(\theta)}{d\theta} = \dfrac{p(1-\theta q) + pq\theta}{(1-\theta q)^2} = \dfrac{p}{(1-\theta q)^2}$ $\qquad (q=1-p)$

and $\quad \dfrac{d^2 G(\theta)}{d\theta} = \dfrac{2pq}{(1-\theta q)^3}.$

Thus $\quad E(X) = \dfrac{p}{(1-q)^2} = \dfrac{1}{p}$

and $\quad E(X^2) - E(X) = \dfrac{2pq}{(1-q)^3} = \dfrac{2q}{p^2},$

so that $\quad Var(X) = \dfrac{2q}{p^2} + \dfrac{1}{p} - \dfrac{1}{p^2} = \dfrac{q}{p^2}.$

The cumulative distribution function is given by

$$F(x) = \sum_{i=1}^{[x]} pq^{i-1} = \dfrac{p(1-q^{[x]})}{1-q} = 1 - q^{[x]}.$$

For k = 1,2,3....

$$P(X \leqslant x+k \,|\, X > x) = \dfrac{P(x < X \leqslant x+k)}{P(X > x)} = \dfrac{F(x+k) - F(x)}{1 - F(x)}$$

$$= \dfrac{1 - q^{[x+k]} - 1 + q^{[x]}}{q^{[x]}}$$

$$= 1 - q^{[x+k]-[x]} = 1 - q^k$$

$$= F(k) = P(X \leqslant k).$$

20. A fair coin is tossed until a head appears. If X denotes the number of tails obtained before the first head appears, find the probability distribution of X and its mean and variance.

¶ X takes the value x if x successive tails are followed by a head. Thus

$$P(X = x) = (\tfrac{1}{2})^{x+1} \qquad (x = 0,1,2,.....).$$

If $G(\theta)$ is the probability generating function of X,

$$G(\theta) = \sum_{x=0}^{\infty} \theta^x (\tfrac{1}{2})^{x+1} = \dfrac{1}{2} \sum_{x=0}^{\infty} (\tfrac{\theta}{2})^x = (2-\theta)^{-1}.$$

Thus $\quad \dfrac{dG(\theta)}{d\theta} = (2-\theta)^{-2}$ and $E(X) = 1,$

while $\quad \dfrac{d^2 G(\theta)}{d\theta^2} = 2(2-\theta)^{-3}$ and $E(X^2) = 2+1 = 3,$

giving $\quad Var(X) = 3-1 = 2.$

21. A machine produces washers which must satisfy certain size and quality specifications. It produces a defective article with probability p. Every hour a sample of 10 washers is inspected and if two or more washers are defective the machine is stopped and overhauled. Assuming that the machine is not malfunctioning,

write down an expression for the probability that production must be stopped after a particular sample. If this probability is α, write down an expression for the expected time between stoppages.

¶
$$\alpha = \sum_{i=2}^{10} {}^{10}C_i p^i (1-p)^{10-i} = 1 - (1-p)^9 (1+9p).$$

Suppose a stoppage occurs at time t and that subsequent samples are taken at times t+1, t+2,.... If the next stoppage occurs at time t+X then

$$P(X = x) = \alpha(1-\alpha)^{x-1} \quad (x = 1,2,....)$$

as α is the probability of a stoppage on a given sample. Hence

$$E(X) = \frac{1}{\alpha}.$$

So the expected time between stoppages is α^{-1} hours.

22. Let X be a random variable with non-zero probabilities on the set $\{1,2,....,2n+1\}$ where n is an integer greater than or equal to 1. If the distribution is symmetric about the value (n+1), i.e. $P(X = n+1-j) = P(X = n+1+j)$, prove that $E(X) = n+1$.

¶
$$E(X) = \sum_{x=1}^{2n+1} xP(X=x) = \sum_{j=-n}^{n} (n+1+j)P(X = n+1+j) \quad (j=x-n-1)$$

$$= n + 1 + \sum_{j=-n}^{n} jP(X = n+1+j) \quad \text{since} \sum_{j=-n}^{n} P(X = n+1+j) = 1$$

$$= n + 1 + \sum_{j=-n}^{-1} jP(X=n+1+j) + \sum_{j=1}^{n} jP(X=n+1+j)$$

$$= n + 1 - \sum_{j=1}^{n} jP(X=n+1-j) + \sum_{j=1}^{n} jP(X=n+1+j)$$

$$= n + 1 \quad \text{as } P(X=n+1-j) = P(X=n+1+j).$$

23. A counter is placed at the origin marked on a line. It is moved one unit to the left or right depending upon whether the outcome of tossing a fair coin is heads or tails respectively. Let X_n denote the position of the counter after n tosses of the coin. Determine the probability distribution of X_n for n = 1,....,8 and

calculate the probability that the counter is no more than 2 units away from the origin in each case. What is $E(X_n)$? Conjecture what this probability and expectation might be as n approaches infinity.

¶ Let r be the number of moves to the right and let ℓ be the number of moves to the left in the first n moves. If n is *odd* then the counter can be at any *odd* integer point between -n and +n inclusive. Suppose it is at x after n moves. Then $x = r - \ell$ so that $r = (n+x)/2$ since $r + \ell = n$. There are ^nC_r ways in which the counter can reach x in n moves as this is the number of different ways of arranging r moves to the right and n-r moves to the left. Each possibility has probability $(\frac{1}{2})^n$. Thus when n is odd

$$P(X_n = x) = {}^nC_r (\tfrac{1}{2})^n \qquad \text{if x is odd,}$$
$$= 0 \qquad \text{otherwise,}$$

where $r = (n+x)/2$.

Similarly, if n is *even* then the counter can be at any *even* integer point between -n and +n inclusive and

$$P(X_n = x) = {}^nC_r (\tfrac{1}{2})^n \qquad \text{if x is even,}$$
$$= 0 \qquad \text{otherwise,}$$

where, again, $r = (n+x)/2$.

These formulae yield the following results

n	$P(-2 \leqslant X_n \leqslant 2)$	$E(X_n)$
1	1	0
2	1	0
3	$\frac{3}{4}$	0
4	$\frac{7}{8}$	0
5	$\frac{5}{8}$	0
6	$\frac{25}{32}$	0
7	$\frac{35}{64}$	0
8	$\frac{91}{128}$	0

For example, $P(-2 \leqslant X_8 \leqslant 2) = ({}^8C_3 + {}^8C_4 + {}^8C_5)(\tfrac{1}{2})^8 = \frac{91}{128}$.

$E(X_n) = 0$ for all n, as is obvious by symmetry.

$P(-2 \leqslant X_n \leqslant 2)$ decreases steadily as n increases through odd values. It also decreases steadily as n increases through even values. This suggests that $P(-2 \leqslant X_n \leqslant 2)$ approaches zero as n approaches infinity and it can be shown that this is the case.

24. A man has 5 similar door keys in his pocket. He is faced with the problem of opening a locked door and only one key will fit. He does not know which key will open the door and so he selects one at random, discarding it if it does not fit. If X denotes the number of keys tried before the door is opened find E(X). Repeat this problem if the man is in a drunken state and consequently replaces the key in his pocket each time.

¶   If he discards keys which do not fit then

$$P(X=1) = P(X=2) = P(X=3) = P(X=4) = P(X=5) = \frac{1}{5}.$$

For example, $P(X=4) = \frac{4}{5} \times \frac{3}{4} \times \frac{2}{3} \times \frac{1}{2} = \frac{1}{5}.$

Thus $E(X) = 1 \times \frac{1}{5} + 2 \times \frac{1}{5} + 3 \times \frac{1}{5} + 4 \times \frac{1}{5} + 5 \times \frac{1}{5} = 3.$

If instead he replaces the key in his pocket each time, then on each occasion he chooses the correct key with probability $\frac{1}{5}$.
Hence
$$P(X=x) = \left(\frac{4}{5}\right)^{x-1} \times \frac{1}{5} \qquad (x = 1,2,3,\ldots.)$$

   and $E(X) = 5.$ (Question 19, page 124.)

In general, if he has n keys, then in the first case $E(X) = \frac{n+1}{2}$ while $E(X) = n$ in the second case.

25. Suppose that a sequence of Bernoulli trials with success probability p is performed until n successes have been obtained. Show that the number of trials X necessary to achieve this has the *negative binomial* probability function

$$p_x = P(X = x) = {}^{x-1}C_{n-1}\,p^n\,(1-p)^{x-n} \qquad (x = n,n+1,n+2,\ldots.).$$

¶   Let the nth success be achieved at the xth trial. Any sequence of length x leading to this result must end with a success and must contain n-1 successes and x-n failures in the first x-1 trials. There are ${}^{x-1}C_{n-1}$ such sequences each occurring with probability $p^n(1-p)^{x-n}$ since there are x trials and n successes in all.

Thus

$$P(X = x) = {}^{x-1}C_{n-1}\,p^n\,(1-p)^{x-n}.$$

Since at least n trials are necessary this holds for x=n,n+1,n+2,...

26. A street 1 kilometer long has n+1 lamp posts equally spaced along it from one end to the other. Two different lamp posts are selected at random. Find expressions for the mean and variance of their distance apart.

¶ Two different lamp posts can be selected in ${}^{n+1}C_2 = (n+1)n/2$ equally likely ways. Let the distance between them be X kilometers. The number of selections which result in $X = \frac{1}{n}$ is n, since the left hand lamp post can be any one of n. Thus

$$P(X = \tfrac{1}{n}) = \frac{2n}{(n+1)n}$$

Similarly $\qquad P(X = \tfrac{k}{n}) = \frac{2(n-k+1)}{(n+1)n} \qquad (k = 1,2,\ldots,n).$

$$E(X) = \sum_{k=1}^{n} \frac{k}{n}\,\frac{2(n-k+1)}{(n+1)n} = \frac{2}{n^2}\sum_{k=1}^{n} k - \frac{2}{n^2(n+1)}\sum_{k=1}^{n} k^2$$

$$= \frac{2}{n^2}\,\frac{n(n+1)}{2} - \frac{2}{n^2(n+1)}\,\frac{n(n+1)(2n+1)}{6}$$

$$= \frac{n+2}{3n}.$$

$$E(X^2) = \sum_{k=1}^{n} \frac{k^2}{n^2}\,\frac{2(n-k+1)}{(n+1)n} = \frac{2}{n^3}\sum_{k=1}^{n} k^2 - \frac{2}{n^3(n+1)}\sum_{k=1}^{n} k^3$$

$$= \frac{2}{n^3}\,\frac{n(n+1)(2n+1)}{6} - \frac{2}{n^3(n+1)}\,\frac{n^2(n+1)^2}{4} = \frac{(n+1)(n+2)}{6n^2}$$

Thus $\quad \mathrm{Var}(X) = \frac{(n+1)(n+2)}{6n^2} - \frac{(n+2)^2}{9n^2} = \frac{(n-1)(n+2)}{18n^2}.$

27. Charles is collecting toy cars, one of which comes free in each packet of cereal. There are five types of car and each type is equally likely to be found in a packet of cereal. Charles wants to have a complete set of all five types. Calculate the expected number of packets that he must buy in order to complete his collection.

¶ The first packet will give Charles a car of some colour. After this, he will either obtain the colour he already has or a new one.

The probability that he finds a new colour in a given packet is $\frac{4}{5}$.
Let X be the number of packets he needs to buy before he finds a
new colour. Then

$$P(X = x) = \frac{4}{5}(\frac{1}{5})^{x-1} \qquad (x = 1,2,3,\ldots.)$$

Thus X has a geometric distribution with success probability $\frac{4}{5}$ and
$E(X) = \frac{5}{4}$. (See problem 19, page 124).
Now that Charles has two colours, he has probability $\frac{3}{5}$ of finding
a new colour and he can expect to buy $\frac{5}{3}$ packets before he finds one.
Continuing the argument, we find that he can expect to buy

$$1 + \frac{5}{4} + \frac{5}{3} + \frac{5}{2} + 5 = \frac{137}{12} \approx 11.4$$

packets in order to complete his collection.

28. (a) Let X be a binomial random variable with parameters n and p.
Prove that, if q = 1-p,

$$P(X = x) = \frac{(n-x+1)}{x} \frac{p}{q} P(X = x-1), \quad x = 1,\ldots,n.$$

(b) Denote by k the unique integer for which

$$(n+1)p - 1 < k \leqslant (n+1)p.$$

If (n+1)p is not an integer, show that as x goes from 0 to n,
$P(X = x)$ increases up to a maximum value, occuring at x=k, and
then decreases. If k = (n+1)p, however, show that $P(X = x)$
increases up to $\overset{\prime}{\underset{\wedge}{P}}(X = k-1)$ which is equal to $P(X = k)$ and then
decreases.

(c) Check the result of (b) if (i) n=6, p=0.25, (ii) n=7, p=0.25.

¶ (a) $$\frac{P(X = x)}{P(X = x-1)} = \frac{n!}{x!(n-x)!} \frac{(x-1)!(n-x+1)!}{n!} \frac{p^x q^{n-x}}{p^{x-1}q^{n-x+1}}$$

$$= \frac{(n-x+1)}{x} \frac{p}{q}.$$

(b) It follows from (a) that
$$P(X = x) > P(X = x-1)$$
if and only if
$$(n-x+1)p > xq = x(1-p)$$
i.e. $$x < (n+1)p.$$
Let k be as defined. If (n+1)p is not an integer then
k < (n+1)p and we have k-r < (n+1)p for r = 0,1,2,... so that
$$P(X = k-r) > P(X = k-r-1)$$
and, in particular,
$$P(X = k) > P(X = k-1).$$

Also $k+r \nmid (n+1)p$ for $r=1,2,\ldots$ so that $P(X=k+r) < P(X=k+r-1)$ and, in particular, $P(X=k+1) < P(X=k)$.

Thus $P(X = x)$ increases to a maximum value at $x=k$ and decreases thereafter. Suppose now that $(n+1)p$ is an integer.

Then $\dfrac{P(X = k)}{P(X = k-1)} = \dfrac{(n-k+1)p}{k(1-p)} = 1$ since $k = (n+1)p$.

Thus $P(X = k) = P(X = k-1)$

but, for $r = 1,2,\ldots,$ $k-r < k = (n+1)p$ and $k+r > k = (n+1)p$

so that $P(X = k-r) > P(X = k-r-1)$

and $P(X = k+r) < P(X = k+r-1)$ as required.

N.B. When $0 < p < 1$ we have $(n+1)p - 1 < np < (n+1)p$.

It follows that if np, the expected value of X, is an integer then the most probable or most likely value of X is equal to np.

(c) (i) If $n=6$, $p=0.25$ then $(n+1)p = 1.75$, $k = [1.75] = 1$ and X has the probability distribution

x	0	1	2	3	4	5	6
p_x	0.1780	0.3560	0.2966	0.1318	0.0330	0.0044	0.0002

(ii) If $n=7$, $p=0.25$ then $k = (n+1)p = 2$ and X has the probability distribution

x	0	1	2	3	4	5	6	7
p_x	0.1335	0.3115	0.3115	0.1730	0.0577	0.0115	0.0013	0.0001

29. In a sequence of n independent trials with constant probability p of success let p_n denote the probability of an odd number of successes. Establish the recurrence formula

$$P_n = qp_{n-1} + p(1-p_{n-1}) \quad (n = 1,2,\ldots.)$$

where $p_0 = 0$, and $q = 1-p$. Verify that the solution is

$$P_n = \tfrac{1}{2}(1-(q-p)^n).$$

¶ Consider the event that there is an odd number of successes in n trials. There are two possibilities.

(i) The first (n-1) trials contain an odd number of successes and the nth trial is a failure.

(ii) The first (n-1) trials contain an even number of successes and the nth trial is a success.

It follows by the law of total probability that

$$P_n = qp_{n-1} + p(1-p_{n-1}).$$

The boundary condition is $p_0 = 0$, since an odd number of successes cannot occur in zero trials.

Suppose p_n is as given in the question.

Consider
$$p_n - qp_{n-1} - p(1-p_{n-1}) = p_n - (q-p)p_{n-1} - p$$
$$= \frac{1}{2} - \frac{1}{2}(q-p)^n - (q-p)\frac{1}{2}[1 - (q-p)^{n-1}] - p$$
$$= 0.$$

Thus p_n satisfies the equation.

Furthermore,
$$p_0 = \frac{1}{2}[1 - (q-p)^0] = 0$$

so that the boundary condition is also satisfied.

30. To encourage sales of a certain brand of breakfast cereal each packet contains a gift token with probability p. To secure a particular prize 10 tokens must be obtained. Find the probability function of the number of packets that must be bought to obtain 10 tokens.

¶ If X is the number of packets bought to obtain 10 tokens then X has a negative binomial distribution (see problem 25, page 128) and
$$P(X = x) = {}^{x-1}C_9 p^{10} q^{x-10} \qquad (x = 10,11,12,\ldots.; \; q = 1-p).$$
Note that $E(X) = \frac{10}{p}$ and $Var(X) = \frac{10q}{p^2}$ – see Question 26, page 236.

31. An entomologist knows that 80% of the leaves he examines carry no insect of the type he is looking for. Assuming a Poisson distribution of these insects among leaves find the probability that if he finds one on a leaf there is at least one more on the same leaf.

¶ Let X be the number of insects on a leaf and assume that X has a Poisson distribution with mean λ.

We require
$$P(X \geqslant 2 \mid X \geqslant 1) = \frac{P(X \geqslant 2)}{P(X \geqslant 1)}$$
$$= \frac{1 - P(X \leqslant 1)}{1 - P(X = 0)}$$
$$= \frac{1 - (e^{-\lambda} + \lambda e^{-\lambda})}{1 - e^{-\lambda}}.$$
$$= 0.1074$$

since $P(X = 0) = e^{-\lambda} = 0.8$ and $\lambda = -\ln 0.8 = 0.223144$.

32. A bag contains n balls numbered 1 to n. If m balls are drawn at random without replacement and if X is the largest number drawn show that

$$p_x = \frac{m(x-1)(x-2)\ldots(x-m+1)}{n(n-1)(n-2)\ldots(n-m+1)} \qquad (x = m, m+1, \ldots, n)$$

and that

$$E(X) = \frac{m(n+1)}{m+1}, \quad Var(X) = \frac{m(n+1)(n-m)}{(m+1)^2(m+2)}$$

Hint:
$$\sum_{x=m}^{n} \frac{x!}{m!(x-m)!} = \frac{(n+1)!}{(m+1)!(n-m)!}$$

If n is unknown but it is given that X = x how might n be estimated?

¶ The number of selections of m balls from n is ^nC_m. Consider those selections with largest value x. The remaining m-1 balls have to be selected out of the x-1 balls numbered from 1 to x-1. Thus by the equally likely principle,

$$P(X = x) = \frac{^{x-1}C_{m-1}}{^nC_m} = \frac{m(x-1)(x-2)\ldots(x-m+1)}{n(n-1)(n-2)\ldots(n-m+1)}$$

and this holds for x = m, m+1, ..., n.

$$E(X) = \sum_{x} xP(X = x) = \sum_{x=m}^{n} x\frac{m(n-m)!(x-1)!}{n!(x-m)!}$$

$$= \frac{m(n-m)!m!}{n!}\sum_{x=m}^{n}\frac{x!}{m!(x-m)!} = \frac{m(n-m)!m!}{n!}\frac{(n+1)!}{(m+1)!(n-m)!}$$

$$= \frac{m(n+1)}{m+1}.$$

$$E(X^2) = \sum_{x=m}^{n} x^2\frac{m(n-m)!(x-1)!}{n!(x-m)!} = \sum_{x=m}^{n}(x+1-1)\frac{m(n-m)!x!}{n!(x-m)!}$$

$$= \frac{m(n-m)!(m+1)!}{n!}\sum_{x=m}^{n}\frac{(x+1)!}{(m+1)!(x-m)!} - \frac{m(n+1)}{m+1}$$

$$= \frac{m(n-m)!(m+1)!}{n!}\sum_{y=m+1}^{n+1}\frac{y!}{(m+1)!(y-m-1)!} - \frac{m(n+1)}{m+1} \qquad (y=x+1)$$

$$= \frac{m(n-m)!(m+1)!}{n!}\frac{(n+2)!}{(m+2)!(n-m)!} - \frac{m(n+1)}{m+1}$$

$$= \frac{m(n+1)(mn+m+n)}{(m+1)(m+2)}.$$

$$\text{Var}(X) = \frac{m(n+1)(mn+m+n)}{(m+1)(m+2)} - \frac{m^2(n+1)^2}{(m+1)^2}$$

$$= \frac{m(n+1)(n-m)}{(m+2)(m+1)^2} \quad \text{as required.}$$

Suppose that n is unknown but that X=x. If we replace E(X) by x we obtain

$$x = \frac{m(n+1)}{m+1} \quad \text{or} \quad n = \frac{(m+1)x}{m} - 1.$$

This suggests that we take the value taken by the random variable

$$N = \frac{(m+1)X}{m} - 1$$

as the estimate of n. Note that $E(N) = n$

$$\text{and} \quad \text{Var}(N) = \frac{(m+1)^2}{m^2}\text{Var}(X) = \frac{(n+1)(n-m)}{m(m+2)}.$$

For example, if we select 19 balls at random without replacement and the largest number drawn is 38 then m=19, X=38 and the estimate of the total number of balls is 39. We can get some idea of the reliability of this estimate by considering the standard deviation of N. The expression for Var(N) involves the unknown number n but if we replace n by its estimate 39 we find that Var(N) $\approx$ 2 so that the standard deviation of N is approximately equal to $\sqrt{2}$. This does at least show that the estimate is unlikely to be greatly in error.

33. A shopkeeper buys certain items daily for a pence each and sells them for b pence each (b > a); there is no refund on unsold items. The daily demand X is a random variable with probability function $p_x = P(X = x)$. If he buys n items daily, show that his expected daily profit is given by

$$E_n = nb \sum_{x=n+1}^{\infty} p_x + b \sum_{x=0}^{n} x p_x - na.$$

Show further that

$$E_n - E_{n-1} = b \sum_{x=n}^{\infty} p_x - a$$

and explain how this result can be used to find the value of n which maximises E_n.

A newsagent buys a daily publication (under the above conditions) for 30 pence/copy and sells for 40 pence/copy. If the demand is Poisson with mean 10, how many copies per day would you advise him to buy?

Calculate his expected daily profit with this value of n, and investigate the sensitivity of E_n with respect to n by calculating the values of E_n for n equal to 1 more and 1 less than your optimal value.

¶ Let X = demand, Y = number sold. Then, since n are bought,

$$Y = X \quad \text{if } X \leqslant n,$$
$$= n \quad \text{if } X > n,$$

and the profit is bY - na.

Therefore

$$E_n = bE(Y) - na = b\left(\sum_{x=0}^{n} xp_x + \sum_{x=n+1}^{\infty} np_x\right) - na$$

$$= nb\sum_{x=n+1}^{\infty} p_x + b\sum_{x=0}^{n} xp_x - na$$

and

$$E_n - E_{n-1} = nb\sum_{x=n+1}^{\infty} p_x + b\sum_{x=0}^{n-1} xp_x + bnp_n - na$$

$$- (n-1)b\sum_{x=n+1}^{\infty} p_x - (n-1)bp_n - b\sum_{x=0}^{n-1} xp_x + (n-1)a$$

$$= b\sum_{x=n+1}^{\infty} p_x + bp_n - a = b\sum_{x=n}^{\infty} p_x - a.$$

Therefore $E_n - E_{n-1} > 0$ as long as $\displaystyle\sum_{x=n}^{\infty} p_x > \frac{a}{b}$ or $\displaystyle\sum_{x=0}^{n-1} p_x < 1 - \frac{a}{b}$.

Thus E_n will be maximised by the largest n satisfying this inequality.

When a=30, b=40 and the demand is Poisson with mean 10, we require the largest value of n for which

$$\sum_{x=0}^{n-1} e^{-10} \frac{10^x}{x!} < \frac{1}{4}.$$

Using tables, we find that n=8 is the required number of copies and that

$$E_8 = 320(1 - 0.33282) + 40 \times 2.2022 - 240$$
$$= 61.59.$$

To find E_7 and E_9 we can use the formula for $E_n - E_{n-1}$.

Thus $E_7 = E_8 - 40(1 - 0.22022) + 30 = 61.59 - 1.19 = 60.40$

and $E_9 = E_8 + 40(1 - 0.33282) - 30 = 61.59 - 3.31 = 58.28.$

34. An airline books n passengers on a flight with only m seats (n > m). If passengers have probability p of not turning up for the flight, find an expression for the expected number of passengers who actually take the flight. Find an approximation for this number when p = 0.04, n = 250 and m = 240.

¶ Let X be the number of passengers who fail to turn up for the flight and let Y be the number who actually take the flight.

Then $\quad Y = n-X \quad$ if $X > n-m$,

$\qquad\quad = m \qquad$ if $X \leqslant n-m$.

Now X is binomially distributed with parameters n and p.

Therefore $E(Y) = \sum_{x=n-m+1}^{n} (n-x)\,^nC_x p^x q^{n-x} + \sum_{x=0}^{n-m} m\,^nC_x p^x q^{n-x} \quad (q=1-p)$

$$= \sum_{x=0}^{n} (n-x)\,^nC_x p^x q^{n-x} - \sum_{x=0}^{n-m} (n-x-m)\,^nC_x p^x q^{n-x}$$

$$= n - np - (n-m)\sum_{x=0}^{n-m} {}^nC_x p^x q^{n-x} + \sum_{x=1}^{n-m} x\,^nC_x p^x q^{n-x},$$

using the fact that the mean of X is np.

Therefore, using the Poisson approximation to the binomial probability function,

$$E(Y) \approx nq - (n-m)\sum_{x=0}^{n-m} e^{-\lambda}\frac{\lambda^x}{x!} + \sum_{x=1}^{n-m} e^{-\lambda}\frac{\lambda^x}{(x-1)!} \quad (\lambda = np)$$

$$= nq - (n-m)\sum_{x=0}^{n-m} e^{-\lambda}\frac{\lambda^x}{x!} + \lambda\sum_{y=0}^{n-m-1} e^{-\lambda}\frac{\lambda^y}{y!} \quad (y = x-1).$$

When p = 0.04, n = 250 and m = 240, so that $\lambda = 250\times0.04 = 10$, we find, using tables, that

$$E(Y) \approx 240 - 10(0.58304 - 0.45793) = 238.75.$$

35. A group of 2n people (n $\geqslant$ 2) is to be screened for a certain disease by means of a blood test. In an attempt to reduce the number of tests the following procedure is adopted. Blood samples, one from each person, are pooled and the pool is tested for the presence of the disease. If the result is negative then no further tests are required. However, if one or more people have the disease the result will be positive and in this case the 2n people are divided at random into two subgroups of size n and new pools, one per group,

are formed and tested for the disease. If the result for a particular subgroup is negative it can be concluded that all n members are disease-free but if the result is positive then all n are tested individually. The probability that a randomly chosen member of the group has the disease is 0.1, independently of all other members. Find the expected number of tests required to screen the 2n people by this method. When is this number less than 2n?

¶ Let X be the number of tests required to screen the group. The number of tests is 1 if the first test is negative or is n+3 if the first is positive and only one of the tests on the pooled samples from the two subgroups is positive or is 2n+3 if the first is positive and both tests on the new pools are positive.

The probability function of X is

x	1	n+3	2n+3
p_x	0.9^{2n}	$2(0.9)^n(1-0.9^n)$	$(1-0.9^n)^2$

Therefore $E(X) = 0.9^{2n} + 2(n+3)(0.9)^n(1-0.9^n) + (2n+3)(1-0.9^n)^2$

$$= 2n + 3 - 2\times0.9^{2n} - 2n\times0.9^n.$$

We find by trial and error that $E(X) < 2n$ if and only if $n \leqslant 27$. Clearly this is not a good procedure when $2n > 54$. See Question 23, page 233 for a more successful method.

4
Continuous Distributions

Exercises 4.1 Continuous Random Variables

1. The amount X of petrol (in thousands of gallons) sold per week in a certain garage has probability density function

$$f(x) = kx^3(9-x^2) \quad \text{if } 0 \leqslant x \leqslant 3,$$
$$= 0 \quad \text{otherwise.}$$

Evaluate k and find the mean and standard deviation of X, converting these to gallons.

¶   Since $\displaystyle\int_{-\infty}^{\infty} f(x)\,dx = 1$, $\quad k\displaystyle\int_0^3 x^3(9-x^2)\,dx = 1$

whence $\quad k = \dfrac{4}{243}$.

$$E(X) = \frac{4}{243}\int_0^3 (9x^4 - x^6)\,dx$$

$$= \frac{4}{243}[\frac{9x^5}{5} - \frac{x^7}{7}]_0^3 \quad = \quad \frac{72}{35}, \text{ i.e. } \approx 2057 \text{ gallons.}$$

$$E(X^2) = \frac{4}{243}\int_0^3 (9x^5 - x^7)\,dx$$

$$= \frac{4}{243}[\frac{9x^6}{6} - \frac{x^8}{8}]_0^3 \quad = \quad \frac{9}{2}.$$

Therefore $\quad Var(X) = E(X^2) - [E(X)]^2$

$$= \frac{9}{2} - (\frac{72}{35})^2 = 0.26816.$$

$$S.D.(X) = 0.5178. \text{ i.e. } \approx 517.8 \text{ gallons.}$$

2. The random variable X has probability density function

$$f(x) = kx^2 \quad \text{if } 0 \leqslant x \leqslant 2,$$
$$= 0 \quad \text{otherwise.}$$

Find (i)   the value of k,

   (ii)   the mode,

   (iii) the median,

   (iv)   the interquartile range.

¶   (i)
$$\int_{-\infty}^{\infty} f(x)\,dx = 1 \quad \text{so that} \quad k\int_0^2 x^2\,dx = 1, \text{ whence } k = \frac{3}{8}.$$

   (ii)   Since f(x) increases over the range [0,2], the mode occurs at x=2.

   (iii) The median m satisfies $\dfrac{3}{8}\displaystyle\int_0^m x^2\,dx = \dfrac{1}{2}$,

$$\frac{3}{8}\cdot\frac{m^3}{3} = \frac{1}{2},$$

whence m = $\sqrt[3]{4}$ = 1.5874.

   (iv)   The upper quartile u satisfies

$$\frac{3}{8}\int_0^u x^2\,dx = \frac{3}{4}, \quad \text{whence } u = \sqrt[3]{6}.$$

The lower quartile ℓ satisfies

$$\frac{3}{8}\int_0^\ell x^2\,dx = \frac{1}{4}, \quad \text{whence } \ell = \sqrt[3]{2}.$$

Interquartile range = u - ℓ = $\sqrt[3]{6}$ - $\sqrt[3]{2}$ = 0.5572.

3. The random variable X has mean μ and probability density function f(x). Defining the variance of X as

$$\text{Var}(X) = \int_{-\infty}^{\infty} (x-\mu)^2 f(x)\,dx$$

show that an alternative expression is given by

$$\text{Var}(X) = \int_{-\infty}^{\infty} x^2 f(x)\,dx - \mu^2.$$

¶
$$\text{Var}(X) = \int_{-\infty}^{\infty} (x-\mu)^2 f(x)\,dx = \int_{-\infty}^{\infty} (x^2-2\mu x+\mu^2) f(x)\,dx$$

$$= \int_{-\infty}^{\infty} x^2 f(x)\,dx - 2\mu \int_{-\infty}^{\infty} x f(x)\,dx + \mu^2 \int_{-\infty}^{\infty} f(x)\,dx$$

$$= \int_{-\infty}^{\infty} x^2 f(x)\,dx - 2\mu^2 + \mu^2 = \int_{-\infty}^{\infty} x^2 f(x)\,dx - \mu^2.$$

4. The continuous random variable X has the cumulative distribution function F(x) defined by

$$
\begin{aligned}
F(x) &= 0 && \text{if } x < 0, \\
&= \frac{x}{3} && \text{if } 0 \leqslant x \leqslant 1, \\
&= k && \text{if } 1 < x \leqslant 2, \\
&= ax^2 && \text{if } 2 < x \leqslant 3, \\
&= \frac{x}{4} && \text{if } 3 < x \leqslant 4, \\
&= 1 && \text{if } x > 4.
\end{aligned}
$$

(i) Determine the values of the constants a and k.

(ii) Determine the probability density function f(x).

(iii) Evaluate the probability $P(\frac{1}{2} \leqslant X \leqslant 2\frac{1}{2})$.

¶   (i)   Since X is a continuous random variable, there are no 'jumps' in the graph of F(x).

Therefore $k = F(1) = \frac{1}{3}$.

Also $k = F(2) = 4a$, whence $a = \frac{1}{12}$.

(ii) By differentiation we find that the probability density function is given by

$$
\begin{aligned}
f(x) &= 0 && \text{if } x < 0, \\
&= \frac{1}{3} && \text{if } 0 \leqslant x \leqslant 1, \\
&= 0 && \text{if } 1 < x \leqslant 2, \\
&= \frac{x}{6} && \text{if } 2 < x \leqslant 3, \\
&= \frac{1}{4} && \text{if } 3 < x \leqslant 4, \\
&= 0 && \text{if } x > 4.
\end{aligned}
$$

(iii) $P(0.5 \leqslant X \leqslant 2.5) = F(2.5) - F(0.5) = \frac{25}{48} - \frac{1}{6} = \frac{17}{48}$.

5. The random variable X has probability density function

$$f(x) = ke^{-x} \quad \text{if } x \geqslant 0,$$
$$= 0 \quad \text{otherwise.}$$

   Determine (i)   the value of k,

   (ii)   the cumulative distribution function of X,

   (iii)   the median of the distribution.

¶ (i)   Since $\int_{-\infty}^{\infty} f(x)\,dx = 1,$ $k\int_{0}^{\infty} e^{-x}\,dx = 1,$ whence $k = 1.$

   (ii)   The cumulative distribution function F(x) is given by

$$F(x) = 0 \quad \text{if } x < 0,$$
$$= \int_{0}^{x} e^{-y}\,dy = 1 - e^{-x} \quad \text{if } x \geqslant 0.$$

   (iii) The median m satisfies

$$\int_{0}^{m} e^{-x}\,dx = \frac{1}{2}. \quad \text{Thus } 1 - e^{-m} = \frac{1}{2}$$

$$\text{or } m = \ln 2 = 0.69315.$$

6. Let X be a continuous random variable with probability density function f(x), mean μ and variance σ^2.   If a and b are any two constants prove that

   (i) $E(aX+b) = a\mu+b,$ (ii) $Var(aX+b) = a^2\sigma^2.$

   If the random variable Z is defined by $Z = \dfrac{(X-\mu)}{\sigma}$ prove that it has zero mean and unit variance.

¶ (i) $E(aX+b) = \int_{-\infty}^{\infty} (ax+b)f(x)\,dx = a\int_{-\infty}^{\infty} xf(x)\,dx + b\int_{-\infty}^{\infty} f(x)\,dx$

$$= aE(X) + b = a\mu + b.$$

   (ii) $Var(aX+b) = \int_{-\infty}^{\infty} (ax+b-(a\mu+b))^2 f(x)\,dx = a^2\int_{-\infty}^{\infty} (x-\mu)^2 f(x)\,dx$

$$= a^2\,Var(X) = a^2\sigma^2.$$

   Using these results,

$$E(Z) = E\left(\frac{X}{\sigma} - \frac{\mu}{\sigma}\right) = \frac{\mu}{\sigma} - \frac{\mu}{\sigma} = 0, \quad Var(Z) = Var\left(\frac{X}{\sigma} - \frac{\mu}{\sigma}\right) = \frac{1}{\sigma^2}Var(X) = 1.$$

7. A continuous random variable X has the cumulative distribution function

$$F(x) = 0 \qquad\qquad \text{if } x < 0,$$
$$= \frac{x^2}{10} \qquad\qquad \text{if } 0 \leqslant x < 2,$$
$$= 1 - \frac{1}{15}(5 - x)^2 \quad \text{if } 2 \leqslant x < 5,$$
$$= 1 \qquad\qquad \text{if } x \geqslant 5.$$

Sketch the probability density function of X and calculate (i) its mean, (ii) its median, (iii) its mode.

¶ Let f(x) be the probability density function. Then, differentiating,

$$f(x) = 0 \qquad\qquad \text{if } x < 0,$$
$$= \frac{x}{5} \qquad\qquad \text{if } 0 \leqslant x < 2,$$
$$= \frac{2}{15}(5-x) \qquad \text{if } 2 \leqslant x < 5,$$
$$= 0 \qquad\qquad \text{if } x \geqslant 5.$$

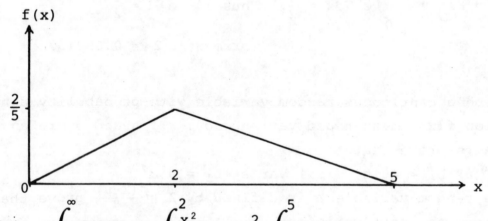

(i) $$E(X) = \int_{-\infty}^{\infty} x f(x)\, dx = \int_{0}^{2} \frac{x^2}{5}\, dx + \frac{2}{15}\int_{2}^{5} x(5-x)\, dx$$

$$= [\frac{x^3}{15}]_0^2 + \frac{2}{15}[\frac{5x^2}{2} - \frac{x^3}{3}]_2^5 = \frac{7}{3}.$$

(ii) Since $F(2) = \frac{4}{10}$ and the median m satisfies $F(m) = \frac{1}{2}$, it follows that m > 2 and

$$1 - \frac{1}{15}(5-m)^2 = \frac{1}{2}.$$

Hence $m = 5 - \sqrt{15/2} = 2.2614.$

(iii) From the diagram, the mode is 2.

8. The random variable X has probability density function

$$f(x) = kx^2(1-x) \qquad \text{if } 0 \leqslant x \leqslant 1,$$
$$= 0 \qquad\qquad\quad \text{otherwise.}$$

(i)   Find the value of k.

(ii) Find the probability that X lies in the range $(0,\frac{1}{2})$.

(iii) In 100 independent observations of X, how many on average will fall in the range $(0,\frac{1}{2})$?

¶   (i) $k \int_0^1 x^2(1-x)\,dx = 1$,   whence k = 12.

(ii) $P(0 < X < \frac{1}{2}) = 12 \int_0^{1/2} x^2(1-x)\,dx = \frac{5}{16}.$

(iii) The number of observations lying in the interval $(0,\frac{1}{2})$ is binomially distributed with parameters n=100 and $p = \frac{5}{16}$, so that

Mean number of observations in $(0,\frac{1}{2})$ = np = 31.25.

9. The random variable X has probability density function

$$f(x) = \lambda e^{-\lambda x} \quad \text{if } x \geqslant 0,$$
$$= 0 \quad \text{otherwise.}$$

Find expressions for (i) the mean, (ii) the standard deviation σ, (iii) the mode, (iv) the median.

Show that the interquartile range equals $\sigma \log_e 3$.

¶   (i) & (ii) $E(X) = \frac{1}{\lambda}, \quad \sigma = \sqrt{\text{Var}(X)} = \frac{1}{\lambda}.$

[See Question 3 on page 149 for a detailed solution.]

(iii) The mode is x=0 since this value maximises $f(x)$.

(iv) The median m is given by

$$\int_0^m \lambda e^{-\lambda x}\,dx = \frac{1}{2}, \quad \text{whence } m = \frac{1}{\lambda}\log_e 2.$$

If u and ℓ denote the upper and lower quartiles,

$$\int_0^u \lambda e^{-\lambda x}\,dx = \frac{3}{4} \quad \text{and} \quad \int_0^\ell \lambda e^{-\lambda x}\,dx = \frac{1}{4}$$

whence $u = \frac{1}{\lambda}\log_e 4$ and $\ell = \frac{1}{\lambda}\log_e \frac{4}{3}.$

The interquartile range equals

$$\frac{1}{\lambda}\log_e 4 - \frac{1}{\lambda}\log_e \frac{4}{3} = \frac{1}{\lambda}\log_e 3 = \sigma \log_e 3.$$

10. A factory produces discs to operate fruit machines. The slots in the fruit machines are 3 cm long and the factory is requested to make discs whose diameters are no more than 2.9 cm and no less than 2.7 cm in length. The probability density function of R, the disc diameter, is

$$f(r) = \frac{3000}{32}(3.1 - r)(r - 2.7) \text{ if } 2.7 \leqslant r \leqslant 3.1,$$

$$= 0 \qquad\qquad\qquad \text{otherwise.}$$

A disc is chosen at random. Find

(i)   the probability that the disc does not meet the required specification,

(ii) the probability that the disc does not meet the required specification but will still fit in the slot,

(iii) the probability that the disc is too large, given that it does not meet the specification.

¶   (i) $P(2.9 < R \leqslant 3.1) = \dfrac{3000}{32} \displaystyle\int_{2.9}^{3.1}(3.1-r)(r-2.7)\,dr$

$$= \frac{1}{2} \quad \text{(by symmetry or otherwise).}$$

(ii) $P(2.9 < R \leqslant 3.0) = \dfrac{3000}{32} \displaystyle\int_{2.9}^{3.0}(3.1-r)(r-2.7)\,dr = \dfrac{11}{32}.$

(iii) $P(R > 3.0 \,|\, R > 2.9) = \dfrac{P(R > 3.0)}{P(R > 2.9)} = \dfrac{1 - (\frac{1}{2} + \frac{11}{32})}{\frac{1}{2}} = \dfrac{5}{16}$

$$\text{since } P(2.7 \leqslant R \leqslant 2.9) = \frac{1}{2}.$$

11. The random variable X has cumulative distribution function

$$F(x) = 0 \qquad\qquad\qquad\qquad \text{if } x < 0,$$

$$= \frac{3x^2}{41} \qquad\qquad\qquad \text{if } 0 \leqslant x < 1,$$

$$= \frac{3}{41} \qquad\qquad\qquad\quad \text{if } 1 \leqslant x < 2,$$

$$= \frac{3}{41} + \frac{2}{41}(x^3 - 8) \text{ if } 2 \leqslant x < 3,$$

$$= 1 \qquad\qquad\qquad\qquad \text{if } x \geqslant 3.$$

Determine the probability density function $f(x)$ and find the probability that X lies between 1/2 and 5/2.

¶   Differentiating we find that

$$f(x) = 0 \qquad \text{if } x < 0,$$
$$= \frac{6x}{41} \qquad \text{if } 0 \leqslant x < 1,$$
$$= 0 \qquad \text{if } 1 \leqslant x < 2,$$
$$= \frac{6x^2}{41} \qquad \text{if } 2 \leqslant x < 3,$$
$$= 0 \qquad \text{if } x \geqslant 3.$$

$$P(\tfrac{1}{2} \leqslant X \leqslant \tfrac{5}{2}) = F(\tfrac{5}{2}) - F(\tfrac{1}{2}) = \frac{3}{41} + \frac{2}{41}((\tfrac{5}{2})^3 - 8) - \frac{3}{41}(\tfrac{1}{2})^2$$

$$= \frac{70}{164} = 0.42683.$$

12. A random variable X is said to have a *Cauchy* distribution if its probability density function is given by

$$f(x) = \frac{1}{\pi(1+x^2)} \qquad (-\infty < x < +\infty).$$

   (i)   Verify that it is a valid probability density function and sketch its graph.

   (ii)   Find the cumulative distribution function F(x).

   (iii) Find $P(-1 \leqslant X \leqslant 1)$.

¶   (i)   We must show that $\displaystyle\int_{-\infty}^{\infty} f(x)\,dx = 1$ and $f(x) > 0$ all x.

   Now $\displaystyle\int_{-\infty}^{\infty} \frac{dx}{\pi(1+x^2)} = \frac{1}{\pi}[\tan^{-1}x]_{-\infty}^{\infty} = \frac{1}{\pi}(\frac{\pi}{2} - (\frac{-\pi}{2})) = 1.$

   Also $\dfrac{1}{\pi(1+x^2)} \geqslant 0$ all x .

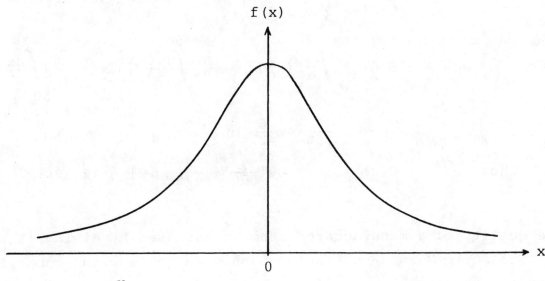

   (ii) $F(x) = \dfrac{1}{\pi}\displaystyle\int_{-\infty}^{x} \frac{dy}{1+y^2} = \frac{1}{\pi}[\tan^{-1}y]_{-\infty}^{x} = \frac{1}{\pi}(\tan^{-1}x + \frac{\pi}{2}).$

(iii) $P(-1 \leqslant X \leqslant 1) = F(1) - F(-1) = \frac{1}{\pi}(\tan^{-1}1 + \frac{\pi}{2}) - \frac{1}{\pi}(\tan^{-1}(-1) + \frac{\pi}{2}) = \frac{1}{2}.$

13. The operational lifetime in days of a battery-operated toy may be regarded as a continuous random variable with probability density function

$$f(x) = \frac{kx(50+x)}{5000} \qquad \text{if } 0 \leqslant x \leqslant 50,$$

$$= k \qquad\qquad \text{if } 50 < x \leqslant 100,$$

$$= 0 \qquad\qquad \text{otherwise.}$$

(i) Find the value of k and determine the mean operational lifetime of the toy.

(ii) If battery-costs amount to 2p a day and the purchase price of the toy is £5.00 determine the average overall cost per day to the buyer.

¶ (i) $\quad k\int_{0}^{50}\frac{x(50+x)}{5000}dx + k\int_{50}^{100}dx = 1, \quad$ whence $k = \frac{6}{425}.$

$$E(X) = \frac{6}{425}\int_{0}^{50}\frac{x^2(50+x)}{5000}dx + \frac{6}{425}\int_{50}^{100}xdx$$

$$\doteqdot \frac{1075}{17} = 63.235 \text{ days.}$$

(ii) Let the toy last for X days. Then, if C is the overall cost per day,

$$C = 2 + \frac{500}{X}.$$

$$E(C) = 2 + 500E(\frac{1}{X}).$$

Now $\quad E(\frac{1}{X}) = \int_{-\infty}^{\infty}\frac{1}{x}f(x)dx = \frac{6}{425}\int_{0}^{50}\frac{(50+x)}{5000}dx + \frac{6}{425}\int_{50}^{100}\frac{dx}{x}$

$$= \frac{9}{850} + \frac{6}{425}\ln 2.$$

Thus $\quad E(C) = 2 + 500[\frac{9}{850} + \frac{6}{425}\ln 2] = 12.19p.$

14. The quality of a manufactured item is assessed by giving it a score X. The score X is a continuous random variable with probability density function

$$f(x) = kx \qquad \text{if } 0 \leqslant x \leqslant 1,$$

$$= k\theta \qquad \text{if } 1 < x \leqslant 2,$$

$$= 0 \qquad \text{otherwise,}$$

where $0 \leqslant \theta \leqslant 1$.

(a) Express k in terms of θ.

(b) The quality of the item is assessed before sale. Three units of profit are made if $X > 1$ but only one unit of profit is made if $X \leqslant 1$. The manufacturer selects the value of θ at a cost of θ units.

  (i) Write down an expression involving θ for the net profit when the score is X.

  (ii) Find the expected net profit.

  (iii) Find the value of θ which maximises the expected net profit.

¶ (a)
$$k \int_0^1 x\,dx + k\theta \int_1^2 dx = 1, \text{ whence } k = \frac{2}{(1+2\theta)}.$$

(b) (i) If P is the net profit,
$$P = 1-\theta \quad \text{if } X \leqslant 1,$$
$$= 3-\theta \quad \text{if } X > 1.$$

(ii)
$$E(P) = (1-\theta)P(X \leqslant 1) + (3-\theta)P(X > 1)$$

$$= (1-\theta) \int_0^1 f(x)\,dx + (3-\theta) \int_1^2 f(x)\,dx$$

$$= (1-\theta)\frac{1}{(1+2\theta)} + (3-\theta)\frac{2\theta}{(1+2\theta)}$$

$$= \frac{1 + 5\theta - 2\theta^2}{(1+2\theta)}$$

(iii)
$$\frac{dE(P)}{d\theta} = \frac{(5-4\theta)(1+2\theta) - 2(1+5\theta-2\theta^2)}{(1+2\theta)^2}$$

$$= \frac{3 - 4\theta - 4\theta^2}{(1+2\theta)^2} = \frac{(3+2\theta)(1-2\theta)}{(1+2\theta)^2}.$$

Rejecting the negative root we find that
$$\frac{dE(P)}{d\theta} = 0 \text{ when } \theta = \frac{1}{2}.$$

Since $\frac{d^2E(P)}{d\theta^2} < 0$, $E(P)$ is maximised when $\theta = \frac{1}{2}$.

15. A continuous random variable X has cumulative distribution function $F(x)$. If $F'(x)$ is positive only in the range $(0,b)$, show that
$$E(X) = \int_0^b (1 - F(x))\,dx.$$

¶   If f(x) is the probability density function of X,

$$E(X) = \int_0^b xf(x)\,dx = \int_0^b x\frac{dF(x)}{dx}\,dx$$

$$= [xF(x)]_0^b - \int_0^b F(x)\,dx$$

$$= b - \int_0^b F(x)\,dx \qquad (F(b)=1)$$

$$= \int_0^b [1 - F(x)]\,dx.$$

Exercises 4.2 Some Special Distributions

1. The time of departure of the train standing at platform 9 is a uniformly distributed random variable. If the train's expected time of departure is 11.05 a.m. and the probability that it leaves between 11.07 a.m. and 11.09 a.m. is 0.2, find the probability that the train departs before 11.03 a.m.

¶   Let time be measured in terms of minutes past 11 a.m. and let a and b be the endpoints of the distribution (a < b). If X is the time of departure,

$$E(X) = \frac{a+b}{2} = 5 \quad \text{so that} \quad a+b = 10.$$

Also $P(7 \leqslant X \leqslant 9) = \dfrac{9-7}{b-a} = \dfrac{1}{5}$ so that $b-a = 10$.

So a=0 and b=10 and

$$P(X < 3) = \frac{3-a}{b-a} = \frac{3}{10} = 0.3.$$

Therefore the train leaves before 11.03 a.m. with probability 0.3.

2. The first bus of the day arrives at a certain stop at 7 a.m. Thereafter, buses arrive at ten minute intervals. A girl arrives at the stop at a time which is uniformly distributed between 7.15 a.m. and 7.45 a.m. Find the probability she waits for a bus for (a) less than two minutes, (b) more than.4 minutes.

¶   (a) She waits less than two minutes if she arrives during any of the time intervals (7.18,7.20], (7.28,7.30], (7.38,7.40]. The total length of these intervals is 6 minutes and there are 30 minutes between 7.15 a.m. and 7.45 a.m. So the probability that she waits for less than two minutes is 6/30 = 0.2.

(b) She waits more than four minutes if she arrives during one of the intervals [7.15,7.16), [7.20,7.26), [7.30,7.36) and [7.40,7.45]. The total of these intervals is 18 minutes. So the probability that she waits for more than four minutes is 18/30 = 0.6.

3. If the random variable X has an exponential distribution with parameter λ show that $E(X) = 1/\lambda$ and $Var(X) = 1/\lambda^2$.

¶

$$E(X) = \lambda \int_0^\infty x e^{-\lambda x} dx$$

$$= [-x e^{-\lambda x}]_0^\infty + \int_0^\infty e^{-\lambda x} dx \quad \text{(integrating by parts)}$$

$$= 0 - \frac{1}{\lambda}[e^{-\lambda x}]_0^\infty \quad \text{(since } \lambda > 0\text{)}$$

$$= \frac{1}{\lambda}.$$

$$E(X^2) = \lambda \int_0^\infty x^2 e^{-\lambda x} dx$$

$$= [-x^2 e^{-\lambda x}]_0^\infty + 2 \int_0^\infty x e^{-\lambda x} dx$$

$$= 0 + \frac{2}{\lambda^2} \quad \text{(using the first result)}$$

$$= \frac{2}{\lambda^2}$$

Therefore $Var(X) = \frac{2}{\lambda^2} - \frac{1}{\lambda^2} = \frac{1}{\lambda^2}$.

N.B. For $\lambda > 0$,

$$x e^{-\lambda x} = \frac{x}{1 + \lambda x + \frac{(\lambda x)^2}{2!} + \ldots} = \frac{1}{\frac{1}{x} + \lambda + \frac{\lambda^2 x}{2!} + \ldots}$$

and this clearly decreases to zero as x increases to infinity. Similarly we can show that $x^k e^{-\lambda x}$ decreases to zero for any fixed integer k.

4. The continuous random variable X has probability density function

$$f(x) = e^{-x} \qquad x \geqslant 0,$$
$$= 0 \qquad \text{otherwise.}$$

Find constants a,b,c (0 < a < b < c) such that

$P(0 \leqslant X < a) = P(a \leqslant X < b) = P(b \leqslant X < c) = P(c \leqslant X < \infty) = 0.25.$

It is claimed that the 20 numbers below come from this distribution. Examine the frequency distribution with classes [0,a), [a,b), [b,c), [c,∞) to see if this is a reasonable claim.

1.46, 0.07, 0.34, 0.85, 0.21, 0.40, 1.10, 4.50, 0.31, 0.12, 0.46, 0.04, 2.80, 0.68, 1.37, 0.26, 1.50, 0.70, 0.75, 1.87.

¶ The cumulative distribution function of X is

$$F(x) = \int_0^x e^{-y}dy = 1 - e^{-x} \qquad (0 \leqslant x < \infty)$$

$0.25 = P(0 \leqslant X < a) = F(a) = 1 - e^{-a}$, so that $e^{-a} = 0.75$, a=0.288.

$0.25 = P(a \leqslant X < b) = F(b) - 0.25 = (1 - e^{-b}) - 0.25$,
so that $e^{-b} = 0.5$, b=0.693.

$0.25 = P(b \leqslant X < c) = F(c) - 0.5 = (1 - e^{-c}) - 0.5$,
so that $e^{-c} = 0.25$, c=1.386.

Assume that the 20 numbers were obtained by making 20 independent observations on X. We find that each of the four classes [0,0.288), [0.288,0.693), [0.693,1.386) and [1.386,∞) contains one quarter of the 20 numbers. This is the sort of result we would expect to get if the claim is true but this does not prove that the claim is true. Many other distributions could give rise to the same result.

5. If Z has the distribution N(0,1) find the following probabilities.
   (i) $P(Z \leqslant 1.96)$, (ii) $P(Z \leqslant 2.33)$, (iii) $P(Z \leqslant -1.65)$, (iv) $P(Z \geqslant 0)$,
   (v) $P(Z \geqslant 1 | Z \geqslant 0)$, (vi) $P(-0.5 \leqslant Z \leqslant 1.5)$, (vii) $P(|Z| \geqslant 0.75)$,
   (viii) $P(Z^2 - Z - 2 \leqslant 0)$, (ix) $P(2Z + 1 \leqslant 6)$, (x) $P(|Z-1| \leqslant 1)$.

¶ (i) $P(Z \leqslant 1.96) = \Phi(1.96) = 0.97500.$

(ii) $P(Z \leqslant 2.33) = \Phi(2.33) = 0.99010.$

(iii) $P(Z \leqslant -1.65) = \Phi(-1.65) = 1 - \Phi(1.65)$

$$= 1 - 0.95053 = 0.04947.$$

(iv) $P(Z \geqslant 0) = 1 - P(Z \leqslant 0) = 1 - \Phi(0)$

$$= 1 - 0.5 = 0.5.$$

(v) $P(Z \geqslant 1 | Z \geqslant 0) = \dfrac{P(Z \geqslant 1 \text{ and } Z \geqslant 0)}{P(Z \geqslant 0)} = \dfrac{P(Z \geqslant 1)}{P(Z \geqslant 0)}$

$$= \frac{1 - P(Z \leqslant 1)}{1 - P(Z \leqslant 0)} = \frac{1 - \Phi(1)}{1 - \Phi(0)}$$

$$= \frac{1 - 0.84134}{1 - 0.5} = 0.31732.$$

(vi) $P(-0.5 \leqslant Z \leqslant 1.5) = \Phi(1.5) - \Phi(-0.5)$

$$= \Phi(1.5) - (1 - \Phi(0.5))$$

$$= \Phi(1.5) + \Phi(0.5) - 1$$

$$= 0.93319 + 0.69146 - 1$$

$$= 0.62465.$$

(vii) $P(|Z| \geqslant 0.75) = 1 - P(|Z| \leqslant 0.75)$

$$= 1 - P(-0.75 \leqslant Z \leqslant 0.75)$$

$$= 1 - (\Phi(0.75) - \Phi(-0.75))$$

$$= 1 - (2\Phi(0.75) - 1)$$

$$= 2(1 - 0.77337)$$

$$= 0.45326.$$

(viii) $P(Z^2 - Z - 2 \leqslant 0) = P((Z-2)(Z+1) \leqslant 0)$

$$= P(-1 \leqslant Z \leqslant 2)$$

$$= \Phi(2) - \Phi(-1)$$

$$= \Phi(2) - (1 - \Phi(1))$$

$$= 0.97725 + 0.84134 - 1$$

$$= 0.81859.$$

(ix) $P(2Z+1 \leqslant 6) = P(Z \leqslant 2.5) = \Phi(2.5)$

$$= 0.99379.$$

(x) $P(|Z-1| \leqslant 1) = P(0 \leqslant Z \leqslant 2)$

$$= \Phi(2) - \Phi(0)$$

$$= 0.97725 - 0.5$$

$$= 0.47725.$$

6. If X has the distribution N(6,25) find the following probabilities.
   (i) $P(X \leqslant 11)$, (ii) $P(X \geqslant 0)$, (iii) $P(-4 \leqslant X \leqslant 16)$,
   (iv) $P(|X-6| \leqslant 5)$, (v) $P(2X+5 \leqslant 17)$.

¶ The standardised variable $Z = \dfrac{X-6}{5}$ is N(0,1).

(i) $P(X \leqslant 11) = P(Z \leqslant \dfrac{11-6}{5}) = P(Z \leqslant 1) = \Phi(1) = 0.84134.$

(ii) $P(X \geqslant 0) = P(Z \geqslant \dfrac{0-6}{5}) = P(Z \geqslant -1.2) = 1 - P(Z \leqslant -1.2)$

$$= 1 - \Phi(-1.2) = 1 - (1 - \Phi(1.2)) = \Phi(1.2) = 0.88493.$$

(iii) $P(-4 \leqslant X \leqslant 16) = P(\frac{-4-6}{5} \leqslant Z \leqslant \frac{16-6}{5})$

$= P(-2 \leqslant Z \leqslant 2) = \Phi(2) - \Phi(-2)$

$= \Phi(2) - (1 - \Phi(2)) = 2\Phi(2) - 1$

$= 2 \times 0.97725 - 1 = 0.9545.$

(iv) $P(|X-6| \leqslant 5) = P(|Z| \leqslant 1) = P(-1 \leqslant Z \leqslant 1)$

$= 2\Phi(1) - 1 = 2 \times 0.84134 - 1$

$= 0.68268.$

(v) $P(2X+5 \leqslant 17) = P(X \leqslant 6) = P(Z \leqslant \frac{6-6}{5})$

$= P(Z \leqslant 0) = \Phi(0) = 0.5.$

7. If X has the distribution $N(\mu, \sigma^2)$ find

(i) the probability that X differs from its mean by more than 3 standard deviations,

(ii) the probability that X is at most 2 standard deviations away from the mean,

(iii) the probability that X does not differ from its mean by more than 3 standard deviations given that it does differ from its mean by more than 2 standard deviations.

¶ The standardised variable $Z = \frac{X-\mu}{\sigma}$ is $N(0,1)$.

(i) $P(|X-\mu| > 3\sigma) = P(|Z| > 3) = 1 - P(|Z| \leqslant 3)$

$= 1 - P(-3 \leqslant Z \leqslant 3) = 1 - (2\Phi(3) - 1)$

$= 2(1 - \Phi(3)) = 2(1 - 0.99865)$

$= 0.0027.$

(ii) $P(|X-\mu| \leqslant 2\sigma) = P(|Z| \leqslant 2) = 2\Phi(2) - 1$

$= 2 \times 0.97725 - 1$

$= 0.9545.$

(iii) $P(|X-\mu| \leqslant 3\sigma | |X-\mu| > 2\sigma) = P(|Z| \leqslant 3 | |Z| > 2)$

$= \frac{P(2 < |Z| \leqslant 3)}{P(|Z| > 2)}$

$= \frac{P(|Z| \leqslant 3) - P(|Z| \leqslant 2)}{P(|Z| > 2)}$

$= \frac{(1 - 0.0027) - 0.9545}{1 - 0.9545}$

$= 0.9407.$

8. The random variable X has a uniform distribution over the interval (a,b). If the mean and variance of X are 5 and 3 respectively calculate a and b.

¶
$$E(X) = \frac{a+b}{2} = 5 \quad \text{so that} \quad a+b = 10.$$

$$Var(X) = \frac{(b-a)^2}{12} = 3 \quad \text{so that} \ (b-a)^2 = 36.$$

Therefore $(10 - 2a)^2 = 36$

which reduces to $(a-2)(a-8) = 0.$

Therefore a=2 and b=8 since a < b.

9. The random variable X has probability density function

$$f(x) = \frac{1}{4} \quad \text{if } 2 \leqslant x \leqslant 4,$$

$$= \frac{1}{2} \quad \text{if } 6 \leqslant x \leqslant 7,$$

$$= 0 \quad \text{otherwise.}$$

Determine the cumulative distribution function and sketch it. Calculate (i) $P(3.5 \leqslant X \leqslant 6.5)$, (ii) $E(X)$.

¶ Let F(x) denote the cumulative distribution function. Then

$$F(x) = 0 \qquad \text{if } x < 2,$$

$$= \int_{2}^{x} \frac{dy}{4} = \frac{(x-2)}{4} \quad \text{if } 2 \leqslant x \leqslant 4,$$

$$= \frac{1}{2} \qquad \text{if } 4 < x < 6,$$

$$= \frac{1}{2} + \int_{6}^{x} \frac{dy}{2} = \frac{1}{2} + \frac{(x-6)}{2} \quad \text{if } 6 \leqslant x \leqslant 7,$$

$$= 1 \qquad \text{if } x > 7.$$

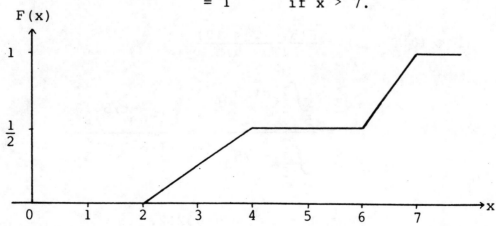

(i) $P(3.5 \leqslant X \leqslant 6.5) = F(6.5) - F(3.5) = \frac{1}{2} + (\frac{6.5-6}{2}) - (\frac{3.5-2}{4})$

$$= \frac{3}{8}.$$

(ii) $\qquad E(X) = \int_{-\infty}^{\infty} xf(x)\,dx = \int_{2}^{4} \frac{xdx}{4} + \int_{6}^{7} \frac{xdx}{2}$

$$= 4.75.$$

10. A value c is chosen at random in the range $(-5,5)$. Calculate the probability that the equation $x^2 - 2x + c^2 = 0$ has no real roots.

¶ The equation will have real roots if $4-4c^2 \geqslant 0$ i.e. $-1 \leqslant c \leqslant 1$. Therefore $P(\text{real roots}) = \frac{2}{10} = \frac{1}{5}$ since c is distributed uniformly on $(-5,5)$. Therefore $P(\text{no real roots}) = \frac{4}{5}$.

11. The time T between any two successive arrivals in a hospital casualty department has probability density function f(t) defined by
$$f(t) = \lambda e^{-\lambda t} \quad \text{if } t \geqslant 0,$$
$$= 0 \qquad \text{otherwise.}$$
The total of 100 successive inter-arrival times was found to be 500 hours. From this data estimate the value of λ. Use this estimate to calculate the following probabilities.
(i) $P(0 < T < 5)$, (ii) $P(T < 10 | T > 5)$.

¶ An estimate of $E(T)$ is $\frac{500}{100} = 5$. As $E(T) = \frac{1}{\lambda}$ we take $\frac{1}{5}$ as the estimate of λ.

(i) $\qquad P(0 < T < 5) = \int_{0}^{5} \frac{1}{5}e^{-t/5}dt = [-e^{-t/5}]_{0}^{5} = 1 - e^{-1} = 0.63212.$

(ii) $\qquad P(T < 10 | T > 5) = \frac{P(5 < T < 10)}{P(T > 5)}$

$$= \frac{\int_{5}^{10} \frac{1}{5}e^{-t/5}dt}{\int_{5}^{\infty} \frac{1}{5}e^{-t/5}dt} = \frac{[-e^{-t/5}]_{5}^{10}}{[-e^{-t/5}]_{5}^{\infty}}$$

$$= 1 - e^{-1} = 0.63212.$$

12. A positive, continuous random variable X is said to be "memoryless" if, for any positive number s,

$$P(X > s+t \mid X > t) = P(X > s),$$

when t > 0. Show that this requirement is equivalent to

$$P(X > s+t) = P(X > s)P(X > t)$$

and deduce that exponential random variables are memoryless. Does X possess this property when

$$f(x) = \lambda^2 x e^{-\lambda x} \quad \text{if } x \geqslant 0,$$
$$= 0 \qquad \text{otherwise?}$$

¶ $$P(X > s+t \mid X > t) = \frac{P(X > s+t)}{P(X > t)}.$$

So if $P(X > s+t \mid X > t) = P(X > s)$ then $P(X > s+t) = P(X > s)P(X > t)$ and conversely.

If X has the probability density function
$$f(x) = \lambda e^{-\lambda x} \quad (x \geqslant 0)$$

then $P(X > s+t) = e^{-\lambda(s+t)} = e^{-\lambda s}e^{-\lambda t} = P(X > s)P(X > t)$ and X is memoryless.

If instead $\quad f(x) = \lambda^2 x e^{-\lambda x} \quad (x \geqslant 0)$

then for any x > 0
$$P(X > x) = \int_{x}^{\infty} \lambda^2 y e^{-\lambda y} dy$$
$$= (\lambda x + 1) e^{-\lambda x} \quad \text{(integrating by parts)}$$

Therefore $P(X > s+t) = (\lambda(s+t) + 1)e^{-\lambda(s+t)}$

$$\neq P(X > s)P(X > t) = (\lambda s + 1)(\lambda t + 1)e^{-\lambda(s+t)}$$

So X is no longer memoryless.

In fact exponential random variables are the only continuous variables possessing the lack of memory property. Geometric random variables have a similar property in the discrete case – see Question 19, page 124.

13. If X has the distribution N(4,16) find
    (i)   the number a such that $P(|X-4| \leqslant a) = 0.95$,
    (ii) the median,
    (iii) the 90th percentile,
    (iv) the interquartile range.

¶   The standardised variable $Z = \frac{X-4}{4}$ is $N(0,1)$.

(i) $P(|X-4| \leqslant a) = P(|Z| \leqslant \frac{a}{4}) = P(-\frac{a}{4} \leqslant Z \leqslant \frac{a}{4}) = 2\Phi(\frac{a}{4}) - 1$.

We require the a for which

$$2\Phi(\frac{a}{4}) - 1 = 0.95 \quad \text{i.e.} \quad \Phi(\frac{a}{4}) = 0.975.$$

Now $\Phi(1.96) = 0.975$. Therefore $\frac{a}{4} = 1.96$. i.e. $a = 7.84$.

(ii)   The normal probability density function is symmetric about its mean.

Therefore, median = mean = 4.

(iii) The 90th percentile (or 9th decile) x_{90} satisfies

$$0.9 = P(X \leqslant x_{90}) = P(Z \leqslant \frac{x_{90}-4}{4}) = \Phi(\frac{x_{90}-4}{4}).$$

Interpolating in tables,

$$\frac{x_{90}-4}{4} = 1.2816$$

Therefore $x_{90} = 9.126$.

(iv)   The upper quartile u satisfies

$$0.75 = P(X \leqslant u) = P(Z \leqslant \frac{u-4}{4}) = \Phi(\frac{u-4}{4}).$$

Interpolating in tables,

$$\frac{u-4}{4} = 0.6745.$$

Therefore $u = 6.698$.

Using symmetry, the interquartile range $= 2(6.698-4) = 5.396$.

14. A factory produces electrical components. Originally 5% of the components had a lifetime in excess of 1000 hours. The production engineer predicted that a certain change in the manufacturing process would increase the mean lifetime by 100 hours. After this change it was found that 20% of the lifetimes exceeded 1000 hours. Assuming that component lifetimes are normally distributed and that the predicted increase did take place find the mean and standard deviation of lifetimes before the change.

¶   Let X be the lifetime (in hours) and let its distribution be $N(\mu,\sigma^2)$. We are given that

$$P(X > 1000) = 1 - P(X \leqslant 1000) = 1 - \Phi(\frac{1000-\mu}{\sigma}) = 0.05,$$

whence $\quad \frac{1000-\mu}{\sigma} = 1.645.$

Suppose that the mean lifetime increases to $\mu+100.$

Then $\quad P(X > 1000) = 1 - \phi(\frac{1000-(\mu+100)}{\sigma}) = 0.2$

and, interpolating in tables,

$$\frac{900-\mu}{\sigma} = 0.8416.$$

Solving these equations, we find that

$$\mu = 795.2 \text{ and } \sigma = 124.5.$$

15. A teacher set and marked an examination and found that the distribution of marks was $N(42,14^2)$. The school's policy is to present scaled marks whose distribution is $N(50,15^2)$. What linear transformation should the teacher apply to the raw marks to accomplish this and what would the raw mark of 40 be transformed to?

¶ If X is $N(\mu,\sigma^2)$ and $Y=aX+b$ where a and b are constants, then

$$F(y) = P(Y \leqslant y) = P(X \leqslant \frac{y-b}{a})$$

$$= \frac{1}{\sigma\sqrt{2\pi}} \int_{-\infty}^{\frac{y-b}{a}} e^{-(x-\mu)^2/2\sigma^2} dx$$

$$= \frac{1}{|a|\sigma\sqrt{2\pi}} \int_{-\infty}^{y} e^{-(z-a\mu-b)^2/2a^2\sigma^2} dz \qquad (z=ax+b)$$

Thus Y is $N(a\mu+b,a^2\sigma^2)$. (See also Question 6 on page 176.) In the present case we must find a and b such that

$$50 = 42a + b \quad \text{and} \quad 15^2 = 14^2 a^2.$$

Solving we find that

$$a = \frac{15}{14} \quad \text{and} \quad b = 5.$$

$(a = -\frac{15}{14},$ b = 95 is also a solution but the transformation

$Y = -\frac{15}{14}X + 95$ gives the lowest marks to the most successful

candidates.)

So the required transformation is $Y = \frac{15}{14}X + 5.$

If X = 40 then $Y = 47\frac{6}{7}$ or 48, rounding to the nearest integer.

Exercises 4.3 Normal Approximation to Binomial and Poisson Distributions

1. The random variable X is B(100,0.5). Find the following
   probabilities. (i) $P(X \leqslant 65)$, (ii) $P(X \geqslant 46)$, (iii) $P(45 \leqslant X \leqslant 60)$,
   (iv) $P(X \leqslant 30)$, (v) $P(X \geqslant 65)$, using (a) the binomial tables,
   (b) the normal approximation.

¶ (a) Using tables of the binomial cumulative distribution function
   $F(x;n,p)$,

   (i) $P(X \leqslant 65) = F(65;100,0.5) = 0.99911$.

   (ii) $P(X \geqslant 46) = 1 - P(X \leqslant 45) = 1 - F(45;100,0.5)$
   $= 1 - 0.18410 = 0.81590$.

   (iii) $P(45 \leqslant X \leqslant 60) = F(60;100,0.5) - F(44;100,0.5)$
   $= 0.98240 - 0.13563 = 0.84677$.

   (iv) $P(X \leqslant 30) = F(30;100,0.5) = 0.00004$.

   (v) $P(X \geqslant 65) = 1 - P(X \leqslant 64) = 1 - F(64;100,0.5)$
   $= 1 - 0.99824 = 0.00176$.

   (b) If n=100 and p=0.5 then np=50 and $np(1-p) = 5^2$.
   So let Y be $N(50,5^2)$.

   (i) $P(X \leqslant 65) \approx P(Y \leqslant 65.5) = \Phi(\frac{65.5-50}{5}) = \Phi(3.1) = 0.99903$.

   (ii) $P(X \geqslant 46) \approx P(Y \geqslant 45.5) = 1 - \Phi(\frac{45.5-50}{5})$
   $= 1 - \Phi(-0.9) = \Phi(0.9) = 0.81594$.

   (iii) $P(45 \leqslant X \leqslant 60) \approx P(44.5 \leqslant Y \leqslant 60.5)$
   $= \Phi(\frac{60.5-50}{5}) - \Phi(\frac{44.5-50}{5})$
   $= \Phi(2.1) - \Phi(-1.1) = 0.98214 - 0.13567$
   $= 0.84647$.

   (iv) $P(X \leqslant 30) \approx P(Y \leqslant 30.5) = \Phi(\frac{30.5-50}{5}) = \Phi(-3.9) = 0.00005$.

   (v) $P(X \geqslant 65) \approx P(Y \geqslant 64.5) = 1 - \Phi(\frac{64.5-50}{5})$
   $= 1 - \Phi(2.9) = 0.00187$.

2. It is known that in a certain district 30% of the population will
   vote Conservative. A sample of 100 people is asked how they would
   vote. If X represents the number who say they will vote
   Conservative, find $P(25 \leqslant X \leqslant 35)$. What assumptions have to be
   made to answer this question?

¶ The number of Conservative voters in the sample can be taken to be binomially distributed only if certain conditions are satisfied. Firstly the number of voters in the district must be much greater than the sample size of 100. Otherwise drawing a person from the population may alter appreciably the proportion of Conservatives in the remaining population. Secondly a person's response must be independent of other people's responses. This can be achieved by using a random selection procedure in which each person has an equal chance of being selected. Assuming that these conditions are satisfied and also that people tell the truth about their voting intentions, X is B(n,p) with n=100 and p=0.3. Since np=30 and np(1-p) = 21 let Y be N(30,21).

Then $\quad P(25 \leqslant X \leqslant 35) \approx P(24.5 \leqslant Y \leqslant 35.5)$

$$= \Phi(\frac{35.5-30}{\sqrt{21}}) - \Phi(\frac{24.5-30}{\sqrt{21}})$$

$$\approx \Phi(1.2) - \Phi(-1.2) = 2\Phi(1.2) - 1$$

$$= 2\times0.88493 - 1 = 0.76986.$$

Alternatively, using tables of the binomial distribution,

$$P(25 \leqslant X \leqslant 35) = P(X \leqslant 35) - P(X \leqslant 24)$$

$$= 0.88392 - 0.11357 = 0.77035.$$

3. 90% of all items produced by a manufacturing process are satisfactory. Find an approximation for the probability that a sample of 250 items contains exactly 25 which are defective. What assumptions have to be made to answer this question?

¶ Let X be the number of defectives in the sample. To answer the question we make the assumption that each item inspected has probability 0.1 of being defective, independently of the quality of the other items inspected. This implies, for example, that if the first 9 items inspected are all defective then the (conditional) probability that the 10th item is defective is still 0.1. (This would be unrealistic for many manufacturing processes.) Then X is B(n,p) with n=250 and p=0.1. Since np=25 and np(1-p) = 22.5 let Y be N(25,22.5).

$$P(X = 25) \approx P(24.5 \leqslant Y \leqslant 25.5)$$

$$= \Phi(\frac{25.5-25}{\sqrt{22.5}}) - \Phi(\frac{24.5-25}{\sqrt{22.5}})$$

$$= \Phi(0.1054) - \Phi(-0.1054) = 2\Phi(0.1054) - 1$$

$$\approx 2\times0.541974 - 1 \quad \text{(interpolating in tables)}$$

$$= 0.08395.$$

Although p is small, both np and n(1-p) are considerably greater than 10. So we can expect the normal approximation to be quite good. In fact the exact value is 0.08382.

4. The random variable X is B(30,0.2). Calculate the probability $P(8 \leqslant X \leqslant 13)$ using (a) the binomial tables, (b) the Poisson approximation, (c) the normal approximation.

¶   (a) $P(8 \leqslant X \leqslant 13) = P(X \leqslant 13) - P(X \leqslant 7)$

$$= 0.99910 - 0.76079$$

$$= 0.23831.$$

(b) Using the Poisson approximation

$$P(8 \leqslant X \leqslant 13) \approx \sum_{x=0}^{13} e^{-6} \frac{6^x}{x!} - \sum_{x=0}^{7} e^{-6} \frac{6^x}{x!}$$

$$= 0.99637 - 0.74398$$

$$= 0.25239.$$

(c) Let Y be N(6,4.8). Then

$$P(8 \leqslant X \leqslant 13) \approx P(7.5 \leqslant Y \leqslant 13.5)$$

$$= \Phi\left(\frac{13.5-6}{\sqrt{4.8}}\right) - \Phi\left(\frac{7.5-6}{\sqrt{4.8}}\right)$$

$$= \Phi(3.4233) - \Phi(0.68465)$$

$$\approx 0.99969 - 0.75321 \quad \text{(interpolating)}$$

$$= 0.24648.$$

5. A certain material emits α-particles in such a way that the number emitted per minute is Poisson distributed with mean 9.5. Use the Poisson tables and the normal approximation to find the probability that, in a particular minute, the number of particles emitted is (i) not more than 10, (ii) at least 12, (iii) between 8 and 11 inclusive.

¶   Let X be the number of α-particles emitted during one minute.

   (i)   Using tables of the Poisson cumulative distribution function $F(x,\lambda)$, $P(X \leqslant 10) = F(10,9.5) = 0.64533$.

       Using the normal approximation and letting Y be N(9.5,9.5),

$$P(X \leqslant 10) \approx P(Y \leqslant 10.5)$$

$$= \Phi\left(\frac{10.5-9.5}{\sqrt{9.5}}\right) = \Phi(0.3244)$$

$$\approx 0.6272 \quad \text{(using linear interpolation)}.$$

(ii) Using Poisson tables,

$$P(X \geqslant 12) = 1 - P(X \leqslant 11)$$
$$= 1 - F(11, 9.5)$$
$$= 0.24801.$$

Using the normal approximation

$$P(X \geqslant 12) \approx 1 - P(Y \leqslant 11.5)$$
$$= 1 - \Phi\left(\frac{11.5 - 9.5}{\sqrt{9.5}}\right)$$
$$= 1 - \Phi(0.6489)$$
$$\approx 1 - 0.7418 \quad \text{(using linear interpolation)}$$
$$= 0.2582.$$

(iii) Using Poisson tables

$$P(8 \leqslant X \leqslant 11) = F(11, 9.5) - F(7.9.5) = 0.48333.$$

Using the normal approximation

$$P(8 \leqslant X \leqslant 11) \approx P(7.5 \leqslant Y \leqslant 11.5)$$
$$= \Phi\left(\frac{11.5 - 9.5}{\sqrt{9.5}}\right) - \Phi\left(\frac{7.5 - 9.5}{\sqrt{9.5}}\right)$$
$$= 2\Phi(0.6489) - 1$$
$$= 2 \times 0.7418 - 1$$
$$= 0.4836.$$

6. If X is Poisson distributed with mean λ, carry out the following operations for $\lambda = 4$, 9, 16 and 25.

(i) Construct a probability table showing $P(X = x)$ evaluated for appropriate values of x.

(ii) Draw an area diagram on graph paper.

(iii) Draw on the same axes the approximating normal curve

$$f(x) = \frac{1}{\sqrt{2\pi\lambda}} e^{-(x-\lambda)^2/2\lambda}.$$

Comment on the fit of the normal approximation.

¶   For $\lambda = 4$,

x	0	1	2	3	4	5	6	7	8	9
p_x	0.018	0.073	0.147	0.195	0.195	0.156	0.104	0.060	0.030	0.013
f(x)	0.027	0.065	0.121	0.176	0.199	0.176	0.121	0.065	0.027	0.009

	λ=9			λ=16			λ=25	
x	p_x	f(x)	x	p_x	f(x)	x	p_x	f(x)
3	0.015	0.018	8	0.012	0.013	14	0.006	0.007
4	0.034	0.033	9	0.021	0.022	15	0.010	0.011
5	0.061	0.055	10	0.034	0.032	16	0.015	0.016
6	0.091	0.081	11	0.050	0.046	17	0.023	0.022
7	0.117	0.106	12	0.066	0.060	18	0.032	0.030
8	0.132	0.126	13	0.081	0.075	19	0.042	0.039
9	0.132	0.133	14	0.093	0.088	20	0.052	0.048
10	0.119	0.126	15	0.099	0.097	21	0.062	0.058
11	0.097	0.106	16	0.099	0.100	22	0.070	0.067
12	0.073	0.081	17	0.093	0.097	23	0.076	0.074
13	0.050	0.055	18	0.083	0.088	24	0.080	0.078
14	0.032	0.033	19	0.070	0.075	25	0.080	0.080
15	0.019	0.018	20	0.056	0.060	26	0.076	0.078
16	0.011	0.009	21	0.043	0.046	27	0.071	0.074
			22	0.031	0.032	28	0.063	0.067
			23	0.022	0.022	29	0.054	0.058
			24	0.014	0.013	30	0.045	0.048
			25	0.009	0.008	31	0.037	0.039
						32	0.029	0.030
						33	0.022	0.022
						34	0.016	0.016
						35	0.011	0.011
						36	0.008	0.007

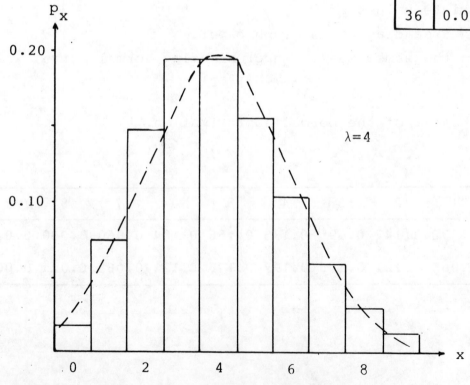

λ=4

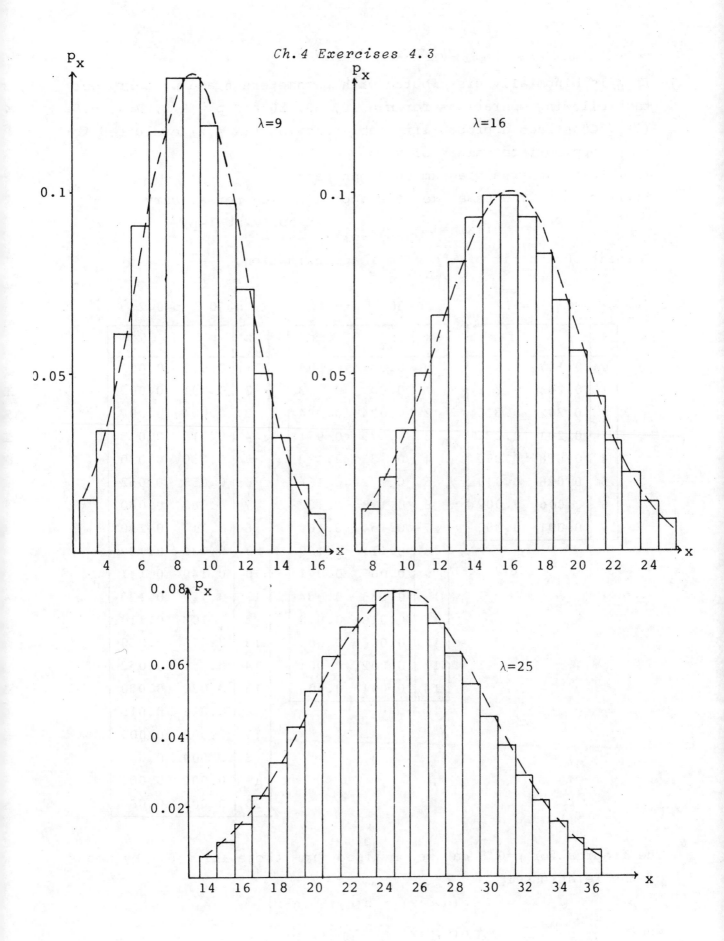

7. If X is binomially distributed with parameters n and p, carry out the following operations for n = 10, 30, 50 and p = 0.2, 0.5, 0.8.

   (i)   Construct a probability table showing $P(X = x)$ evaluated for appropriate values of x.

   (ii) Draw an area diagram on graph paper.

   (iii) Draw on the same axes the approximating normal curve

$$f(x) = \frac{1}{\sqrt{2\pi np(1-p)}} e^{-(x-np)^2/2np(1-p)}$$

Comment on the fit of the normal approximation.

	n=10 p=0.2			n=30 p=0.2			n=50 p=0.2	
x	p_x	f(x)	x	p_x	f(x)	x	p_x	f(x)
0	0.107	0.090	0	0.001	0.004	1	0.000	0.001
1	0.268	0.231	1	0.009	0.013	2	0.001	0.003
2	0.302	0.315	2	0.034	0.034	3	0.004	0.007
3	0.201	0.231	3	0.079	0.071	4	0.013	0.015
4	0.088	0.090	4	0.133	0.120	5	0.030	0.030
5	0.026	0.019	5	0.172	0.164	6	0.055	0.052
6	0.006	0.002	6	0.179	0.182	7	0.087	0.080
7	0.001	0.000	7	0.154	0.164	8	0.117	0.110
			8	0.111	0.120	9	0.136	0.133
			9	0.068	0.071	10	0.140	0.141
			10	0.035	0.034	11	0.127	0.133
			11	0.016	0.013	12	0.103	0.110
			12	0.006	0.004	13	0.075	0.080
			13	0.002	0.001	14	0.050	0.052
			14	0.001	0.000	15	0.030	0.030
						16	0.016	0.015
						17	0.008	0.007
						18	0.004	0.003
						19	0.002	0.001
						20	0.001	0.000

The figures for p=0.8 can be obtained from those for p=0.2 by means of the relationship

$$b(n,p;x) = b(n,1-p;n-x)$$

where

$$b(n,p;x) = {}^nC_x p^x (1-p)^{n-x}.$$

By symmetry, $p_x = p_{n-x}$ for p = 0.5.

n=10   p=0.5

x	$p_x=p_{n-x}$	f(x)
0	0.001	0.002
1	0.010	0.010
2	0.044	0.042
3	0.117	0.113
4	0.205	0.207
5	0.246	0.252

n=30   p=0.5

x	$p_x=p_{n-x}$	f(x)
6	0.001	0.001
7	0.002	0.002
8	0.005	0.006
9	0.013	0.013
10	0.028	0.028
11	0.051	0.050
12	0.081	0.080
13	0.112	0.112
14	0.135	0.136
15	0.144	0.146

n=50   p=0.5

x	$p_x=p_{n-x}$	f(x)
14	0.001	0.001
15	0.002	0.002
16	0.004	0.004
17	0.009	0.009
18	0.016	0.016
19	0.027	0.027
20	0.042	0.042
21	0.060	0.060
22	0.079	0.079
23	0.096	0.096
24	0.108	0.108
25	0.112	0.113

n=10   p=0.8

x	p_x	f(x)
3	0.001	0.000
4	0.006	0.002
5	0.026	0.019
6	0.088	0.090
7	0.201	0.231
8	0.302	0.315
9	0.268	0.231
10	0.107	0.090

n=30   p=0.8

x	p_x	f(x)
16	0.001	0.000
17	0.002	0.001
18	0.006	0.004
19	0.016	0.013
20	0.035	0.034
21	0.068	0.071
22	0.111	0.120
23	0.154	0.164
24	0.179	0.182
25	0.172	0.164
26	0.133	0.120
27	0.079	0.071
28	0.034	0.034
29	0.009	0.013
30	0.001	0.004

n=50   p=0.8

x	p_x	f(x)
30	0.001	0.000
31	0.002	0.001
32	0.004	0.003
33	0.008	0.007
34	0.016	0.015
35	0.030	0.030
36	0.050	0.052
37	0.075	0.080
38	0.103	0.110
39	0.127	0.133
40	0.140	0.141
41	0.136	0.133
42	0.117	0.110
43	0.087	0.080
44	0.055	0.052
45	0.030	0.030
46	0.013	0.015
47	0.004	0.007
48	0.001	0.003
49	0.000	0.001

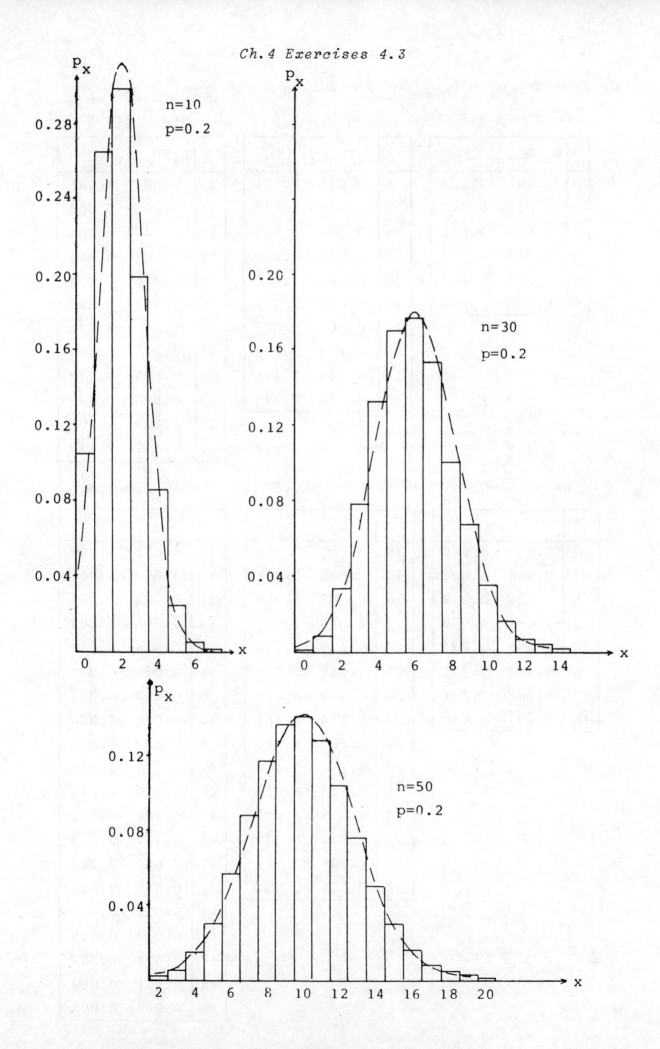

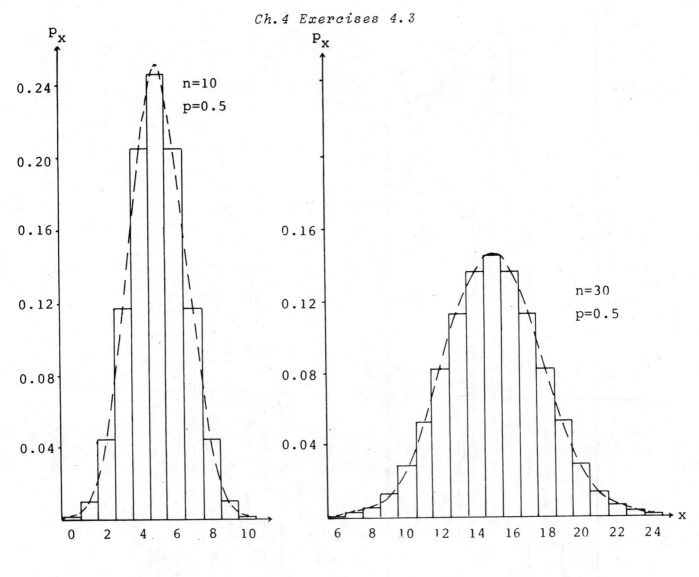

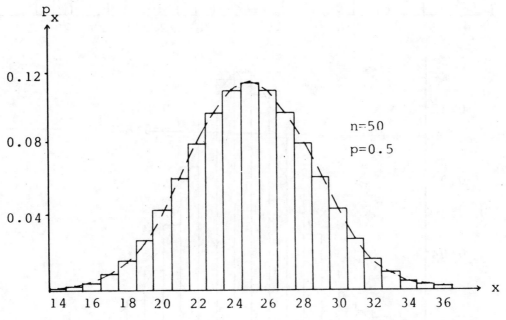

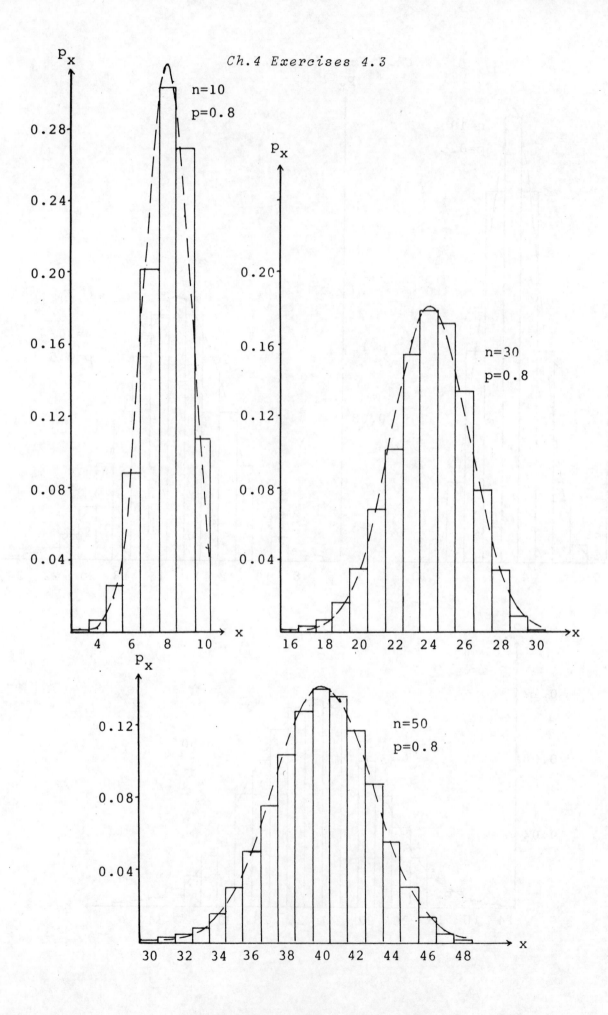

n=10
p=0.8

n=30
p=0.8

n=50
p=0.8

8. Of the football supporters in a certain area, it is known that 40%
   support 'City' and 60% support 'United'. Use the binomial
   distribution and the normal approximation to find the probability
   that of 100 supporters selected at random there are more 'City'
   supporters than 'United' supporters.

¶ Let X be the number of City supporters in the sample.
   Then X is B(100,0.4), assuming that City and United have many more
   than 100 supporters.
   We require
   $$P(X \geqslant 51) = 1 - P(X \leqslant 50)$$
   $$= 1 - F(50;100,0.4)$$
   $$= 0.01676$$
   or, using the normal approximation,
   $$P(X \geqslant 51) = 1 - P(X \leqslant 50)$$
   $$\approx 1 - P(Y \leqslant 50.5)$$
   $$= 1 - \Phi(\frac{50.5-40}{\sqrt{24}})$$
   $$= 1 - \Phi(2.1433)$$
   $$\approx 1 - 0.98395 \text{ (using linear interpolation)}$$
   $$= 0.01605.$$
   The relative error in the approximation is just over 4%.

9. The random variable X is B(n,p). The parameters n and p are such
   that one could use an approximation to evaluate probabilities.
   If the Poisson approximation is used, the mean is 10. If the
   normal approximation is used, the mean and variance are 10 and 9
   respectively. Calculate the values of n and p and use the tables
   to decide which approximation is better for calculating the
   probability that X $\geqslant$ 10.

¶ It is given that np=10 and np(1-p) = 9 so that p=0.1 and n=100.
   Thus X is B(100,0.1).
   Using tables of the binomial distribution,
   $$P(X \geqslant 10) = 1 - P(X \leqslant 9) = 1 - 0.45129 = 0.54871.$$
   Using the Poisson approximation with λ=np=10
   $$P(X \geqslant 10) = 1 - \sum_{x=0}^{9} e^{-10} \frac{10^x}{x!} = 1 - 0.45793 = 0.54207.$$
   Using the normal approximation,
   $$P(X \geqslant 10) \approx P(Y \geqslant 9.5) \qquad \text{where Y is N}(10,9)$$

$$= 1 - \Phi(\frac{9.5-10}{\sqrt{9}})$$

$$= \Phi(\frac{1}{6}) = 0.56618 \quad \text{(using linear interpolation)}.$$

The relative error in the normal approximation is only 3% but the Poisson approximation is preferable in this case.

10. A man buys a new die and throws it 600 times.

   (i)   Find the probability that he obtains between 90 and 100 'sixes' if the die is fair.

   (ii) Between what two limits symmetrically placed about 100 would the number of sixes obtained lie with probability 0.95 if the die is fair?

   (iii) What might he conclude if he obtained 120 sixes?

¶   Let X be the number of sixes obtained. Then X is $B(n,p)$ with $n=600$ and $p=\frac{1}{6}$ if the die is fair. Let Y be $N(100,\frac{250}{3})$.

   (i) $P(90 \leqslant X \leqslant 100) \approx P(89.5 \leqslant Y \leqslant 100.5)$

$$= \Phi(\frac{100.5-100}{\sqrt{250/3}}) - \Phi(\frac{89.5-100}{\sqrt{250/3}})$$

$$= \Phi(0.0548) - \Phi(-1.1502)$$

$$\approx 0.3968 \text{ (using linear interpolation)}.$$

   (ii) We wish to find a positive integer N such that
$$P(99.5-N \leqslant Y \leqslant 100.5+N) = 0.95$$

   i.e. $\Phi(\frac{N+0.5}{\sqrt{250/3}}) - \Phi(-\frac{N+0.5}{\sqrt{250/3}}) = 0.95$

   or $\Phi(\frac{N+0.5}{\sqrt{250/3}}) = 0.975.$

   Thus $\frac{N+0.5}{\sqrt{250/3}} = 1.96.$

   This equation does not have an integer solution but the integer which most nearly satisfies it is N=17. In fact $P(83 \leqslant X \leqslant 117) \approx 0.945.$

   (iii) He might well conclude that there is some evidence that the die is unfair since 120 is an unexpectedly large number of sixes if the die is fair.

11. A newsagent knows from past experience that the weekly demand for a certain magazine is Poisson distributed with mean 20. How many should he stock to be able to satisfy the weekly demand with

probability 0.95?

Suppose that he stocks this number of magazines and finds that after an advertising campaign he is unable to satisfy the demand in one week in four on average. Assuming that the weekly demand remains Poisson distributed, to what value has the mean risen?

¶   Let the newsagent stock N magazines. If X_1 is the weekly demand, we require
$$P(X_1 \leqslant N) = \sum_{x=0}^{N} e^{-20} \frac{20^x}{x!} = 0.95$$

or, using the normal approximation,
$$\Phi(\frac{N+0.5-20}{\sqrt{20}}) = 0.95$$

whence
$$\frac{N-19.5}{\sqrt{20}} = 1.645.$$

Therefore   N = 27   (to the nearest integer).

Let X_2 be the weekly demand after the advertising campaign. Since the new demand is not satisfied in one week in four on average, $P(X_2 \leqslant 27) = 0.75$.

Using the normal approximation, this leads to the equation
$$\Phi(\frac{27.5-\lambda}{\sqrt{\lambda}}) = 0.75$$

where λ is the new mean.

Thus
$$\frac{27.5-\lambda}{\sqrt{\lambda}} = 0.6745$$

or $\lambda + 0.6745\sqrt{\lambda} - 27.5 = 0$.

Solving this quadratic in $\sqrt{\lambda}$ we find that
$$\sqrt{\lambda} = 4.9176 \quad \text{and} \quad \lambda = 24.18.$$

12. The random variable X is Poisson distributed with mean λ. If $P(30 \leqslant X \leqslant 42) = 0.6$, use the normal approximation, together with trial and error, to find the two possible values of λ correct to the nearest integer.

¶ $P(30 \leqslant X \leqslant 42)$ decreases to zero both as λ increases to infinity and as λ decreases to zero. It attains a maximum value between $\lambda=35$ and $\lambda=36$. We can construct the following table with the aid of the approximation
$$P(30 \leqslant X \leqslant 42) \approx \Phi(\frac{42.5-\lambda}{\sqrt{\lambda}}) - \Phi(\frac{29.5-\lambda}{\sqrt{\lambda}}).$$

λ	30	31	32	35	36	39	40	41
$P(30{\leqslant}X{\leqslant}42)$	0.5251	0.5868	0.6390	0.7213	0.7213	0.6483	0.6052	0.5564

We see that the required values are $\lambda=31$ and $\lambda=40$.

Exercises 4.4 Transformations

1. The random variable X has probability density function

$$f(x) = \frac{15x^2(1-x^2)}{2} \quad \text{if } 0 \leqslant x \leqslant 1,$$

$$= 0 \qquad \text{otherwise.}$$

Find the probability density function of $Y = 1-X^2$.

¶ Let X have cumulative distribution function $F(x)$ and let Y have cumulative distribution function $G(y)$ and probability density function $g(y)$. Then, for $0 \leqslant x \leqslant 1$,

$$F(x) = \frac{15}{2}\int_C^x (z^2-z^4)\,dz = \frac{15}{2}(\frac{x^3}{3} - \frac{x^5}{5}).$$

Thus for $0 \leqslant y \leqslant 1$,

$$G(y) = P(Y \leqslant y) = P(1-X^2 \leqslant y)$$
$$= P(X \geqslant \sqrt{1-y}) = 1 - P(X \leqslant \sqrt{1-y})$$
$$= 1 - F(\sqrt{1-y})$$
$$= 1 - \frac{15}{2}(\frac{(1-y)^{3/2}}{3} - \frac{(1-y)^{5/2}}{5})$$

and

$$g(y) = G'(y)$$
$$= \frac{15y\sqrt{1-y}}{4}.$$

Alternatively, since $y=1-x^2$ $(0 \leqslant x \leqslant 1)$ is a strictly decreasing function of x,

$$g(y) = -f(\sqrt{1-y})\frac{dx}{dy}$$
$$= \frac{15(1-y)(1-(1-y))}{2}\cdot\frac{1}{2\sqrt{1-y}} \quad \text{as } \frac{dy}{dx} = -2x = -2\sqrt{1-y}$$
$$= \frac{15}{4}y\sqrt{1-y} \quad \text{as before.}$$

2. The random variable X has probability density function

$$f(x) = \frac{e^{-x/2}}{\sqrt{2\pi x}} \quad \text{if } x > 0,$$

$$= 0 \qquad \text{otherwise.}$$

Find the probability density function of $Y = \sqrt{X}$ and explain its relationship with the standardised normal distribution.

¶ Since $y = \sqrt{x}$ $(x > 0)$ is a strictly increasing function of x, the probability density function of $Y = \sqrt{X}$ is given by

$$g(y) = f(y^2)\frac{dx}{dy}$$

$$= \frac{e^{-y^2/2}}{\sqrt{2\pi y}} \cdot 2y$$

$$= \sqrt{\frac{2}{\pi}}e^{-y^2/2}, \quad y \geqslant 0.$$

Clearly $g(y) = 0$ for $y < 0$.

This is the probability density function of $W = |Z|$ where Z is $N(0,1)$. In fact let $H(w)$ be the cumulative distribution function of W. Then, for $w \geqslant 0$,

$$H(w) = P(|Z| \leqslant w) = 2P(0 \leqslant Z \leqslant w) = 2(\Phi(w) - \Phi(0))$$

and $\quad H'(w) = 2\Phi'(w) = \sqrt{\frac{2}{\pi}}e^{-w^2/2}$

since $\quad \Phi(x) = \displaystyle\int_{-\infty}^{x} \frac{e^{-z^2/2}}{\sqrt{2\pi}}dz$, so that $\quad \Phi'(x) = \dfrac{e^{-x^2/2}}{\sqrt{2\pi}}$.

3. Find the probability density function of Y in the following cases, where $f(x)$ denotes the probability density function of X.

(i) $\quad Y = X^3 \qquad$ if $f(x) = \dfrac{3x^2}{64} \quad (0 \leqslant x \leqslant 4)$.

(ii) $\quad Y = -\lambda\log_e X \quad$ if $f(x) = 1 \qquad (0 < x < 1)$.

(iii) $Y = \cos X \qquad$ if $f(x) = \dfrac{2}{\pi} \qquad (0 \leqslant x \leqslant \frac{\pi}{2})$.

¶ Let Y have probability density function $g(y)$.

(i) $\quad y = x^3$ $(0 \leqslant x \leqslant 4)$ is a strictly increasing function of x with range $0 \leqslant y \leqslant 64$ and so

$$g(y) = f(x)\frac{dx}{dy}$$

$$= \frac{3}{64}y^{2/3} \cdot \frac{1}{3}y^{-2/3}$$

$$= \frac{1}{64}, \qquad 0 \leqslant y \leqslant 64.$$

(ii) $\quad y = -\lambda\log_e x$ $(0 < x < 1)$ is a strictly decreasing function of x and takes values between 0 and ∞. For any $y > 0$,

$$g(y) = -f(x)\frac{dx}{dy}$$

$$= -1 \cdot (-\frac{1}{\lambda}e^{-y/\lambda}) \qquad \text{since } x = e^{-y/\lambda}$$

$$= \frac{1}{\lambda}e^{-y/\lambda}.$$

(iii) In the range $0 \leqslant x \leqslant \frac{\pi}{2}$, $y = \cos x$ is a strictly decreasing function of x taking values in $[0,1]$.

For $0 \leqslant y \leqslant 1$,

$$g(y) = -f(x)\frac{dx}{dy}$$

$$= -\frac{2}{\pi}(\frac{1}{-\sin x}) \qquad \text{since } \frac{dx}{dy} = 1\bigg/\frac{dy}{dx}$$

$$= \frac{2}{\pi} \cdot \frac{1}{\sqrt{1-y^2}}.$$

4. The radius R of a certain make of tennis ball is uniformly distributed on the interval (a,b). Assuming that the ball is hollow, consisting of a shell of material of small thickness t and density ρ, find the probability density function of (i) the external volume V, (ii) the weight W.

[It may be assumed that $W = 4\pi R^2 t\rho$.]

¶ The probability density function of R is given by

$$f(r) = \frac{1}{b-a} \qquad \text{if } a < r < b$$

$$= 0 \qquad \text{otherwise.}$$

(i) Let $g(v)$ be the probability density function of V, where

$$V = \frac{4\pi R^3}{3}.$$

Then, for $\frac{4\pi a^3}{3} < v < \frac{4\pi b^3}{3}$,

$$g(v) = f(r)\frac{dr}{dv} \quad \text{as } v=\frac{4\pi r^3}{3} \text{ is a strictly}$$
$$\text{increasing function of r}$$

$$= (\frac{3}{4\pi})^{1/3}\frac{v^{-2/3}}{3(b-a)}.$$

(ii) Let $h(w)$ be the probability density function of W. Then, for $4\pi t\rho a^2 < w < 4\pi t\rho b^2$,

$$h(w) = f(r)\frac{dr}{dw}$$

$$= \frac{1}{\sqrt{4\pi t\rho}}\frac{w^{-1/2}}{2(b-a)}$$

as $w=4\pi t\rho r^2$ is a strictly increasing function of r.

5. On a certain 4 km stretch of motorway cars are observed to travel at constant speeds which are uniformly distributed between 80 and 128 km per hour. Find the probability distribution of the time T (in minutes) taken to cover the distance by the next car to enter the stretch. Also find (i) $P(2 \leqslant T \leqslant 3)$, (ii) $E(T)$ and (iii) $E(V)$, where V is the car's speed. Is it true that $E(V) = 240/E(T)$?

¶   The probability density function of the speed V is given by

$$f(v) = \frac{1}{48} \qquad \text{if } 80 < v < 128$$
$$= 0 \qquad \text{otherwise.}$$

Let T be the time taken to cover 4 km, and let g(t) be the probability density function of T. Then

$$T = \frac{240}{V}.$$

For $\frac{15}{8} < t < 3$, $\qquad g(t) = -f(v)\frac{dv}{dt}$ as $t = \frac{240}{V}$ is a strictly decreasing function of v.

$$= \frac{1}{48} \cdot \frac{240}{t^2}$$

$$= \frac{5}{t^2}.$$

(i) $\qquad\qquad P(2 \leqslant T \leqslant 3) = \int_{2}^{3} \frac{5}{t^2} dt = [-\frac{5}{t}]_{2}^{3} = \frac{5}{6}.$

(ii) $\qquad\qquad E(T) = \int_{15/8}^{3} t \cdot \frac{5}{t^2} dt = 5[\ln t]_{15/8}^{3}$

$$= 5 \ln(8/5) = 2.35.$$

(iii) $\qquad\qquad E(V) = 104.$

Therefore $\quad E(V)E(T) = 104 \times 5 \ln(8/5) = 244.4$
$$\neq 240.$$

In fact $\quad E(V) = E(\frac{240}{T}) = 240E(\frac{1}{T}).$

6. The marks in a mathematics examination are $N(60,100)$. It is desired to rescale the marks so that
   (i)   75% of students pass (i.e. obtain a mark of 40 or more) and
   (ii) 10% of students get grade A (i.e. obtain a mark of 75 or more).
   What linear transformation of the original scores is required?

¶ The linear function y=ax+b (a≠0) is strictly increasing when a > 0 and strictly decreasing when a < 0. So if X is $N(\mu,\sigma^2)$ then Y=aX+b has the probability density function

$$g(y) = \frac{e^{-(x-\mu)^2/2}}{\sigma\sqrt{2\pi}}\left|\frac{dx}{dy}\right|$$

$$= \frac{e^{-(y-a\mu-b)^2/2a^2\sigma^2}}{|a|\sigma\sqrt{2\pi}} \quad (-\infty < y < \infty)$$

and Y is $N(a\mu+b,a^2\sigma^2)$.

In the present case, $\mu = 60$ and $\sigma^2 = 100$ so that Y is $N(60a+b,10^2a^2)$. It is required that

$$0.75 = P(Y \geqslant 40) = 1 - P(Y < 40) = 1 - \phi(\frac{40-60a-b}{10a}).$$

Hence $\phi(\frac{60a+b-40}{10a}) = 0.75$

and $\frac{60a+b-40}{10a} = 0.6745.$ \hfill (1)

It is also required that

$$0.1 = P(Y \geqslant 75) = 1 - P(Y < 75) = 1 - \phi(\frac{75-60a-b}{10a})$$

so that $\phi(\frac{75-60a-b}{10a}) = 0.9$

and $\frac{75-60a-b}{10a} = 1.2816.$ \hfill (2)

Solving equations (1) and (2), we find that

$$a = 1.7893, \quad b = -55.288.$$

So the required transformation is

$$Y = 1.7893X - 55.288.$$

7. The random variable X has probability density function

$$f(x) = 2x \quad \text{if } 0 < x < 1,$$
$$= 0 \quad \text{otherwise.}$$

Find a function h such that Y = h(X) defines a random variable Y which is distributed uniformly on the interval (0,1).

¶ Let X,Y have cumulative distribution functions F(x), G(y) respectively. Then, for 0 < x < 1,

$$F(x) = 2 \int_0^x z\,dz = x^2.$$

Assume that h(x) is strictly increasing and denote by $h^{-1}(y)$ the unique value x such that h(x)=y.

Then
$$G(y) = P(Y \leqslant y) = P(h(X) \leqslant y) = P(X \leqslant h^{-1}(y))$$
$$= F(h^{-1}(y)) = [h^{-1}(y)]^2, \quad 0 < y < 1.$$

Now Y is uniformly distributed on $(0,1)$ if
$$G(y) = P(Y \leqslant y) = y$$

so we require
$$[h^{-1}(y)]^2 = y,$$

i.e. $\quad h^{-1}(y) = \sqrt{y},$

i.e. $\quad y = h(\sqrt{y}).$

Putting $x = \sqrt{y}$, it follows that $h(x) = x^2$ is the required function. Note that, as assumed, it is strictly increasing on $(0,1)$.

(See also Question 31, page 202.)

8. A diameter PD is drawn on a circle of unit radius and a chord PX makes an acute angle Y with PD. If Y is a random variable with probability density function
$$f(y) = \frac{2}{\pi} \quad \text{if } 0 \leqslant y \leqslant \frac{\pi}{2},$$
$$= 0 \quad \text{otherwise,}$$
find the probability density function of the length of the chord. Find, also, the probability that the length of the chord (i) exceeds $\sqrt{2}$, (ii) lies between 1 and 2, (iii) exceeds $\sqrt{2}$, given that it exceeds unity.

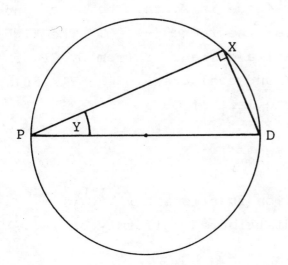

Let C be the length of the chord PX. Then
$$C = 2 \cos Y.$$
Let Y, C have cumulative distribution functions $F(y)$, $G(c)$ respectively.
Then $F(y) = 0 \quad$ if $y < 0$,
$$= \frac{2y}{\pi} \quad \text{if } 0 \leqslant y \leqslant \frac{\pi}{2},$$
$$= 1 \quad \text{if } y > \frac{\pi}{2}.$$

For $0 \leqslant c \leqslant 2$, as $c = 2 \cos y$ $(0 \leqslant y \leqslant \frac{\pi}{2})$ is a decreasing function of y,
$$G(c) = P(C \leqslant c) = P(2 \cos Y \leqslant c) = P(Y \geqslant \cos^{-1}(\tfrac{c}{2}))$$
$$= 1 - P(Y < \cos^{-1}(\tfrac{c}{2})) = 1 - F(\cos^{-1}(\tfrac{c}{2}))$$

$$= 1 - \frac{2 \cos^{-1}(\frac{c}{2})}{\pi}.$$

So the probability density function of the length of the chord is

$$G'(c) = \frac{2}{\pi\sqrt{4-c^2}} \quad \text{if } 0 < c < 2,$$

$$= 0 \qquad \text{otherwise.}$$

(i) $\quad P(C > \sqrt{2}) = 1 - P(C \leqslant \sqrt{2}) = 1 - G(\sqrt{2}) = \frac{1}{2}.$

(ii) $\quad P(1 \leqslant C \leqslant 2) = G(2) - G(1) = \dfrac{2\cos^{-1}(\frac{1}{2}) - 2\cos^{-1}(1)}{\pi} = \frac{2}{3}.$

(iii) $\quad P(C > \sqrt{2} \mid C > 1) = \dfrac{P(C > \sqrt{2})}{P(C > 1)} = \dfrac{1 - G(\sqrt{2})}{1 - G(1)} = \dfrac{\cos^{-1}(\frac{1}{\sqrt{2}})}{\cos^{-1}(\frac{1}{2})} = \frac{3}{4}.$

9. A searchlight S is placed 50 metres from a perimeter fence as shown in the diagram below.

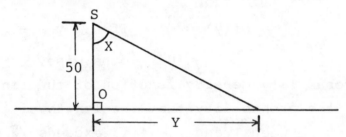

When the light is switched on, the angle it makes with the perpendicular SO to the perimeter fence is X, this being a random variable distributed uniformly over the range $(-\frac{\pi}{2}, \frac{\pi}{2})$. The light beam strikes the perimeter fence at a distance Y from O. Find the probability density function of Y and evaluate $P(-50 \leqslant Y \leqslant 50)$, where negative distances are to the left of O.

¶ The relationship between Y and X is

$$Y = 50 \tan X.$$

Let X,Y have cumulative distribution functions F(x), G(y) respectively. Then, since X is distributed uniformly on $(-\frac{\pi}{2}, \frac{\pi}{2})$,

$$F(x) = \frac{x}{\pi} + \frac{1}{2} \quad (-\frac{\pi}{2} < x < \frac{\pi}{2})$$

and

$$G(y) = P(Y \leqslant y) = P(50 \tan X \leqslant y)$$

$$= P(X \leqslant \tan^{-1}(\frac{y}{50})) = F(\tan^{-1}(\frac{y}{50}))$$

$$= \frac{1}{\pi}\tan^{-1}(\frac{y}{50}) + \frac{1}{2}.$$

The probability density function of Y is

$$G'(y) = \frac{50}{\pi(y^2+2500)} \qquad (-\infty < y < \infty).$$

Thus Y has a Cauchy distribution.

$$P(-50 \leqslant Y \leqslant 50) = G(50) - G(-50) = \frac{1}{\pi}(\tan^{-1}(1) - \tan^{-1}(-1))$$

$$= \frac{1}{\pi}(\frac{\pi}{4} - (-\frac{\pi}{4})) = \frac{1}{2}.$$

10. A point P is chosen at random on a fixed radius of the unit circle so that its distance X measured from the centre of the circle has a uniform distribution on the interval [0,1]. A chord is now drawn through P perpendicular to the fixed radius. If Y denotes the angle that the chord subtends at the centre, find the probability density function of Y and calculate its mean and variance.

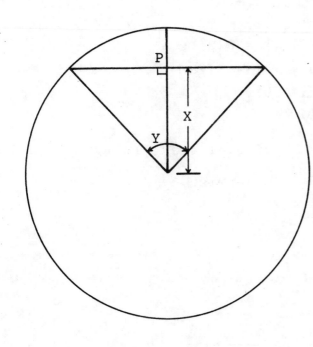

The relationship between X and Y is $X = \cos(Y/2)$

or $Y = 2\cos^{-1}X.$

Since $y = 2\cos^{-1}x \;(0 \leqslant x \leqslant 1)$ is a strictly decreasing function of x and the probability density function of X is

$$f(x) = 1 \quad \text{if } 0 \leqslant x \leqslant 1,$$
$$= 0 \quad \text{otherwise,}$$

the probability density function of Y is given by

$$g(y) = 1.\left|\frac{dx}{dy}\right| = \frac{1}{2}\sin(\frac{y}{2})$$

for $0 \leqslant y \leqslant \pi$; $g(y)=0$ otherwise.

Hence
$$E(Y) = \frac{1}{2}\int_0^\pi y \sin(\frac{y}{2})\,dy = 2 \text{ radians},$$

using integration by parts.

Similarly $\quad E(Y^2) = \frac{1}{2}\int_0^\pi y^2 \sin(\frac{y}{2})\,dy = 4\pi - 8 \text{ radians}^2$

whence $\quad \text{Var}(Y) = (4\pi - 8) - 2^2 = 4(\pi-3) \text{ radians}^2.$

11. A mass-produced square plate should be 1 cm square but, in fact, the length of its sides is distributed uniformly in the range 0.9 cm to 1.1 cm. Let the random variable A denote the area of the square plate. Find (i) the probability density function of A, (ii) the median area, (iii) the mean area.
Explain why (a) the median area = (median of the side)^2, (b) the mean area $\neq$ (mean of the side)^2.

¶ Let L be the length of a side, so that L is uniformly distributed on [0.9,1.1] and $A = L^2$.

(i) Let $F(\ell)$, $G(a)$ denote respectively the distribution functions of L,A. We are given that

$$F(\ell) = 0 \qquad\qquad \text{if } \ell < 0.9,$$
$$= 5(\ell-0.9) \quad \text{if } 0.9 \leqslant \ell \leqslant 1.1,$$
$$= 1 \qquad\qquad \text{if } \ell > 1.1.$$

For $0.81 \leqslant a \leqslant 1.21$,

$$G(a) = P(A \leqslant a) = P(L^2 \leqslant a)$$
$$= P(L \leqslant \sqrt{a}) = F(\sqrt{a})$$
$$= 5(\sqrt{a}-0.9).$$

The density of A is given by

$$G'(a) = \frac{5}{2\sqrt{a}} \qquad \text{if } 0.81 \leqslant a \leqslant 1.21,$$
$$= 0 \qquad\qquad \text{otherwise.}$$

(ii) The median area m_A satisfies

$$G(m_A) = \frac{1}{2}$$

i.e. $\sqrt{m_A}-0.9 = 0.1$

Therefore $m_A = 1$.

(iii) $$E(A) = \frac{5}{2} \int_{0.81}^{1.21} \sqrt{a}\,da = 1.00\dot{3}.$$

If m_S is the median of the side, we see that $m_A = m_S = 1$

whereas $E(A) = E(L^2) = 1.003 \neq [E(L)]^2 = 1$.

In general, for any positive random variable X, if m is the median of X then m^2 is the median of X^2. In fact

$$0.5 = P(X < m) = P(X^2 < m^2).$$

On the other hand, unless Var(X)=0, $E(X^2) \neq [E(X)]^2$.

12. A botanist observed that the distribution of X, the leaf-length of a certain species of plant, could be described by the density function

$$f(x) = 2xe^{-x^2} \quad (0 \leqslant x < \infty).$$

The amount of oxygen output from the leaf is proportional to the surface area of the leaf which is itself proportional to the length of the leaf. If Y is the random variable which represents the oxygen output, find the probability density function of Y. It was found that the mean oxygen output per leaf was 5 units. Find the probability that the oxygen output of a randomly selected leaf exceeds this figure.

¶ We are given that $\quad Y = kX$

where k is a constant of proportionality.

Let F(x), G(y) be the cumulative distribution functions of X and Y respectively. Then, for $x \geqslant 0$,

$$F(x) = \int_0^x 2ze^{-z^2}\, dz = [-e^{-z^2}]_0^x = 1 - e^{-x^2}.$$

For $y > 0$, $\quad G(y) = P(Y \leqslant y) = P(X \leqslant \frac{y}{k}) = F(\frac{y}{k}) = 1 - e^{-y^2/k^2}$

and the probability density function of Y is

$$G'(y) = \frac{2y}{k^2}e^{-y^2/k^2}.$$

$$E(Y) = \frac{2}{k^2}\int_0^\infty y \cdot y e^{-y^2/k^2}\, dy$$

$$= [-ye^{-y^2/k^2}]_0^\infty + \int_0^\infty e^{-y^2/k^2}\, dy$$

$$= 0 + \frac{k}{\sqrt{2}}\int_0^\infty e^{-z^2/2}\, dz \qquad (y = kz/\sqrt{2})$$

$$= \frac{k\sqrt{\pi}}{2} \qquad \text{as} \qquad \int_0^\infty \frac{e^{-z^2/2}}{\sqrt{2\pi}}\, dz = \frac{1}{2}.$$

It is given that $E(Y) = 5$.

Therefore $\quad k = \frac{10}{\sqrt{\pi}}$,

$$G'(y) = \frac{\pi y}{50}e^{-\pi y^2/100},$$

$$G(y) = 1 - e^{-\pi y^2/100} \qquad (y \geqslant 0).$$

We require
$$P(Y > 5) = 1 - G(5)$$
$$= e^{-25\pi/100}$$
$$= 0.4559 \text{ (to 4 decimal places)}.$$

Miscellaneous Problems

1. The weekly demand (in thousands of gallons) for 2-star petrol at a filling station is a continuous random variable with probability density function

$$f(x) = 48(x - \tfrac{1}{2})(1 - x) \quad \text{if } \tfrac{1}{2} \leqslant x \leqslant 1,$$
$$= 0 \qquad\qquad\qquad \text{otherwise.}$$

The storage tank, which can hold 940 gallons, is replenished each week at the same time. Calculate the probability the station runs out of 2-star petrol before the next delivery.

¶ Let X be the weekly demand. Then we require

$$P(X > 0.94) = 48 \int_{0.94}^{1} (x - \tfrac{1}{2})(1 - x)\,dx$$
$$= 0.03974.$$

2. Show that the points of inflection of the normal curve
$$f(x) = \frac{1}{\sqrt{2\pi}} e^{-(x-\mu)^2/2\sigma^2}$$
occur at $x = \mu \pm \sigma$.

¶
$$f(x) = \frac{1}{\sigma\sqrt{2\pi}} e^{-(x-\mu)^2/2\sigma^2}$$

$$f'(x) = \frac{-(x-\mu)}{\sigma^3\sqrt{2\pi}} e^{-(x-\mu)^2/2\sigma^2}$$

$$f''(x) = \frac{-e^{-(x-\mu)^2/2\sigma^2}}{\sigma^3\sqrt{2\pi}} + \frac{(x-\mu)^2}{\sigma^5\sqrt{2\pi}} e^{-(x-\mu)^2/2\sigma^2}$$

The points of inflection satisfy
$$f''(x) = 0$$
which leads to
$$\frac{(x-\mu)^2}{\sigma^2} = 1.$$

Thus
$$x = \mu \pm \sigma.$$

3. The random variable X has probability density function

$$f(x) = \frac{3}{x^4} \quad \text{if } x \geqslant 1,$$
$$= 0 \quad \text{otherwise.}$$

Find the mode, mean and median of X and calculate its variance and interquartile range.

¶ Since $f(x)$ decreases in the range $x \geqslant 1$, it follows that the mode is 1.

$$E(X) = 3\int_1^\infty \frac{dx}{x^3} = \frac{3}{2}[-\frac{1}{x^2}]_1^\infty = \frac{3}{2}.$$

The median m satisfies

$$3\int_m^\infty \frac{dx}{x^4} = \frac{1}{2}$$

$$[-\frac{1}{x^3}]_m^\infty = \frac{1}{2}$$

whence
$$m = \sqrt[3]{2} = 1.260.$$

$$E(X^2) = 3\int_1^\infty \frac{dx}{x^2} = 3[-\frac{1}{x}]_1^\infty = 3,$$

so that
$$Var(X) = E(X^2) - [E(X)]^2$$
$$= 3 - \frac{9}{4}$$
$$= \frac{3}{4}.$$

The upper quartile u satisfies

$$3\int_u^\infty \frac{dx}{x^4} = \frac{1}{4}$$

whence
$$u = \sqrt[3]{4}.$$

The lower quartile ℓ satisfies

$$3\int_\ell^\infty \frac{dx}{x^4} = \frac{3}{4}$$

whence
$$\ell = \sqrt[3]{4/3}$$

So the interquartile range is $\sqrt[3]{4} - \sqrt[3]{4/3} = 0.4868$.

4. Two similar discs are placed on a spindle and spun about their centres independently of one another. Each disc has a 10 cm radius and has a hole drilled in it of 1 cm radius, the centre of the hole

being 5 cm from the centre of the disc. Find the probability that the two holes will overlap when the discs have stopped spinning.

¶

Suppose the hole in one disc stops with its centre at B as shown. If the two holes are to overlap, the centre of the hole in the other disc must lie on the arc between A and C. Since the chords AB and BC are both of length 2, the probability that the holes overlap equals

$$\frac{\text{Angle AOC}}{2\pi} = \frac{4\sin^{-1}(1/5)}{2\pi}$$

$$= 0.1282.$$

5. Let X be a continuous random variable with probability density function f(x) and mean E(X). If f(x) is symmetrical about the point c prove that E(X) = c.

¶   Consider

$$E(X-c) = \int_{-\infty}^{\infty} (x-c)f(x)\,dx = \int_{-\infty}^{\infty} yf(y+c)\,dy \quad (y=x-c)$$

$$= \int_{-\infty}^{0} yf(y+c)\,dy + \int_{0}^{\infty} yf(y+c)\,dy$$

$$= \int_{0}^{\infty} -yf(-y+c)\,dy + \int_{0}^{\infty} yf(y+c)\,dy$$

$$= \int_{0}^{\infty} y[f(y+c) - f(-y+c)]\,dy$$

$$= 0$$

since, by the symmetry of f(x) about c, f(y+c) = f(-y+c).

Thus   E(X) = c.

6. The *moments* of the standardised normal distribution are defined by

$$\mu_r = \frac{1}{\sqrt{2\pi}} \int_{-\infty}^{\infty} x^r e^{-\frac{1}{2}x^2} dx. \qquad (r=0,1,2,3,\ldots)$$

Use integration by parts to show that

$$\mu_{r+2} = (r+1)\mu_r \qquad (r \geqslant 0).$$

Hence verify that

$$\mu_r = 0 \qquad\qquad (r \text{ odd})$$

$$= \frac{(r-1)!}{2^{(r/2)-1}(\frac{r}{2} - 1)!} \qquad (r \text{ even})$$

$$\mu_r = \frac{1}{\sqrt{2\pi}} \int_{-\infty}^{\infty} x^r e^{-\frac{1}{2}x^2} dx$$

$$= \frac{1}{\sqrt{2\pi}} \left[\frac{e^{-\frac{1}{2}x^2} x^{r+1}}{(r+1)} \right]_{-\infty}^{\infty} + \frac{1}{\sqrt{2\pi}} \int_{-\infty}^{\infty} \frac{x^{r+1}}{(r+1)} \cdot xe^{-\frac{1}{2}x^2} dx$$

$$= \frac{1}{\sqrt{2\pi}} \frac{1}{(r+1)} \int_{-\infty}^{\infty} x^{r+2} e^{-\frac{1}{2}x^2} dx$$

$$= \frac{\mu_{r+2}}{(r+1)},$$

i.e. $\qquad \mu_{r+2} = (r+1)\mu_r.$

Now $\qquad\qquad \mu_1 = 0$

so that $\qquad\quad \mu_3 = 3\mu_1 = 0$

and similarly for $r = 5,7,\ldots$

Also $\qquad\qquad \mu_0 = 1$

so that $\qquad\quad \mu_2 = \mu_0 = 1.$

Suppose, for even r,

$$\mu_r = \frac{(r-1)!}{2^{(r/2)-1}(\frac{r}{2}-1)!}$$

Then $\qquad\quad \mu_{r+2} = \frac{(r+1)!}{2^{r/2}(\frac{r}{2})!}$

and $\qquad\quad \dfrac{\mu_{r+2}}{\mu_r} = \dfrac{r(r+1)}{2 \cdot \frac{r}{2}} = r+1,$

confirming that this μ_r satisfies the equation

$$\mu_{r+2} = (r+1)\mu_r.$$

7. The random variable X has a $N(\mu,\sigma^2)$ distribution. Find the probability density function of the random variable $Y = (\frac{X-\mu}{\sigma})^2$. Y is said to have a *chi-square* distribution with 1 degree of freedom. Find the mode, median and mean of this distribution.

¶ Let the cumulative distribution function of Y be G(y). Then, for $0 \leqslant y < \infty$,

$$G(y) = P(Y \leqslant y) = P((\frac{X-\mu}{\sigma})^2 \leqslant y) = P(-\sqrt{y} \leqslant \frac{X-\mu}{\sigma} \leqslant \sqrt{y})$$

$$= 2\Phi(\sqrt{y}) - 1$$

and
$$g(y) = G'(y) = 2\Phi'(\sqrt{y})\frac{1}{2\sqrt{y}} = \frac{1}{\sqrt{2\pi y}}e^{-y/2}.$$

Clearly $g(y) = 0$ when $y < 0$.

Since $g(y)$ increases to infinity as y decreases to zero, the mode of $g(y)$ is $y=0$.

For the median m,
$$2\Phi(\sqrt{m}) - 1 = 0.5 \quad \text{or} \quad \Phi(\sqrt{m}) = 0.75.$$

Therefore $\sqrt{m} = 0.6745$ and $m = 0.455$ (to 3 decimal places).

Finally $E(Y) = E[(\frac{X-\mu}{\sigma})^2] = \frac{1}{\sigma^2}E[(X-\mu)^2] = \frac{1}{\sigma^2}\sigma^2 = 1.$

Note that this last result holds for any random variable X with mean μ and variance σ^2.

8. The probability density function of X has the form
$$f(x) = a + bx + cx^2 \quad \text{if } 0 \leqslant x \leqslant 4,$$
$$= 0 \quad \text{otherwise.}$$

If $E(X) = 2$ and $Var(X) = \frac{12}{5}$, determine the values of a,b,c.

¶ We are given that

$$\int_{-\infty}^{\infty} xf(x)\,dx = \int_0^4 (ax+bx^2+cx^3)\,dx = 8a + \frac{64b}{3} + 64c = E(X) = 2$$

and
$$\int_{-\infty}^{\infty} x^2 f(x)\,dx = \int_0^4 (ax^2+bx^3+cx^4)\,dx = \frac{64a}{3} + 64b + \frac{1024c}{5}$$

$$= Var(X) + [E(X)]^2 = \frac{32}{5}.$$

Also
$$\int_{-\infty}^{\infty} f(x)\,dx = \int_0^4 (a+bx+cx^2)\,dx = 4a + 8b + \frac{64c}{3} = 1.$$

Solving these equations,

$$a = \frac{3}{4}$$

$$b = -\frac{3}{4}$$

$$c = \frac{3}{16}$$

Therefore $\quad f(x) = \frac{3}{16}(x-2)^2, \quad 0 \leqslant x \leqslant 4.$

9. Calculate the mean and variance of the *Laplace* distribution with probability density function

$$f(x) = \frac{1}{2}e^x \qquad \text{if } x < 0,$$

$$= \frac{1}{2}e^{-x} \qquad \text{if } x \geqslant 0.$$

Sketch $f(x)$ and find the probabilities of being within one, two and three standard deviations of the mean. Compare these values with the corresponding ones for the normal distribution.

¶ Let X have the given probability density function.

Then $\quad E(X) = 0, \quad$ by symmetry.

Therefore $Var(X) = E(X^2) = \frac{1}{2}\int_{-\infty}^{0} x^2 e^x dx + \frac{1}{2}\int_{0}^{\infty} x^2 e^{-x} dx = \int_{-\infty}^{0} x^2 e^x dx = 2.$

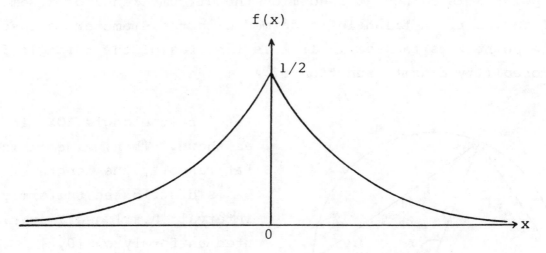

$$f(x)$$

$$1/2$$

$$0$$

$$x$$

The standard deviation is $\sqrt{2}$ so we require

$$P(-\sqrt{2} \leqslant X \leqslant \sqrt{2}) = \int_{-\sqrt{2}}^{\sqrt{2}} f(x)dx = \int_{-\sqrt{2}}^{0} e^x dx = 1 - e^{-\sqrt{2}} = 0.7569.$$

The corresponding normal probability is $2\Phi(1) - 1 = 0.6827.$

Also $P(-2\sqrt{2} \leqslant X \leqslant 2\sqrt{2}) = 1 - e^{-2\sqrt{2}} = 0.9409$,

compared with $2\Phi(2) - 1 = 0.9545$,

and $P(-3\sqrt{2} \leqslant X \leqslant 3\sqrt{2}) = 1 - e^{-3\sqrt{2}} = 0.9856$,

compared with $2\Phi(3) - 1 = 0.9973$.

10. A heavy goods vehicle runs for an average of 10,000 miles before breaking down. If the driver undertakes a 2,000 mile round-trip what is the probability that he completes the journey without breakdown if the distance to breakdown is exponentially distributed? What extra information would be needed to answer this question if the distance to breakdown was not memoryless?

¶ Let X be the distance travelled from the start of the journey until the vehicle breaks down. We require $P(X > 2000)$. Since X is exponentially distributed with mean $\lambda^{-1} = 10,000$,

$$P(X > 2000) = e^{-2000\lambda} = e^{-0.2} = 0.8187.$$

If the distribution of the distance to breakdown was not memoryless then we would need to know how far the vehicle had driven since the last breakdown as well as the distribution of the distance to breakdown.

11. A point X is chosen at random on the circumference of a semi-circle of radius r. A triangle is formed with the diameter as base and the point X as the apex. If A is the area of the triangle find the probability density function of A.

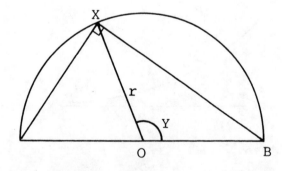

Let Y be the angle BOX (in radians), as shown. Then, since X is chosen "at random", the length of the arc BX is distributed uniformly on the interval $[0,\pi r]$ and Y is distributed uniformly on $[0,\pi]$. The area of the triangle

$$A = \tfrac{1}{2}(2r)(r \sin Y) = r^2 \sin Y.$$

Let A have distribution function $G(a)$. Then, for $0 \leqslant a \leqslant r^2$,

$$G(a) = P(A \leqslant a) = P(\sin Y \leqslant \tfrac{a}{r^2})$$

$$= P(Y \leqslant \sin^{-1}\tfrac{a}{r^2}) + P(Y \geqslant \pi - \sin^{-1}\tfrac{a}{r^2})$$

$$= 2P(Y \leqslant \sin^{-1}\frac{a}{r^2}) = \frac{2}{\pi}\sin^{-1}\frac{a}{r^2}$$

and $\qquad g(a) = G'(a) = \frac{2}{\pi\sqrt{r^4-a^2}}.$

Clearly $g(a) = 0$ elsewhere.

Note that, since $\sin y$ increases on $0 \leqslant y \leqslant \frac{\pi}{2}$ but decreases on

$\frac{\pi}{2} \leqslant y \leqslant \pi$, an unthinking application of the formula $g(a) = f(y)\left|\frac{dy}{da}\right|$

gives the wrong answer.

12. The maximum wind velocity (in km/hr) recorded each year at a weather station is a random variable with probability density function

$$f(x) = \frac{(x-70)}{200}e^{-\left(\frac{x-70}{20}\right)^2} \qquad \text{if } 70 \leqslant x < \infty,$$
$$= 0 \qquad\qquad\qquad \text{otherwise.}$$

Find the probability that the maximum gust in any year will exceed 110 km/hr and calculate the expected number of years until a gust exceeding this speed is recorded.

¶ Let V denote the maximum wind velocity in a year. Then

$$P(V > 110) = \frac{1}{200}\int_{110}^{\infty}(x-70)e^{-(x-70)^2/20^2}dx$$

$$= 2\int_{2}^{\infty}ye^{-y^2}dy \qquad (y = \frac{x-70}{20})$$

$$= [-e^{-y^2}]_{2}^{\infty} = e^{-4} = 0.0183.$$

Let X be the number of years until a gust of more than 110 km/hr is recorded. Then X is geometrically distributed and

$$E(X) = \frac{1}{0.0183} = 54.6 \quad \text{years.}$$

13. Targets at a rifle range are marked with 5 concentric circles of radii 1,2,3,4 and 5 cm. The centre ring is worth 10 points, and the remaining 4 regions are worth 8,6,4 and 2 points respectively. Let the random variable X denote the distance (in cm) of a shot from the centre of the target. If the probability density function of X is

$$f(x) = 0.25e^{-0.25x} \qquad \text{if } x > 0,$$
$$= 0 \qquad\qquad \text{otherwise,}$$

find the expected score. What is the expected number of 10-point scores in 100 independent shots and what is the variance of this number?

¶ The cumulative distribution function of X is

$$F(x) = 1 - e^{-0.25x}.$$

If S denotes the score,

$$P(S = 10) = P(X \leqslant 1) = F(1) = 1 - e^{-0.25} = 0.22120.$$

$$P(S = 8) = P(1 < X \leqslant 2) = F(2) - F(1)$$

$$= e^{-0.25} - e^{-0.5} = 0.17227.$$

Similarly $P(S = 6) = 0.13416$, $P(S = 4) = 0.10449$, $P(S = 2) = 0.08137$

Therefore $E(S) = 10 \times 0.22120 + 8 \times 0.17227 + \ldots + 2 \times 0.08137 = 4.976.$

The number N of 10-point scores in 100 independent shots is B(n,p) with n=100 and p=0.22120. Thus

$$E(N) = np = 22.12$$
$$Var(N) = np(1-p) = 17.23.$$

14. The following test is employed to test whether a rifleman is a marksman or not. Two long strips of wood, 1 cm wide, are knocked into the ground 10 metres and 11 metres away from where the rifleman stands. The rifleman fires at the first target, which is then removed so that he may fire at the second. He is classified as a marksman if he hits both targets. If the only detectable error a rifleman can make is in the horizontal plane, calculate the probability he is classified as a marksman if he is equally likely to fire at an angle Y in the range $(-0.05°, +0.05°)$, $0°$ being the direction of the centre line. It may be assumed that different shots are statistically independent.

¶ Let the target be r metres away from the rifleman. He hits the target if and only if

$$\frac{-0.5}{100r} \leqslant \tan Y \leqslant \frac{0.5}{100r}$$

i.e. $\tan^{-1}(\frac{-0.5}{100r}) \leqslant Y \leqslant \tan^{-1}(\frac{0.5}{100r}).$

If r = 10 then the probability that he hits the target is

$$P(-0.0286479 \leqslant Y \leqslant 0.0286479) = \frac{0.0572958}{0.1} = 0.572958.$$

The corresponding probability when r=11 is

$$P(-0.0260435 \leqslant \theta \leqslant 0.0260435) = \frac{0.0520871}{0.1} = 0.520871.$$

Thus the probability that he is classified as a marksman is
$0.572958 \times 0.520871 = 0.2984$ (to 4 decimal places).

15. The gap (in seconds) between successive vehicles passing a fixed point is a continuous random variable whose probability density function has the form $\lambda^2 t e^{-\lambda t}$ (t > 0). If the mean gap between successive vehicles is 5 seconds long find the probability the next gap exceeds (i) 5 seconds (ii) 10 seconds. If 5 seconds have elapsed since the last vehicle passed, what is the probability that a vehicle fails to arrive during the next 5 seconds?

¶   If T is the time gap (in seconds) between successive vehicles,

$$E(T) = \int_0^\infty \lambda^2 t^2 e^{-\lambda t} dt = \frac{2}{\lambda},$$

using integration by parts twice.
It is given that $E(T) = 5$. Thus $\lambda = \frac{2}{5} = 0.4$.

The cumulative distribution function of T is given for t > 0 by

$$F(t) = \int_0^t \frac{4}{25} x e^{-2x/5} dx = 1 - e^{-2t/5} - \frac{2t}{5} e^{-2t/5}$$

(i) $P(T > 5) = 1 - F(5) = e^{-2} + 2e^{-2} = 0.4060.$

(ii) $P(T > 10) = 1 - F(10) = e^{-4} + 4e^{-4} = 0.09158.$

(iii) $P(T > 10 | T > 5) = \frac{P(T > 10)}{P(T > 5)} = \frac{5e^{-4}}{3e^{-2}} = \frac{5}{3} e^{-2} = 0.22556.$

16. A random variable X is normally distributed with mean μ and variance σ^2. Show that
$$E\{|X-\mu|\} = \sigma\sqrt{2/\pi}.$$

¶ $E(|X-\mu|) = \frac{1}{\sigma\sqrt{2\pi}} \int_{-\infty}^{\infty} |x-\mu| e^{-(x-\mu)^2/2\sigma^2} dx$

$= \frac{\sigma}{\sqrt{2\pi}} \int_{-\infty}^{\infty} |y| e^{-y^2/2} dy \qquad (y = \frac{x-\mu}{\sigma})$

$$= \frac{2\sigma}{\sqrt{2\pi}} \int_0^\infty y e^{-y^2/2} dy \qquad \text{(by symmetry)}$$

$$= \sigma\sqrt{\frac{2}{\pi}} [-e^{-y^2/2}]_0^\infty = \sigma\sqrt{\frac{2}{\pi}}.$$

Alternatively, since $Z = (X-\mu)/\sigma$ is $N(0,1)$ and $|Z|$ has probability density function

$$f(z) = \sqrt{\frac{2}{\pi}} e^{-z^2/2} \qquad (z \geqslant 0)$$

(see Question 2, page 173), it follows that

$$E\left(\frac{|X-\mu|}{\sigma}\right) = \sqrt{\frac{2}{\pi}} \int_0^\infty z e^{-z^2/2} dz = \sqrt{\frac{2}{\pi}}.$$

17. Guided tours of a French chateau take place every thirty minutes.
    (a) If a tourist arrives at a randomly chosen point in time, find the cumulative distribution function of the time he must wait until the start of the next guided tour.
    (b) If the time of arrival of a second tourist has the probability density function
    $$f(x) = \frac{(x-10)^2}{3000}$$
    over the interval $0 \leqslant x \leqslant 30$ between two successive tours, find the cumulative distribution function of his waiting time T and calculate the mean and variance of T.

¶ (a) In this case, his waiting time is uniformly distributed on $[0,30]$, i.e. the distribution function is given by

$$\begin{aligned}
F(t) &= 0 && t < 0 \\
&= \frac{t}{30} && 0 \leqslant t \leqslant 30, \\
&= 1 && t > 30.
\end{aligned}$$

(b) The distribution function of X, the tourist's arrival time, is

$$F(x) = \frac{1}{3000} \int_0^x (z-10)^2 dz = \frac{1}{9000}[(x-10)^3 + 10^3].$$

Let $G(t)$ be the distribution function of his waiting time. Then, for $0 < t < 30$,

$$G(t) = P(T \leqslant t) = P(30-X \leqslant t) = P(X \geqslant 30-t)$$

$$= 1 - F(30-t) = 1 - \frac{1}{9000}[(20-t)^3 + 10^3].$$

Therefore
$$E(T) = \int_0^{30} (1 - G(t))dt \quad \text{(see Question 15, page 147)}$$

$$= \frac{1}{9000} \int_0^{30} [(20-t)^3 + 10^3]dt = 7.5.$$

Alternatively, the probability density function of T is
$$G'(t) = \frac{(20-t)^2}{3000} \quad (0 \leqslant t \leqslant 30)$$

and
$$E(T) = \frac{1}{3000} \int_0^{30} t(20-t)^2 dt = 7.5 \quad \text{as before.}$$

Also
$$E(T^2) = \frac{1}{3000} \int_0^{30} t^2(20-t)^2 dt = 120,$$

so that Var(T) = 120 - 7.5² = 63.75.

18. A number X is selected at random in the interval (0,1). Find the probability that the integer k appears in the first decimal place of $\sqrt{X}$ (k = 0,1,...,9). What is the probability that 3 appears in the second decimal place?

¶ The probability that the integer k appears in the first decimal place of X is
$$P(\frac{k}{10} \leqslant \sqrt{X} < \frac{k+1}{10}) = P(\frac{k^2}{100} \leqslant X < \frac{(k+1)^2}{100})$$

$$= \frac{(k+1)^2 - k^2}{100} \quad \text{(since X is distributed uniformly}$$
$$\text{on (0,1)).}$$

$$= \frac{2k+1}{100} \quad (k = 0,1,2,...,9).$$

Writing k3 for 10×k+3 and k4 for 10×k+4, the probability that 3 appears in the second decimal place is the sum
$$\sum_k P(\frac{k3}{100} \leqslant \sqrt{X} < \frac{k4}{100}) = \sum_k P(\frac{(k3)^2}{10000} \leqslant X < \frac{(k4)^2}{10000})$$

$$= \sum_{k=0}^{9} \frac{(k4)^2 - (k3)^2}{10000} = \sum_{k=0}^{9} \frac{2 \times k3 + 1}{10000} = \sum_{k=0}^{9} \frac{20k+7}{10000}$$

$$= \frac{20}{10000} \times \frac{1}{2} \times 9 \times 10 + \frac{70}{10000} = 0.097.$$

Note that the probability that 3 appears in the first decimal place is only 0.07.

19. The continuous random variable Y has a $N(\mu, 100(1+(\frac{\mu}{100}-1)^2))$
distribution. The *coefficient of variation* (CV), or *relative error*
as it is sometimes called, is defined by
$$CV = \frac{STANDARD\ DEVIATION}{|MEAN|}.$$

If μ is constrained to be positive, sketch a graph of the
coefficient of variation as a function of μ and calculate the
value of μ which minimises it.

¶
$$CV^2 = \frac{100(1 + (1 - \mu/100)^2)}{\mu^2} = \frac{1}{100} - \frac{2}{\mu} + \frac{200}{\mu^2}.$$

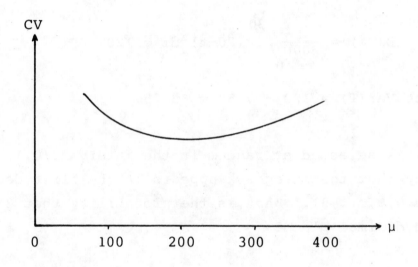

$$\frac{dCV}{d\mu} = \mu^{-2}(1-200\mu^{-1})(\frac{1}{100} - 2\mu^{-1} + 200\mu^{-2})^{-1/2}$$

This vanishes when $\mu=200$, corresponding to the minimum CV.
Note that the standard deviation is minimised when $\mu=100$.

20. The random variable X has probability density function
$$f(x) = \frac{5}{8}(1 - x^4) \quad \text{if } -1 \leqslant x \leqslant 1,$$
$$= 0 \qquad\qquad \text{otherwise.}$$

Find F(x), the cumulative distribution function of X. If $Y = X^2$,
show that G(y), the distribution function of Y, satisfies
$$G(y) = F(\sqrt{y}) - F(-\sqrt{y}).$$

Hence find G(y) and deduce that the probability density function
of Y is
$$g(y) = \frac{5y^{-\frac{1}{2}}}{8}(1 - y^2) \quad \text{if } 0 \leqslant y \leqslant 1,$$
$$= 0 \qquad\qquad \text{otherwise.}$$

¶   For x < -1,   F(x) = 0.
    For x > 1,   F(x) = 1.
For -1 ⩽ x ⩽ 1,
$$F(x) = \frac{5}{8} \int_{-1}^{x} (1-y^4) \, dy = \frac{5}{8}(\frac{4}{5} + x - \frac{x^5}{5})$$

For y > 0,
$$G(y) = P(Y \leqslant y) = P(X^2 \leqslant y) = P(-\sqrt{y} \leqslant X \leqslant +\sqrt{y})$$
$$= F(\sqrt{y}) - F(-\sqrt{y}).$$

For y < 0,   G(y) = 0.
For y > 1,   G(y) = 1.
For 0 ⩽ y ⩽ 1,
$$G(y) = \frac{5}{8}(\frac{4}{5} + \sqrt{y} - \frac{y^{5/2}}{5} - \frac{4}{5} + \sqrt{y} - \frac{y^{5/2}}{5})$$
$$= \frac{5}{8}(2\sqrt{y} - \frac{2y^{5/2}}{5})$$

and $$g(y) = G'(y) = \frac{5}{8}(\frac{1}{\sqrt{y}} - \frac{2}{5}\cdot\frac{5}{2}y^{3/2})$$
$$= \frac{5}{8}y^{-1/2}(1-y^2).$$

21. The random variable X is binomially distributed with parameters n,p. Use the normal approximation to show that, if n is large, the probability that X/n differs from p by more than $1/\sqrt{n}$ is less that 0.05 for all values of p. A biased coin is tossed 400 times, and falls 'heads' 240 times. What can you say about the probability p that the coin falls 'heads' in a single toss?

¶   Using the normal approximation, X is N(np,npq)

$$\text{or } \frac{X}{n} \text{ is } N(p,pq/n) \qquad (q = 1-p).$$

Therefore $$Z = \frac{\frac{X}{n} - p}{\sqrt{\frac{pq}{n}}} \text{ is } N(0,1).$$

Therefore $$P(|\frac{X}{n} - p| > \frac{1}{\sqrt{n}}) = P(|Z| > \frac{1}{\sqrt{pq}})$$
$$< P(|Z| > 2) = 0.04550 < 0.05,$$

since $pq \leqslant \frac{1}{4}$ or $\frac{1}{\sqrt{pq}} \geqslant 2$ for all values of p between 0 and 1.
If n=400 then, for 0 ⩽ p ⩽ 1,
$$P(|\frac{X}{400} - p| > \frac{1}{20}) < 0.05.$$

This is equivalent to

$$P(|\frac{X}{400} - p| \leqslant \frac{1}{20}) > 0.95$$

which can be written as

$$P(\frac{X}{400} - \frac{1}{20} \leqslant p \leqslant \frac{X}{400} + \frac{1}{20}) > 0.95.$$

This shows that the interval whose lower and upper end points are the random variables $\frac{X}{400} - \frac{1}{20}$ and $\frac{X}{400} + \frac{1}{20}$ respectively will enclose p with probability greater than 0.95, no matter what the value of p may be. If it is found that X=240 then

$$\frac{240}{400} \pm \frac{1}{20} = 0.6 \pm 0.05,$$

which suggests that the value of p lies somewhere between 0.55 and 0.65.

22. In a survey on telephone usage, it was found that the length of a conversation T has the probability density function

$$f(t) = \frac{1}{2}\lambda^3 t^2 e^{-\lambda t} \qquad (t \geqslant 0).$$

Use repeated integration by parts to find (a) E(T), (b) Var(T), (c) the coefficient of variation defined in Question 19.

¶
$$\text{Let } I_n = \int_0^\infty t^n e^{-\lambda t} dt.$$

Since it is given that f(t) is a probability density function, the result

$$I_2 = \int_0^\infty t^2 e^{-\lambda t} dt = \frac{2}{\lambda^3}$$

can be written down immediately.

Consider

$$I_3 = \int_0^\infty t^3 e^{-\lambda t} dt = [-\frac{t^3}{\lambda}e^{-\lambda t}]_0^\infty + \frac{1}{\lambda}\int_0^\infty 3t^2 e^{-\lambda t} dt$$

$$= 0 + \frac{3}{\lambda}I_2 = \frac{6}{\lambda^4}.$$

Similarly $I_4 = \frac{4}{\lambda}I_3 = \frac{24}{\lambda^5}.$

(a) $\qquad E(T) = \frac{1}{2}\lambda^3 I_3 = \frac{3}{\lambda}.$

(b) $\qquad E(T^2) = \frac{1}{2}\lambda^3 I_4 = \frac{12}{\lambda^2}.$

$$\text{Therefore } \sigma^2 = Var(T) = \frac{12}{\lambda^2} - \frac{9}{\lambda^2} = \frac{3}{\lambda^2}.$$

(c) In this case the standard deviation is directly proportional to the mean so that the coefficient of variation is a constant. In fact,

$$\sigma = \frac{\sqrt{3}}{\lambda} = \frac{1}{\sqrt{3}}E(T)$$

and

$$CV = \frac{\sigma}{E(T)} = \frac{1}{\sqrt{3}}.$$

23. A continuous random variable X has a $N(\mu,1)$ distribution where the mean μ is unknown. Five independent observations were made and 4 were found to be positive. Write down an expression in terms of μ for the probability that 4 positive scores are observed in five observations and sketch a graph of this probability as a function of μ. If you had to estimate the unknown mean μ what would your value be?

¶ Let N be the number of positive results when five independent observations are made on X. Then

$$P(N = 4) = 5[\Phi(\mu)]^4(1 - \Phi(\mu))$$

since

$$P(X > 0) = P(\frac{X-\mu}{1} > -\mu) = \Phi(\mu) \quad \text{when X is } N(\mu,1).$$

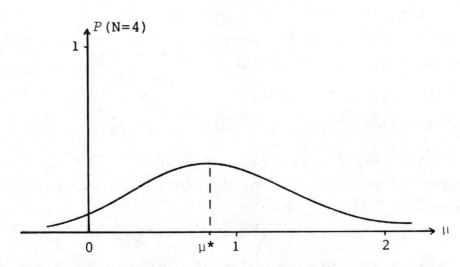

Since 4 is the observed value of N, a sensible estimate is the value of μ which maximises $P(N=4)$. We find that

$$\frac{dP(N=4)}{d\mu} = 5\Phi(\mu)^3\phi(\mu)(4 - 5\Phi(\mu))$$

where

$$\phi(\mu) = \Phi'(\mu) = \frac{e^{-\mu^2/2}}{\sqrt{2\pi}}.$$

So the maximum occurs at μ^* where $\Phi(\mu^*) = \frac{4}{5}$.

Thus we obtain $\mu^*=0.84$ as an estimate of μ.

An alternative method is to equate the observed value of N with its

expected value. This happens to give 0.84 again since
$$E(N) = 5\phi(\mu).$$

24. A firm manufactures components which must have a mean length of 1m
and a standard deviation of no more than 0.5 cm to meet the
requirements of a customer. A quality control officer is employed
to monitor the firm's performance. Each time a component is
inspected he decides that the firm is producing components to the
required specification if and only if the observed length is within
1 cm of the target mean (1m). Let the random variable X denote the
number of items inspected before one is rejected. Find E(X) when
   (i)   the mean of the process is 1m with standard deviation 0.5 cm
         (In Control),
   (ii) the mean of the process is 1.01 m with standard deviation 0.5
         cm (Out of Control).
It may be assumed that the lengths of inspected items are normally
distributed and that they are statistically independent of each
other.

¶   Let L be the length of an inspected item (in centimetres) and let
p be the probability that the item is rejected.
   (i)   If L is $N(100,0.5^2)$ then the process is "in control" and a
         large value of E(X) is desirable.

$$p = 1 - P(99 \leqslant L \leqslant 101)$$

$$= 1 - P(\frac{99-100}{0.5} \leqslant Z \leqslant \frac{101-100}{0.5}) \quad \text{where Z is N(0,1)}$$

$$= 2(1 - \phi(2)) = 2\times0.02275 = 0.0455.$$

Since inspected lengths are independent, X is geometrically
distributed and
$$E(X) = \frac{1}{p} = 22.0 \quad \text{(to 1 decimal place)}.$$

Thus a "false alarm" occurs once, on average, for every 22
items inspected when the process is in control.

   (ii) If L is $N(101,0.5^2)$ then the process is "out of control" and
         a small value of E(X) is desirable.

$$p = 1 - P(\frac{99-101}{0.5} \leqslant Z \leqslant 0) = 1 - (\phi(0) - \phi(-4)) = 0.50003.$$

and $$E(X) = \frac{1}{p} = 2.0.$$

25. There are two telephone booths in a hotel lobby. Mr Jones wishes to make a call but finds he must wait as the first booth is occupied by Mr Smith and the second is occupied by Mr Patel. If no one else is waiting and the duration of telephone calls is exponentially distributed with a mean of two minutes, find the probability that either Mr Smith or Mr Patel is still talking on the telephone when Mr Jones finishes his call.

    (Hint: consider the instant when one of the booths becomes free.)

¶ Consider the instant at which Mr Jones begins his telephone call. At this instant, either Mr Smith or Mr Patel is still speaking. Due to the 'memoryless' property of the exponential distribution, the distributions of the length of Mr Jones' call and the remaining length of the other person's call are identical; both are exponentially distributed with mean two minutes. Thus, by symmetry, Mr Jones has a probability of 1/2 of finishing first, and this is the required probability.

26. Height is distributed normally among a large population of males. What is the probability that a random sample of 100 men contains at least one man whose height exceeds 1.95m if 25% of the males in the population are taller than 1.8m but 10% are shorter than 1.65m?

¶ Let X denote the height of a randomly selected male (in metres). If X is $N(\mu, \sigma^2)$ then
$$P(X > 1.8) = 1 - \phi(\frac{1.8-\mu}{\sigma}) = 0.25$$

and
$$P(X < 1.65) = \phi(\frac{1.65-\mu}{\sigma}) = 0.1,$$

so that
$$\frac{1.8-\mu}{\sigma} = 0.67450$$

and
$$\frac{\mu-1.65}{\sigma} = 1.28155$$

whence $\sigma = 0.076685$ and $\mu = 1.748276$.

Therefore $P(X > 1.95) = 1 - \phi(2.63055) = 0.00426$.

Let Y be the number of males in the sample whose height exceeds 1.95m. Then Y is binomially distributed with n=100 and p=0.00426. Using the Poisson approximation with $\lambda = np = 0.426$,
$$P(Y \geqslant 1) \approx 1 - e^{-0.426} = 0.347 \quad \text{(to 3 decimal places)}.$$

27. The expected proportion p of flies killed by a concentration of x units of a fly spray is expressed in terms of the standard normal cumulative distribution function by

$$p = \Phi\left(\frac{x-\mu}{\sigma}\right)$$

where μ and σ are constants. A toxicity study reveals that $p = 0.30$ when $x = 10$ but $p = 0.95$ when $x = 20$. If the fly spray is used in a room containing 100 flies how many flies can be expected to survive if the concentration is 15 units?

¶ We are given that

$$\Phi\left(\frac{10-\mu}{\sigma}\right) = 0.3 \quad \text{or} \quad \Phi\left(\frac{\mu-10}{\sigma}\right) = 0.7$$

whence

$$\frac{\mu-10}{\sigma} = 0.5244 \qquad (1)$$

Also

$$\Phi\left(\frac{20-\mu}{\sigma}\right) = 0.95$$

so that

$$\frac{20-\mu}{\sigma} = 1.6449 \qquad (2)$$

Solving (1) and (2),

$$\sigma = 4.6098 \quad \text{and} \quad \mu = 12.4174.$$

If $x = 15$ then

$$p = \Phi(0.5602) = 0.71233 \qquad \text{(interpolating)}$$

and the expected number of flies which survive is

$$100(1 - 0.71233) = 28.767.$$

28. A positive random variable X has the probability density function

$$f(x) = e^{-x} \qquad \text{if } x > 0,$$
$$= 0 \qquad \text{otherwise,}$$

and Y is the error when X is rounded to the largest integer below. Show that F(y), the cumulative distribution function of Y, is

$$F(y) = \frac{1-e^{-y}}{1-e^{-1}} \qquad \text{when } 0 \leqslant y < 1.$$

¶ For $0 \leqslant y < 1$, $\qquad F(y) = P(Y \leqslant y) = \sum_{n=0}^{\infty} P(n \leqslant X \leqslant n+y)$

and $\qquad P(n \leqslant X \leqslant n+y) = \int_{n}^{n+y} e^{-x} dx = e^{-n}(1-e^{-y}).$

Therefore $\quad F(y) = (1-e^{-y}) \sum_{n=0}^{\infty} e^{-n} = \frac{1-e^{-y}}{1-e^{-1}} \quad$ as required.

29. A mortar fires a shell at a stationary target. The shell lands X metres from the target but the target is destroyed if the shell lands no more than 10 metres away. X has the probability density function

$$f(x) = \frac{(100-|x|)}{10000} \quad \text{if } |x| < 100,$$

$$= 0 \quad \text{otherwise,}$$

and successive shots are independent. Find the expected number of shots needed to destroy the target.

¶ Let p be the probability that any given shot destroys the target.

$$p = P(-10 \leqslant X \leqslant 10) = \int_{-10}^{10} \frac{(100-|x|)}{10000} dx$$

$$= 2 \int_{0}^{10} \frac{(100-x)}{10000} dx \quad \text{by symmetry}$$

$$= 0.19.$$

Since successive shots are independent, the number of shots N needed to destroy the target is geometrically distributed and

$$E(N) = \frac{1}{p} = 5.263.$$

30. Two numbers X and Y are chosen independently at random from the interval (0,2). Find the probability that Z > 3 when (a) Z=X+Y, (b) Z=XY.

(Hint: Consider the region in the (x,y) plane defined by $0 \leqslant x,y \leqslant 2$ and, in each case, shade the region corresponding to Z > 3.)

¶ (a)

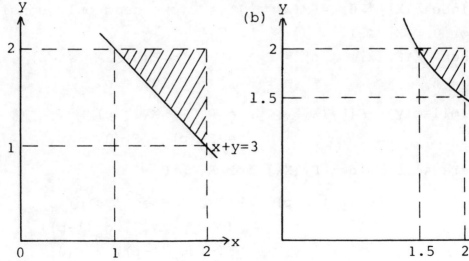

(a) The shaded triangle corresponds to the event $X+Y > 3$.
The area of the square is 4 and the area of the triangle is $\frac{1}{2}$.
Since all points in the square are equally likely,

$$P(X+Y > 3) = \frac{1/2}{4} = \frac{1}{8} = 0.1\dot{2}\dot{5}.$$

(b) The shaded region corresponds to the event $XY > 3$ and its area
is

$$\int_{1.5}^{2} (2 - \frac{3}{x})\,dx = 1 - 3\ln\frac{4}{3} = 0.13695$$

and $\quad P(XY > 3) = \dfrac{0.13695}{4} = 0.03424.$

31. Let X_1, X_2, X_3 be random variables with respective cumulative
distribution functions $F_1(x)$, $F_2(x)$, $F_3(x)$ where

$$
\begin{aligned}
F_1(x) &= 0 && \text{if } x < 0, \\
&= x^2 && \text{if } 0 \leqslant x \leqslant 1, \\
&= 1 && \text{if } x > 1, \\[4pt]
F_2(x) &= 0 && \text{if } x < 0, \\
&= x && \text{if } 0 \leqslant x \leqslant 1, \\
&= 1 && \text{if } x > 1, \\[4pt]
F_3(x) &= 0 && \text{if } x < 0, \\
&= 1-e^{-x} && \text{if } x \geqslant 0.
\end{aligned}
$$

If p is a given number between 0 and 1, find (i) $P(F_1(X_1) \leqslant p)$,
(ii) $P(F_2(X_2) \leqslant p)$, (iii) $P(F_3(X_3) \leqslant p)$.
If $Y_1 = F_1(X_1)$, $Y_2 = F_2(X_2)$, $Y_3 = F_3(X_3)$ what are the probability
density functions of Y_1, Y_2 and Y_3?

¶ (i) Since $P(X_1 < 0) = P(X_1 > 1) = 0$, we need only consider $F_1(X_1)$
for $0 \leqslant X_1 \leqslant 1$.
Then $P(F_1(X_1) \leqslant p) = P(X_1^2 \leqslant p) = P(0 \leqslant X_1 \leqslant \sqrt{p})$
$$= F_1(\sqrt{p}) - F_1(0) = p.$$

(ii) Similarly $\quad P(F_2(X_2) \leqslant p) = P(0 \leqslant X_2 \leqslant p)$
$$= F_2(p) - F_2(0) = p.$$

(iii) Here we consider $F_3(X_3)$ for $X_3 \geqslant 0$.
$$
\begin{aligned}
P(F_3(X_3) \leqslant p) &= P(0 \leqslant 1 - e^{-X_3} \leqslant p) \\
&= P(0 \leqslant X_3 \leqslant -\log_e(1-p)) \\
&= F(-\log_e(1-p)) - F(0) \\
&= 1 - \exp(\log_e(1-p)) = p.
\end{aligned}
$$

Thus $Y_1 = F_1(X_1)$, $Y_2 = F_2(X_2)$, $Y_3 = F_3(X_3)$ are all uniformly distributed on the interval [0,1].

In fact it is always true that if X is a continuous random variable with cumulative distribution function F(x) then the random variable U=F(X) is uniformly distributed on [0,1]. The proof is especially simple if F(x) is a strictly increasing function of x. In this case let $F^{-1}(p)$ denote the unique value of x such that F(x)=p.

Then $\quad P(U \leqslant p) = P(F(X) \leqslant p) = P(X \leqslant F^{-1}(p)) = F(F^{-1}(p)) = p.$

32. Two people A and B agree to meet outside a cinema. They choose independently their times of arrival at random between 6 p.m. and 7 p.m. If A is prepared to wait for 10 minutes and B for 15 minutes what is the probability they meet?

(Hint: Let X,Y be the arrival times of A,B. Consider the region of the (x,y) plane corresponding to 6 p.m. $\leqslant$ X,Y $\leqslant$ 7 p.m. and shade the region within which A,B meet.)

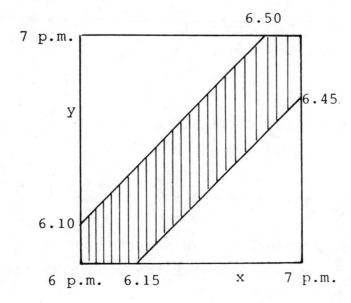

The shaded area corresponds to the event that A and B meet.
Let the square have unit area. Then the area of the shaded region is $\quad 1 - (\frac{1}{2}\times\frac{3}{4}\times\frac{3}{4} + \frac{1}{2}\times\frac{5}{6}\times\frac{5}{6}) = \frac{107}{288} = 0.3715$ (to 4 decimal places) and, since all points in the square are equally likely, this is the required probability.

33. The proportion X of the sky covered by cloud at midday at a certain meteorological station is a random variable with probability density function

$$f(x) = 12x(1-x)^2 \quad \text{if } 0 \leqslant x \leqslant 1,$$
$$= 0 \quad \text{otherwise,}$$

if the sky was red the previous evening, but with probability density function

$$g(x) = 12x^2(1-x) \quad \text{if } 0 \leqslant x \leqslant 1,$$
$$= 0 \quad \text{otherwise,}$$

if it was not. If 25% of evenings have red skies find, for a randomly chosen day, (i) the probability that the sky is more than 90% covered by cloud at midday, (ii) the expected proportion of the sky covered by cloud at midday.

¶ If X has the probability density function

$$f(x) = 12x(1-x)^2 \quad (0 \leqslant x \leqslant 1)$$

then $\quad P(X > 0.9) = 12 \displaystyle\int_{0.9}^{1} x(1-x)^2 dx = 0.0037$

and $\quad E(X) = 12 \displaystyle\int_{0}^{1} x^2(1-x)^2 dx = 12 \int_{0}^{1} (x^2 - 2x^3 + x^4) dx = 0.4.$

If X has the probability density function

$$g(x) = 12x^2(1-x) \quad (0 \leqslant x \leqslant 1)$$

then $\quad P(X > 0.9) = 12 \displaystyle\int_{0.9}^{1} x^2(1-x) dx = 0.0523$

and $\quad E(X) = 12 \displaystyle\int_{0}^{1} x^3(1-x) dx = 0.6.$

The unconditional probability and expectation are found by weighting these in accordance with the probabilities of occurrence or not of a red sky. Thus

(i) $\quad P(X > 0.9) = (0.25 \times 0.0037) + (0.75 \times 0.0523) = 0.04015.$

(ii) $E(X) = (0.25 \times 0.4) + (0.75 \times 0.6) = 0.55.$

34. The *moment generating function* M(t) of a continuous random variable X with probability density function f(x) is defined by

$$M(t) = \int_{-\infty}^{\infty} e^{tx} f(x) dx.$$

Show that

$$\frac{d^k M(t)}{dt^k} \bigg]_{t=0} = E(X^k), \quad (k = 1, 2, 3, \ldots).$$

If X is an exponential random variable with parameter λ show that

$$M(t) = \frac{\lambda}{\lambda - t} \qquad (t < \lambda)$$

and use this result to obtain the mean and variance of X.

¶ Suppose $\qquad M(t) = \displaystyle\int_{-\infty}^{\infty} e^{tx} f(x)\, dx.$

Differentiating with respect to t

$$\frac{dM(t)}{dt} = \int_{-\infty}^{\infty} x e^{tx} f(x)\, dx$$

and, in general,

$$\frac{d^k M(t)}{dt^k} = \int_{-\infty}^{\infty} x^k e^{tx} f(x)\, dx.$$

Putting t=0,

$$\left.\frac{d^k M(t)}{dt^k}\right]_{t=0} = \int_{-\infty}^{\infty} x^k f(x)\, dx = E(X^k).$$

If X is exponentially distributed with parameter λ, its density function is $\qquad f(x) = \lambda e^{-\lambda x} \qquad (x \geqslant 0).$

The moment generating function is

$$M(t) = \lambda \int_{0}^{\infty} e^{tx} e^{-\lambda x}\, dx = \left[-\frac{\lambda}{\lambda - t} e^{-(\lambda - t)x}\right]_{0}^{\infty} = \frac{\lambda}{\lambda - t}$$

as long as $t < \lambda$.

$$M'(t) = \frac{\lambda}{(\lambda - t)^2},$$

$$M''(t) = \frac{2\lambda}{(\lambda - t)^3}$$

so that

$$E(X) = M'(0) = \frac{1}{\lambda},$$

$$E(X^2) = M''(0) = \frac{2}{\lambda^2}$$

and $\qquad \mathrm{Var}(X) = \frac{2}{\lambda^2} - \left(\frac{1}{\lambda}\right)^2 = \frac{1}{\lambda^2}.$

35. A random variable X is $N(\mu, \sigma^2)$. Show that its moment generating function M(t) is given by

$$M(t) = e^{\mu t + \frac{1}{2}\sigma^2 t^2} \qquad \text{for all } t.$$

Use this result to show that $E(X) = \mu$, $Var(X) = \sigma^2$ and find $E(X^3)$ and $E(X^4)$ in terms of μ and σ^2.

¶   If X is $N(\mu,\sigma^2)$ then

$$M(t) = \frac{1}{\sigma\sqrt{2\pi}} \int_{-\infty}^{\infty} e^{tx} e^{-(x-\mu)^2/2\sigma^2} dx$$

$$= \frac{1}{\sigma\sqrt{2\pi}} \int_{-\infty}^{\infty} \exp\{-(x^2-2(\mu+\sigma^2 t)x+\mu^2)/2\sigma^2\} dx$$

$$= \frac{1}{\sigma\sqrt{2\pi}} \int_{-\infty}^{\infty} \exp\{-(x-\mu-\sigma^2 t)^2/2\sigma^2\} e^{\mu t+\frac{1}{2}\sigma^2 t^2} dx$$

$$= e^{\mu t+\frac{1}{2}\sigma^2 t^2} \int_{-\infty}^{\infty} \frac{e^{-\frac{1}{2}z^2}}{\sqrt{2\pi}} dz \qquad (z = \frac{x-\mu-\sigma^2 t}{\sigma})$$

$$= e^{\mu t+\frac{1}{2}\sigma^2 t^2}.$$

$$M'(t) = (\mu+\sigma^2 t)M(t).$$

Therefore $E(X) = M'(0) = \mu M(0) = \mu$ as $M(0) = 1$.

$$M''(t) = \sigma^2 M(t) + (\mu+\sigma^2 t)M'(t).$$

Therefore $E(X^2) = M''(0) = \sigma^2 M(0) + \mu M'(0) = \sigma^2+\mu^2$

so that $Var(X) = E(X^2) - [E(X)]^2 = \sigma^2$.

$$M'''(t) = 2\sigma^2 M'(t) + (\mu+\sigma^2 t)M''(t).$$

Therefore $E(X^3) = M'''(0) = 2\sigma^2 M'(0) + \mu M''(0)$

$$= 2\sigma^2\mu + \mu(\sigma^2+\mu^2)$$

$$= 3\sigma^2\mu + \mu^3.$$

$$M''''(t) = 3\sigma^2 M''(t) + (\mu+\sigma^2 t)M'''(t).$$

Therefore $E(X^4) = M''''(0) = 3\sigma^2 M''(0) + \mu M'''(0)$

$$= 3\sigma^2(\sigma^2+\mu^2) + \mu(3\sigma^2\mu + \mu^3)$$

$$= 3\sigma^4 + 6\sigma^2\mu^2 + \mu^4.$$

36. Show that the moment generating function of a Poisson random variable X with mean λ is given by

$$M_1(\theta) = E[e^{\theta X}] = e^{\lambda(e^\theta-1)}.$$

Deduce that the moment generating function of $Y = \frac{X-\lambda}{\sqrt{\lambda}}$

is given by

$$M_2(\theta) = E[e^{\theta Y}] = e^{-\theta\sqrt{\lambda}} M_1(\frac{\theta}{\sqrt{\lambda}}).$$

Use the exponential series to deduce that, for large θ,

$$M_2(\theta) \approx e^{\frac{1}{2}\theta^2}.$$

Interpret this result in the light of the moment generating function found in Question 35.

¶   The moment generating function of X is

$$M_1(\theta) = E[e^{\theta X}] = \sum_{x=0}^{\infty} e^{\theta x} p_x$$

where $p_x = e^{-\lambda} \dfrac{\lambda^x}{x!}.$

Therefore $M_1(\theta) = \displaystyle\sum_{x=0}^{\infty} e^{\theta x} e^{-\lambda} \dfrac{\lambda^x}{x!} = e^{-\lambda} \sum_{x=0}^{\infty} \dfrac{(\lambda e^{\theta})^x}{x!} = e^{-\lambda} \exp(\lambda e^{\theta})$

$$= \exp\{\lambda(e^{\theta}-1)\}.$$

$$M_2(\theta) = E[e^{\theta Y}] = E[e^{\theta(X-\lambda)/\sqrt{\lambda}}] = e^{-\theta\sqrt{\lambda}} M_1\left(\dfrac{\theta}{\sqrt{\lambda}}\right)$$

$$= e^{-\theta\sqrt{\lambda}} \exp\{\lambda(e^{\theta/\sqrt{\lambda}}-1)\} = \exp\{-\theta\sqrt{\lambda} - \lambda + \lambda e^{\theta/\sqrt{\lambda}}\}.$$

When λ is large,

$$-\theta\sqrt{\lambda} - \lambda + \lambda e^{\theta/\sqrt{\lambda}} = -\theta\sqrt{\lambda} - \lambda + \lambda\left(1 + \dfrac{\theta}{\sqrt{\lambda}} + \dfrac{1}{2!}\left(\dfrac{\theta}{\sqrt{\lambda}}\right)^2 + \dfrac{1}{3!}\left(\dfrac{\theta}{\sqrt{\lambda}}\right)^3 + \ldots\right)$$

$$= \dfrac{1}{2}\theta^2 + \dfrac{\theta^3}{3!\sqrt{\lambda}} + \ldots$$

$$\approx \dfrac{1}{2}\theta^2$$

and $M_2(\theta) \approx e^{\frac{1}{2}\theta^2}.$

As $e^{\frac{1}{2}\theta^2}$ is the moment generating function of the standardised normal distribution, this result indicates that $(X-\lambda)/\sqrt{\lambda}$ is approximately $N(0,1)$ when λ is large.

37. The time T for which a machine runs until breakdown is a random variable with probability density function

$$f(t) = \lambda e^{-\lambda t} \quad \text{if } t \geqslant 0,$$
$$= 0 \quad \text{otherwise.}$$

The machine costs C_1 per hour to run but while it is running it earns an amount C_2 per hour. A hired operator is paid C_3 for each hour for which the machine runs. Find the expected profit.
Suppose instead that the operator must be hired for a pre-arranged number of hours H and is paid for H hours regardless of whether or

not the machine breaks down before that time elapses. Find the expected profit and show that this is maximised when
$$H = -(\log_e(C_3/(C_2-C_1)))/\lambda$$
and C_1, C_2 and C_3 satisfy appropriate conditions. What are the constraints on C_1, C_2 and C_3? What do these constraints represent?

¶ Let P denote the profit.
$$P = (C_2 - C_1 - C_3)T$$

and
$$E(P) = (C_2 - C_1 - C_3)E(T) = \frac{C_2 - C_1 - C_3}{\lambda}.$$

Under the modified conditions,
$$P = (C_2 - C_1)T - C_3H \quad \text{if } T \leqslant H,$$
$$= (C_2 - C_1)H - C_3H \quad \text{if } T > H.$$

Therefore
$$E(P) = \int_0^H ((C_2-C_1)t - C_3H)\lambda e^{-\lambda t}dt + \int_H^\infty (C_2-C_1-C_3)H\lambda e^{-\lambda t}dt$$
$$= \frac{(C_2-C_1)}{\lambda}(1 - e^{-\lambda H}) - C_3H$$

and
$$\frac{dE(P)}{dH} = (C_2-C_1)e^{-\lambda H} - C_3$$

which is zero if
$$\lambda H = -\log_e\left(\frac{C_3}{C_2-C_1}\right).$$

Since $\lambda H > 0$, this condition can only be satisfied when
$$0 < \frac{C_3}{C_2-C_1} < 1.$$

Assuming $C_3 > 0$, we require $C_2 > C_1$ and, given this, $C_3 < C_2 - C_1$, i.e. $C_2 - C_1 - C_3 > 0$, so that the hourly profit when the machine is working is positive.

If $C_2 \ngtr C_1 + C_3$ then the machine should not be operated at all.

Finally
$$\frac{d^2E(P)}{dH^2} = -\lambda(C_2-C_1)e^{-\lambda H} < 0 \quad \text{if } C_2 > C_1.$$

So the expected profit will be maximised if the operator is hired for $-(\log_e(C_3/(C_2-C_1)))/\lambda$ hours.

38. In a study of wood boring larvae, an experiment consists of introducing a larva at one end of a long wooden rod and observing the distance X (in cm) which it has travelled along the rod in a given time t. The probability density function of X is
$$f(x) = \frac{\theta}{(1+x)^{\theta+1}} \quad \text{if } x \geqslant 0,$$
$$= 0 \quad \text{otherwise,}$$

where θ is a constant strictly greater than 0. What values of θ ensure a probability of at least 0.99 that the larva is within 1 cm of the starting point at time t? Show that the probability density function of $Y = \log(1+X)$ is exponential with parameter θ. Deduce that the expectation of Y is given by

$$E(Y) = \frac{E(X)}{1+E(X)}.$$

¶ We require $P(X \leqslant 1) \geqslant 0.99$.

Since
$$P(X \leqslant 1) = \int_0^1 \frac{\theta\,dx}{(1+x)^{\theta+1}} = 1 - 2^{-\theta},$$

we require $1 - 2^{-\theta} \geqslant 0.99$,

i.e. $\theta \geqslant \dfrac{\ln 100}{\ln 2} = 6.644.$

Let X, Y have respective cumulative distribution functions F(x), G(y).

$$F(x) = \int_0^x \frac{\theta\,dz}{(1+z)^{\theta+1}} = 1 - \frac{1}{(1+x)^{\theta}} \qquad (x \geqslant 0)$$

$$G(y) = P(Y \leqslant y) = P[\log(1+X) \leqslant y]$$

$$= P(X < e^y - 1) = F(e^y - 1)$$

$$= 1 - e^{-\theta y} \qquad (y \geqslant 0).$$

The density function of Y is

$$G'(y) = \theta e^{-\theta y} \qquad \text{as required.}$$

$$E(Y) = \int_0^\infty \theta y e^{-\theta y}\,dy = \frac{1}{\theta}.$$

$$E(X) = \int_0^\infty \frac{\theta x\,dx}{(1+x)^{\theta+1}}$$

$$= \frac{1}{\theta-1} \qquad \text{(using integration by parts).}$$

It follows that

$$\frac{E(X)}{1+E(X)} = \frac{1}{\theta-1+1} = \frac{1}{\theta} = E(Y).$$

39. A ship fires at a target, 30 metres wide, which is 900 metres away (measured to its centre). The gun is aimed to hit the centre of the target but the actual angle of the gun is a uniform random

variable over the range $(\theta^\circ-1^\circ,\theta^\circ+1^\circ)$ where θ is the nominal setting. The speed of the shell when it leaves the gun is $\sqrt{1000g}$ m/sec, where g is the acceleration due to gravity. Show that there are two possible settings for θ but that the probability of hitting the target is the same whichever angle is used. Find this probability.

Repeat the calculations for the case where the centre of the target is 990 metres away from the ship.

(Hint: The range of a projectile fired with speed V at an angle θ to the horizontal is $V^2\sin2\theta/g$.)

¶ Since $V = \sqrt{1000g}$, the range R is given by the formula

$$R = 1000\sin2Y$$

where Y is the actual angle. To hit the centre of the target at 900 metres the angle y should satisfy

$$\sin2y = \frac{900}{1000} = 0.9$$

so that we should have

$$y = \frac{1}{2}\sin^{-1}0.9 \quad \text{or} \quad 90 - \frac{1}{2}\sin^{-1}0.9$$

$$= 32.079^\circ \quad \text{or} \quad 57.921^\circ.$$

Since the target is 30 metres wide, the target is hit if and only if $885 \leqslant R \leqslant 915$.

If the nominal setting $\theta = 32.079$, then Y is distributed uniformly between 31.079° and 33.079° and

$$P(885 \leqslant R \leqslant 915) = P(\frac{885}{1000} \leqslant \sin2Y \leqslant \frac{915}{1000})$$

$$= P(31.126 \leqslant Y \leqslant 33.103) + P(56.897 \leqslant Y \leqslant 58.874)$$

$$= P(31.126 \leqslant Y \leqslant 33.079) + 0$$

$$= \frac{33.079 - 31.126}{2}$$

$$= 0.977.$$

Similarly, if the nominal setting is $\theta=57.921$, then Y is distributed uniformly between 56.921° and 58.921° and

$$P(885 \leqslant R \leqslant 915) = P(56.921 \leqslant Y \leqslant 58.874)$$

$$= \frac{58.874 - 56.921}{2}$$

$$= 0.977.$$

So the probabilities of hitting the target are the same whichever setting is used.

If the target is 990 metres away, then y should be $\frac{1}{2}\sin^{-1}0.99$
= 40.945° or 90-40.945 = 49.055°.

If the nominal setting θ=40.945°, then Y is distributed uniformly
between 39.945° and 41.945° and, since the maximum range is 1000
metres,

$$P(975 \leqslant R \leqslant 1005) = P(975 \leqslant R \leqslant 1000)$$

$$= P(\frac{975}{1000} \leqslant \sin 2Y \leqslant 1)$$

$$= P(38.581 \leqslant Y \leqslant 45) + P(45 \leqslant Y \leqslant 51.419)$$

$$= P(39.945 \leqslant Y \leqslant 41.945)$$

$$= 1.$$

Similarly, if the nominal setting is 49.055° then Y is uniformly
distributed between 48.055° and 50.055° and the probability of a
hit is one again.

40. The distribution of a certain measurement X associated with an item
manufactured on a production line is continuous with probability
density function f(x) which is non-zero only in the range (a,b) and
cumulative distribution function F(x). Items are accepted for sale
if X ⩾ c and rejected if X < c, where a < c < b. Let Y be the
value of the same measurement associated with an item that has been
accepted and let Y have probability density function g(y) and
cumulative distribution function G(y). Show that, for y ⩾ c,

$$G(y) = \frac{F(y) - F(c)}{1 - F(c)},$$

and hence that
$$g(y) = \frac{f(y)}{1 - F(c)} \qquad \text{if } y \geqslant c,$$

$$= 0 \qquad \text{otherwise.}$$

The volume of lemonade delivered by an automatic bottle filler is
normally distributed with mean 102 cl and standard deviation 2 cl.
If only bottles containing at least 100 cl are accepted for sale,
calculate the mean volume of lemonade contained in bottles for sale.

¶ Consider, for y ⩾ c,
$$G(y) = P(Y \leqslant y) = P(X \leqslant y | X \geqslant c) = \frac{P(c \leqslant X \leqslant y)}{P(X \geqslant c)}$$

$$= \frac{F(y) - F(c)}{1 - F(c)}.$$

Differentiating,
$$g(y) = \frac{f(y)}{1 - F(c)} \qquad \text{if } y \geqslant c,$$

$$= 0 \qquad \text{otherwise.}$$

Let X be the volume of lemonade delivered by the bottle filler. Let $f(x)$, $F(x)$ be the probability density function and cumulative distribution function of X. Let Y be the volume contained in a bottle for sale. Then Y has probability density

$$g(y) = \frac{f(y)}{1 - F(100)} \quad \text{if } y \geqslant 100,$$

$$= 0 \qquad \text{otherwise.}$$

If X is $N(102, 2^2)$,

$$f(x) = \frac{1}{2\sqrt{2\pi}} e^{-(x-102)^2/8} \quad [a=-\infty, b=\infty \text{ in this case}],$$

$$1 - F(100) = 1 - \Phi(\frac{100-102}{2}) = \Phi(1) = 0.84134$$

and

$$E(Y) = \frac{1}{2\sqrt{2\pi}\Phi(1)} \int_{100}^{\infty} y e^{-(y-102)^2/8} dy$$

$$= \frac{1}{2\sqrt{2\pi}\Phi(1)} \int_{-1}^{\infty} (2z+102) e^{-z^2/2} 2dz \quad (y = 2z+102)$$

$$= \frac{2}{\sqrt{2\pi}\Phi(1)} \int_{-1}^{\infty} z e^{-z^2/2} dz + \frac{102}{\Phi(1)} \int_{-1}^{\infty} \frac{e^{-z^2/2}}{\sqrt{2\pi}} dz$$

$$= \frac{2}{\sqrt{2\pi}\Phi(1)} [-e^{-z^2/2}]_{-1}^{\infty} + \frac{102}{\Phi(1)}\Phi(1)$$

$$= \frac{2}{\sqrt{2\pi}\Phi(1)} e^{-1/2} + 102$$

$$= 102.575 \text{ cl.}$$

5
Joint Distributions

Miscellaneous Problems

1. The random variables X,Y have the following joint probability table.

		Y		
		1	2	3
X	1	$\frac{1}{16}$	$\frac{1}{8}$	$\frac{1}{16}$
	2	$\frac{1}{8}$	$\frac{1}{8}$	$\frac{1}{8}$
	3	$\frac{1}{16}$	$\frac{1}{4}$	$\frac{1}{16}$

(i)   Find the marginal probability functions of X and Y.

(ii) Show that $P(X=1,Y=2) = P(X=1)P(Y=2)$.

Can it be concluded that X and Y are independent?

¶   (i)   The marginal distributions of X and Y are found by summing respectively the rows and columns of the joint probability table. This gives

x	1	2	3
p_x	$\frac{1}{4}$	$\frac{3}{8}$	$\frac{3}{8}$

y	1	2	3
p_y	$\frac{1}{4}$	$\frac{1}{2}$	$\frac{1}{4}$

(ii) It follows that $P(X=1)P(Y=2) = \frac{1}{4} \times \frac{1}{2} = \frac{1}{8}$

$$= P(X=1,Y=2) \quad \text{as required.}$$

It cannot be concluded that X,Y are independent since other values x,y can be found such that

213

$$P(X=x,Y=y) \neq P(X=x)P(Y=y).$$

For example $\quad P(X=2,Y=2) = \frac{1}{8},$

while $\qquad P(X=2)P(Y=2) = \frac{3}{16}.$

2. The random variables X and Y have the following joint probability table.

		Y		
		2	3	4
	1	k	2k	4k
X	2	3k	6k	12k
	3	2k	4k	8k

where k is a constant.

(i) Evaluate k.

(ii) Prove that X and Y are independent.

(iii) Verify that the covariance of X and Y is zero.

¶ (i) Since all the probabilities sum to 1,
$$42k = 1 \quad \text{and} \quad k = \frac{1}{42}.$$

(ii) To prove independence, it is necessary to show that
$$P(X=i,Y=j) = P(X=i)P(Y=j) \quad \text{for all } i,j.$$
Consider, for example, i=2 and j=3.
$$P(X=2,Y=3) = \frac{6}{42} = \frac{1}{7}.$$

Also, by summing the appropriate row and column,
$$P(X=2) = \frac{21}{42} = \frac{1}{2},$$

$$P(Y=3) = \frac{12}{42} = \frac{2}{7},$$

so that the result is true for this pair of values of i,j. It can similarly be shown to hold for all pairs of values.

(iii) The marginal distributions of X and Y are respectively

x	1	2	3
p_x	$\frac{7}{42}$	$\frac{21}{42}$	$\frac{14}{42}$

and

y	2	3	4
p_y	$\frac{6}{42}$	$\frac{12}{42}$	$\frac{24}{42}$

Thus $E(X) = \frac{91}{42} = \frac{13}{6}$ and $E(Y) = \frac{144}{42} = \frac{24}{7}.$

The distribution of Z = XY is as follows

z	2	3	4	6	8	9	12
p_z	$\frac{1}{42}$	$\frac{2}{42}$	$\frac{7}{42}$	$\frac{8}{42}$	$\frac{12}{42}$	$\frac{4}{42}$	$\frac{8}{42}$

and

$$E(XY) = E(Z) = \frac{312}{42} = \frac{52}{7}.$$

Thus

$$Cov(X,Y) = E(XY) - E(X)E(Y)$$
$$= \frac{52}{7} - \frac{13}{6} \times \frac{24}{7}$$
$$= 0 \quad \text{as required.}$$

3. Two random variables X,Y can each take only the values 0 and 1, and their joint probability table is as follows.

Y

X		0	1
	0	a	b
	1	c	d

(i)   Show that Cov(X,Y) = ad-bc.

(ii) Use the definition of independence to verify that ad=bc when X and Y are independent.

(iii) Show that X and Y are independent when ad=bc.

¶   (i)   We find that
$$E(X) = c+d, \quad E(Y) = b+d, \quad E(XY) = d.$$
Therefore
$$Cov(X,Y) = E(XY) - E(X)E(Y)$$
$$= d - (c+d)(b+d)$$
$$= d(1-b-c-d) - bc$$
$$= ad-bc \quad \text{as } a+b+c+d = 1.$$

(ii) If X and Y are independent then $P(X=0,Y=0) = P(X=0)P(Y=0)$.
So   a = (a+b)(a+c)
or a(1-a-b-c) = bc,
i.e.   ad = bc.

(iii) Suppose ad=bc. Then
$$P(X=0)P(Y=0) = (a+b)(a+c)$$
$$= a(a+b+c) + bc = a(1-d) + bc$$
$$= a - (ad-bc) = a = P(X=0,Y=0).$$

215

Similarly $P(X=0,Y=1) = b = P(X=0)P(Y=1)$,

$$P(X=1,Y=0) = c = P(X=1)P(Y=0)$$

and $\qquad P(X=1,Y=1) = d = P(X=1)P(Y=1)$.

Thus X and Y are independent.

4. There are two consecutive stages in building a barrage across an estuary, surveying and construction. The times (in years) to complete the surveying and the construction are independent random variables X and Y with respective probability functions p_x and q_y given by

$$p_x = \frac{7}{10} \quad \text{if } x = 2,$$

$$= \frac{3}{10} \quad \text{if } x = 3,$$

and $\qquad q_y = \frac{1}{5} \quad \text{if } y = 3,$

$$= \frac{3}{5} \quad \text{if } y = 4,$$

$$= \frac{1}{5} \quad \text{if } y = 5.$$

What is the probability that it will take longer than six years to complete the project?

$$P(X+Y \geqslant 7) = P(X=2,Y=5) + P(X=3,Y=4) + P(X=3,Y=5)$$

$$= \frac{7}{10}{\times}\frac{1}{5} + \frac{3}{10}{\times}\frac{3}{5} + \frac{3}{10}{\times}\frac{1}{5}$$

$$= \frac{19}{50}.$$

5. A company has ten employees. The number of years an employee has been with the company and the amount of overtime worked per day are given in the following table.

Employee	1	2	3	4	5	6	7	8	9	10
Years with company	3	3	2	2	2	2	1	1	1	1
Overtime (hours/day)	1.5	1.5	1.5	1.0	1.0	1.0	1.0	1.0	0.5	0.5

An employee is selected at random. Let X denote his years with the company and Y his daily hours of overtime.

(a) Construct the joint probability table of X and Y.

(b) Find the marginal probability functions of X and Y.

(c) Compute $E(X)$, $E(Y)$, $Var(X)$, $Var(Y)$ and $Cov(X,Y)$.

(d) The employee's gross yearly income W (in thousands of pounds) is given by the formula W = 8 + X + 2Y.

Find E(W) and Var(W).

¶ (a) By inspection the joint probability table is as follows.

Y

		0.5	1.0	1.5
	1	$\frac{2}{10}$	$\frac{2}{10}$	0
X	2	0	$\frac{3}{10}$	$\frac{1}{10}$
	3	0	0	$\frac{2}{10}$

(b) The marginal probability functions of X and Y are

x	1	2	3
p_x	$\frac{4}{10}$	$\frac{4}{10}$	$\frac{2}{10}$

and

y	0.5	1.0	1.5
p_y	$\frac{2}{10}$	$\frac{5}{10}$	$\frac{3}{10}$

(c)

$$E(X) = \sum_{x=1}^{3} xP(X=x)$$

$$= 1\times\frac{4}{10} + 2\times\frac{4}{10} + 3\times\frac{2}{10} = 1.8.$$

$$E(X^2) = \sum_{x=1}^{3} x^2 P(X=x)$$

$$= 1^2\times\frac{4}{10} + 2^2\times\frac{4}{10} + 3^2\times\frac{2}{10} = 3.8.$$

Hence Var(X) = $E(X^2) - (E(X))^2$ = 3.8 - 1.8^2 = 0.56.

Similarly E(Y) = 1.05, $E(Y^2)$ = 1.225 and Var(Y) = 0.1225.

$$E(XY) = \sum_{x,y} xyP(X=x,Y=y)$$

$$= \frac{1}{2}\times\frac{2}{10} + 1\times\frac{2}{10} + 2\times\frac{3}{10} + 3\times\frac{1}{10} + \frac{9}{2}\times\frac{2}{10}$$

$$= 2.1.$$

Hence Cov(X,Y) = E(XY) - E(X)E(Y)

= 2.1 - 1.8×1.05

= 0.21.

(d) $\qquad E(W) = 8 + E(X) + 2E(Y)$

$\qquad\qquad\qquad = 11.9.$

$\qquad\quad Var(W) = Var(X+2Y)$

$\qquad\qquad\qquad = Var(X) + 4Var(Y) + 4Cov(X,Y)$

$\qquad\qquad\qquad = 0.56 + 4\times0.1225 + 4\times0.21$

$\qquad\qquad\qquad = 1.89.$

6. The random variables X and Y have the following joint probability table

		Y			
		0	1	2	3
X	-3	2α	α	0	α
	-1	α	2α	α	0
	1	0	α	2α	α
	3	α	0	α	2α

where α is a constant.

Find (i)　the value of α,

　　　(ii)　the marginal probability functions of X and Y,

　　　(iii) E(X), E(Y), E(XY).

Are X and Y independent random variables?

¶　(i)　Since the probabilities sum to 1,　$16\alpha = 1$ and $\alpha = 1/16$.

　(ii)　The marginal probability function of X is

x	-3	-1	1	3
p_x	$\frac{1}{4}$	$\frac{1}{4}$	$\frac{1}{4}$	$\frac{1}{4}$

The marginal probability function of Y is

y	0	1	2	3
p_y	$\frac{1}{4}$	$\frac{1}{4}$	$\frac{1}{4}$	$\frac{1}{4}$

(iii)　$E(X) = (-3\times\frac{1}{4}) + (-1\times\frac{1}{4}) + (1\times\frac{1}{4}) + (3\times\frac{1}{4}) = 0,$

$\qquad E(Y) = (0\times\frac{1}{4}) + (1\times\frac{1}{4}) + (2\times\frac{1}{4}) + (3\times\frac{1}{4}) = 1.5.$

The distribution of Z = XY is given by

z	-9	-6	-3	-2	-1	0	1	2	3	6	9
p_z	$\frac{1}{16}$	0	$\frac{1}{16}$	$\frac{1}{16}$	$\frac{2}{16}$	$\frac{4}{16}$	$\frac{1}{16}$	$\frac{2}{16}$	$\frac{1}{16}$	$\frac{1}{16}$	$\frac{2}{16}$

$E(XY) = E(Z) = (-9\times\frac{1}{16}) + (-6\times0) + (-3\times\frac{1}{16}) + \ldots + (9\times\frac{2}{16}) = 1.$

Since $P(X=1,Y=0) = 0 \neq P(X=1)P(Y=0)$, X and Y are not independent.

7. Each one of a large number of candidates sits two examinations. The distribution of the candidates' marks for the first examination has mean 50 and standard deviation 15. The distribution of the candidates' marks for the second examination has mean 60 and standard deviation 20. What are the mean and standard deviation of the distribution of the average marks of the candidates if the covariance between the two marks of a randomly selected candidate is (a) 0, (b) 137.5, (c) -112.5?

¶ Let X_1 and X_2 be the marks obtained in the two examinations.

Then
$$E(X_1) = 50, \qquad Var(X_1) = 15^2,$$
$$E(X_2) = 60, \qquad Var(X_2) = 20^2.$$

The average mark Y is given by
$$Y = \frac{1}{2}X_1 + \frac{1}{2}X_2.$$

$$E(Y) = \frac{1}{2}E(X_1) + \frac{1}{2}E(X_2) = \frac{1}{2} \times 50 + \frac{1}{2} \times 60 = 55.$$

$$Var(Y) = \frac{1}{4}Var(X_1) + \frac{1}{4}Var(X_2) + \frac{1}{2}Cov(X_1,X_2)$$

$$= \frac{1}{4}(225 + 400) + \frac{1}{2}Cov(X_1,X_2)$$

$$= \frac{625}{4} + \frac{1}{2}Cov(X_1,X_2).$$

(a) If $Cov(X_1,X_2) = 0$, $Var(Y) = \frac{625}{4}$ and the standard deviation is $\frac{25}{2}$.

(b) If $Cov(X_1,X_1) = 137.5$, $Var(Y) = \frac{625}{4} + \frac{275}{4} = 225$ and the standard deviation is 15.

(c) If $Cov(X_1,X_2) = -112.5$, $Var(Y) = \frac{625}{4} - \frac{225}{4} = 100$ and the standard deviation of Y is 10.

8. A number X is selected at random from the set of integers $\{1,2,3,4\}$ and then a number Y is selected at random from the set of positive integers less than or equal to X. Derive the joint probability table of X and Y and investigate whether or not X and Y are independent.

Find the marginal probability function of Y and verify that Y is more likely than not to take the value 1.

¶ $P(X=3,Y=2) = P(Y=2|X=3)P(X=3) = \frac{1}{3} \times \frac{1}{4} = \frac{1}{12}.$

The other joint probabilities are calculated in the same way and the joint probability table is as follows.

		Y		
	1	**2**	**3**	**4**
1	$\frac{1}{4}$	0	0	0
2	$\frac{1}{8}$	$\frac{1}{8}$	0	0
3	$\frac{1}{12}$	$\frac{1}{12}$	$\frac{1}{12}$	0
4	$\frac{1}{16}$	$\frac{1}{16}$	$\frac{1}{16}$	$\frac{1}{16}$

(X is the row label.)

$P(X=1,Y=4) = 0 \neq P(X=1)P(Y=4) = \frac{1}{4} \times \frac{1}{16}.$ So X and Y are not independent.

Y has the marginal probability function

y	1	2	3	4
p_y	$\frac{25}{48}$	$\frac{13}{48}$	$\frac{7}{48}$	$\frac{3}{48}$

$P(Y=1) = \frac{25}{48} > \frac{1}{2}$ and so Y is more likely than not to take the value 1.

9. Three numbers are chosen at random with replacement from the set {1,2,3}. Let X be the smallest number chosen and Y be the largest one chosen. Show that X and Y have the joint probability table

		Y	
	1	**2**	**3**
1	$\frac{1}{27}$	$\frac{6}{27}$	$\frac{12}{27}$
2	0	$\frac{1}{27}$	$\frac{6}{27}$
3	0	0	$\frac{1}{27}$

(X is the row label.)

State whether or not X and Y are independent and find (i) E(XY), (ii) E(X+Y), (iii) Var(X+Y).

¶ The 27 equally likely possibilities are

111	112	113	121	122	123	131	132	133
211	212	213	221	222	223	231	232	233
311	312	313	321	322	323	331	332	333

The tabular values can be checked using these.

X and Y are clearly not independent since

$$P(X=3, Y=1) = 0 \neq P(X=3)P(Y=1).$$

(i)   The probability function of $Z = XY$ is

z	1	2	3	4	6	9
p_z	$\frac{1}{27}$	$\frac{6}{27}$	$\frac{12}{27}$	$\frac{1}{27}$	$\frac{6}{27}$	$\frac{1}{27}$

$$E(XY) = E(Z) = 1 \times \frac{1}{27} + 2 \times \frac{6}{27} + \dots + 9 \times \frac{1}{27} = \frac{98}{27}.$$

(ii) The probability function of $W = X+Y$ is

w	2	3	4	5	6
p_w	$\frac{1}{27}$	$\frac{6}{27}$	$\frac{13}{27}$	$\frac{6}{27}$	$\frac{1}{27}$

$$E(X+Y) = E(W) = 2 \times \frac{1}{27} + \dots + 6 \times \frac{1}{27} = \frac{108}{27} = 4.$$

Alternatively,

$$E(X) = \frac{19+14+3}{27} = \frac{36}{27}, \qquad E(Y) = \frac{1+14+57}{27} = \frac{72}{27},$$

so that $E(X+Y) = E(X) + E(Y) = \frac{36+72}{27} = 4.$

(iii) The formula

$$Var(X+Y) = Var(X) + Var(Y) + 2Cov(X,Y)$$

can be used but instead we can calculate

$$E((X+Y)^2) = E(W^2) = 4 \times \frac{1}{27} + \dots + 36 \times \frac{1}{27} = \frac{452}{27}$$

and $Var(X+Y) = \frac{452}{27} - 4^2 = \frac{20}{27}.$

10. A bag contains 7 black balls, 8 red balls and 5 white balls. Two
    balls are chosen at random without replacement. Let X be the number
    of white balls chosen and Y be the number of black balls chosen.
    Find (i)   the probability functions of X and Y,
         (ii) the joint probability function of X and Y.
    Check that the marginal probability functions of X and Y found from
    the joint probability table are the same as those obtained in (i).

¶ (i) $P(X=0) = P$(both balls black or red) $= \frac{15}{20} \times \frac{14}{19} = \frac{105}{190}$,

$P(X=2) = P$(both balls white) $= \frac{5}{20} \times \frac{4}{19} = \frac{10}{190}$,

and so $P(X=1) = \frac{75}{190}$.

Similarly $P(Y=0) = \frac{13}{20} \times \frac{12}{19} = \frac{78}{190}$,

$P(Y=2) = \frac{7}{20} \times \frac{6}{19} = \frac{21}{190}$,

and so $P(Y=1) = \frac{91}{190}$.

(ii) The joint probability table for X and Y can be found similarly. For example

$P(X=1,Y=1) = P$(one ball white and one ball black)

$= P$(white first, black second)

$+ P$(black first, white second)

$= \frac{5}{20} \times \frac{7}{19} + \frac{7}{20} \times \frac{5}{19} = \frac{35}{190}$.

The result is

		Y			
		0	1	2	
	0	$\frac{28}{190}$	$\frac{56}{190}$	$\frac{21}{190}$	$\frac{105}{190}$
X	1	$\frac{40}{190}$	$\frac{35}{190}$	0	$\frac{75}{190}$
	2	$\frac{10}{190}$	0	0	$\frac{10}{190}$
		$\frac{78}{190}$	$\frac{91}{190}$	$\frac{21}{190}$	

The marginal probability functions are in agreement with the values found in (i).

11. If X and Y are two independent random variables, show that
$E((X-Y)^2) = Var(X) + Var(Y) + (E(X)-E(Y))^2$.

¶ $E((X-Y)^2) = E(X^2 - 2XY + Y^2)$

$= E(X^2) - 2E(XY) + E(Y^2)$

$= E(X^2) - 2E(X)E(Y) + E(Y^2)$ by independence

$= Var(X) + (E(X))^2 - 2E(X)E(Y) + Var(Y) + (E(Y))^2$

$= Var(X) + Var(Y) + (E(X)-E(Y))^2$.

12. Two random variables X and Y have the following joint probability table

	Y		
	1	2	3
X 1	0	k	k
2	k	0	k
3	k	k	0

where k is a constant. Evaluate k and show that the marginal probability functions are both uniform, that is all values are equally likely.

If Z = Min(X,Y) find E(Z).

Describe a simple experiment which would produce this joint probability function.

¶ Since the probabilities must sum to 1, $k = \frac{1}{6}$.

The marginal distributions of X,Y are

x	1	2	3
P_x	$\frac{1}{3}$	$\frac{1}{3}$	$\frac{1}{3}$

and

y	1	2	3
P_y	$\frac{1}{3}$	$\frac{1}{3}$	$\frac{1}{3}$

These are uniform distributions.

$$P(Z=1) = P(X=1 \text{ or } Y=1)$$
$$= P(X=1,Y=1) + P(X=1,Y=2) + P(X=1,Y=3)$$
$$\qquad + P(X=2,Y=1) + P(X=3,Y=1)$$
$$= \frac{4}{6}.$$

Similarly $P(Z=2) = \frac{2}{6}$, $P(Z=3) = 0$.

Hence $E(Z) = 1 \times \frac{4}{6} + 2 \times \frac{2}{6} + 3 \times 0 = \frac{4}{3}$.

Let a bag contain 3 balls numbered 1,2,3. Suppose that 2 are drawn out at random (without replacement). If X,Y are the numbers, respectively, on the 1st and 2nd balls then X,Y have the given joint distribution.

13. Two random variables X and Y have the following joint probability table.

Y

		1	2
	1	0.20	0.15
X	2	0.15	0.20
	3	0.25	0.05

Write down the probability functions of (i) X, (ii) Y, (iii) X/Y.
Does $E(X)/E(Y) = E(X/Y)$?

¶ (i)   Summing rows, we obtain the distribution of X.

x	1	2	3
p_x	0.35	0.35	0.30

(ii)   Summing columns, the distribution of Y is

y	1	2
p_y	0.6	0.4

(iii) Enumerating the possible values, we find that the distribution
of X/Y is

X/Y	$\frac{1}{2}$	1	$\frac{3}{2}$	2	3
Prob	0.15	0.4	0.05	0.15	0.25

$E(X) = 1 \times 0.35 + 2 \times 0.35 + 3 \times 0.3 = 1.95,$

$E(Y) = 1 \times 0.6 + 2 \times 0.4 = 1.4,$

$E(X/Y) = \frac{1}{2} \times 0.15 + 1 \times 0.4 + \ldots + 3 \times 0.25 = 1.6.$

We see that $E(X/Y) \neq \frac{E(X)}{E(Y)}$.

14. Three cards are selected at random from a pack of cards. If X and
    Y denote respectively the number of Kings and the number of Queens
    in the selection, write down the joint probability table for X and Y.
    Show that X and Y are dependent and find (i) $P(X=1|Y=1)$,
    (ii) $P(X \leqslant 1|Y=1)$, (iii) $P(X=1|Y \leqslant 1)$, (iv) $P(X \leqslant 1|Y \leqslant 1)$.

¶ $P(X=x, Y=y) = P(x \text{ Kings}, y \text{ Queens}, 3-x-y \text{ others})$

$$= \frac{{}^4C_x \times {}^4C_y \times {}^{44}C_{3-x-y}}{{}^{52}C_3}, \quad \text{for } x+y \leqslant 3$$

Evaluating this for each pair (x,y), we obtain

Y

X	0	1	2	3
0	13244k	3784k	264k	4k
1	3784k	704k	24k	0
2	264k	24k	0	0
3	4k	0	0	0

where $k = \frac{1}{22100}$.

X and Y are dependent since

$$P(X=3,Y=3) = 0 \neq P(X=3)P(Y=3).$$

Y has marginal distribution

y	0	1	2	3
p_y	17296k	4512k	288k	4k

(i) $P(X=1|Y=1) = \frac{P(X=1,Y=1)}{P(Y=1)} = \frac{704}{4512} \approx 0.1560.$

(ii) $P(X\leqslant 1|Y=1) = \frac{P(X\leqslant 1,Y=1)}{P(Y=1)} = \frac{3784k + 704k}{4512k} = \frac{4488}{4512} \approx 0.9947.$

(iii) $P(X=1|Y\leqslant 1) = \frac{P(X=1,Y\leqslant 1)}{P(Y\leqslant 1)} = \frac{3784k + 704k}{17296k + 4512k} = \frac{4488}{21808} \approx 0.2058.$

(iv) $P(X\leqslant 1|Y\leqslant 1) = \frac{P(X\leqslant 1,Y\leqslant 1)}{P(Y\leqslant 1)} = \frac{13244k + 3784k + 3784k + 704k}{21808k}$

$$= \frac{21516}{21808} \approx 0.9866.$$

15. Two random variables X and Y have the joint probability function

$$P(X=x,Y=y) = k(x+y) \quad \text{if } x=1,2,3 \text{ and } y=1,2,3,4.$$

Evaluate the constant k. Find the marginal probability functions of X and Y and hence show that X and Y are dependent. Show that in this instance

$$E(XY) \neq E(X)E(Y).$$

¶ The joint probability table for X,Y is

Y

X	1	2	3	4
1	2k	3k	4k	5k
2	3k	4k	5k	6k
3	4k	5k	6k	7k

Since all the probabilities sum to 1, $54k = 1$, $k = \frac{1}{54}$.

The marginal probability functions of X and Y are

x	1	2	3
p_x	$\dfrac{14}{54}$	$\dfrac{18}{54}$	$\dfrac{22}{54}$

and

y	1	2	3	4
p_y	$\dfrac{9}{54}$	$\dfrac{12}{54}$	$\dfrac{15}{54}$	$\dfrac{18}{54}$

Since $P(X=1,Y=1) = \dfrac{1}{27} \neq P(X=1)P(Y=1)$, X and Y are dependent.

The distribution of XY is

XY	1	2	3	4	6	8	9	12
Prob	$\dfrac{2}{54}$	$\dfrac{6}{54}$	$\dfrac{8}{54}$	$\dfrac{9}{54}$	$\dfrac{10}{54}$	$\dfrac{6}{54}$	$\dfrac{6}{54}$	$\dfrac{7}{54}$

$$E(XY) = 1 \times \frac{2}{54} + 2 \times \frac{6}{54} + \ldots + 12 \times \frac{7}{54} = \frac{320}{54}.$$

$$E(X) = \frac{116}{54}, \quad E(Y) = \frac{150}{54}.$$

Hence $E(XY) \neq E(X)E(Y)$.

16. A fair coin is tossed three times. Let X denote the number of heads obtained and let Y denote the largest number of consecutive heads or tails obtained. (For example, if the result is HHT, Y=2 while if it is HTH, Y=1.)

Write down the joint probability table of X and Y and find the marginal probability functions of X and Y. Are X and Y independent?

¶ By enumeration we find the the joint probability function is

		Y		
		1	2	3
	0	0	0	$\dfrac{1}{8}$
	1	$\dfrac{1}{8}$	$\dfrac{2}{8}$	0
X	2	$\dfrac{1}{8}$	$\dfrac{2}{8}$	0
	3	0	0	$\dfrac{1}{8}$

For example, $P(X=1,Y=2) = P(\text{HTT or TTH}) = \dfrac{2}{8}$

The marginal distributions are

x	0	1	2	3
p_x	$\frac{1}{8}$	$\frac{3}{8}$	$\frac{3}{8}$	$\frac{1}{8}$

and

y	1	2	3
p_y	$\frac{2}{8}$	$\frac{4}{8}$	$\frac{2}{8}$

Since $P(X=0,Y=1) = 0 \neq P(X=0)P(Y=1)$, X and Y are not independent.

17. Three coins are tossed and those falling heads are tossed again. If X and Y denote respectively the number of heads obtained on the first and second tosses, write down the joint probability table for X and Y. Hence find the probability functions of X,Y and X+Y and verify that

$$E(X+Y) = E(X) + E(Y).$$

Calculate Cov(X,Y), the covariance of X and Y, and verify that
$$Var(X+Y) = Var(X) + Var(Y) + 2Cov(X,Y).$$

¶ $P(X=2,Y=1) = P(Y=1 \mid X=2)P(X=2) = \frac{1}{2} \times \frac{3}{8} = \frac{3}{16}.$

The other probabilities are calculated similarly and the following joint probability function is obtained.

Y

X		0	1	2	3
	0	$\frac{1}{8}$	0	0	0
	1	$\frac{3}{16}$	$\frac{3}{16}$	0	0
	2	$\frac{3}{32}$	$\frac{3}{16}$	$\frac{3}{32}$	0
	3	$\frac{1}{64}$	$\frac{3}{64}$	$\frac{3}{64}$	$\frac{1}{64}$

The marginal probability functions of X and Y are

x	0	1	2	3
p_x	$\frac{1}{8}$	$\frac{3}{8}$	$\frac{3}{8}$	$\frac{1}{8}$

and

y	0	1	2	3
p_y	$\frac{27}{64}$	$\frac{27}{64}$	$\frac{9}{64}$	$\frac{1}{64}$

X+Y has the distribution

x+y	0	1	2	3	4	5	6
Prob	$\frac{1}{8}$	$\frac{3}{16}$	$\frac{9}{32}$	$\frac{13}{64}$	$\frac{9}{64}$	$\frac{3}{64}$	$\frac{1}{64}$

We find that

$$E(X) = \frac{3}{2}, \quad E(X^2) = 3 \quad \text{and} \quad \text{Var}(X) = \frac{3}{4},$$

while

$$E(Y) = \frac{3}{4}, \quad E(Y^2) = \frac{9}{8} \quad \text{and} \quad \text{Var}(Y) = \frac{9}{16}.$$

$$E(X+Y) = 0 \times \frac{1}{8} + 1 \times \frac{3}{16} + \ldots + 6 \times \frac{1}{64} = \frac{9}{4}$$

and $E(X+Y) = E(X) + E(Y).$

XY has the distribution

xy	0	1	2	3	4	6	9
Prob	$\frac{27}{64}$	$\frac{3}{16}$	$\frac{3}{16}$	$\frac{3}{64}$	$\frac{3}{32}$	$\frac{3}{64}$	$\frac{1}{64}$

and $E(XY) = 0 \times \frac{27}{64} + 1 \times \frac{3}{16} + \ldots + 9 \times \frac{1}{64} = \frac{3}{2}.$

Hence $\text{Cov}(X,Y) = E(XY) - E(X)E(Y)$

$$= \frac{3}{2} - \frac{3}{2} \times \frac{3}{4} = \frac{3}{8}$$

and $\text{Var}(X) + \text{Var}(Y) + 2\text{Cov}(X,Y) = \frac{3}{4} + \frac{9}{16} + \frac{6}{8} = \frac{33}{16}.$

Finally, $E((X+Y)^2) = 0^2 \times \frac{1}{8} + 1^2 \times \frac{3}{16} + \ldots + 6^2 \times \frac{1}{64} = \frac{57}{8},$

so that $\text{Var}(X+Y) = \frac{57}{8} - (\frac{9}{4})^2 = \frac{33}{16}$ as required.

18. The noon temperature in degrees Fahrenheit at a certain meteorological station on Christmas Day is a random variable X with mean
41 and standard deviation 2.25. Let Y be this temperature
expressed in degrees Centigrade. Find the mean and standard
deviation of Y.

¶ Let W be the average of the temperatures at noon on Christmas Day
in four successive years, i.e.

$$W = \frac{1}{4} \sum_{i=1}^{4} Y_i$$

where Y_1, Y_2, Y_3 and Y_4 are the four temperatures expressed in
degrees Centigrade. Find the mean and standard deviation of W.

¶ Y and X are related by

$$Y = \frac{5}{9}(X-32)$$

so that $\quad E(Y) = \frac{5}{9}(E(X) - 32) = 5^{\circ}C \quad$ as $E(X) = 41^{\circ}C$.

$$Var(Y) = \left(\frac{5}{9}\right)^2 Var(X)$$

and $\quad$ S.D. of $Y = \frac{5}{9} \times$ S.D. of X

$$= \frac{5}{9} \times 2.25 = 1.25^{\circ}C.$$

$$E(W) = \frac{1}{4}E\left(\sum_{i=1}^{4} Y_i\right) = \frac{1}{4}\sum_{i=1}^{4} E(Y_i) = \frac{1}{4} \times 4 \times 5 = 5^{\circ}C.$$

$$Var(W) = \frac{1}{16}Var\left(\sum_{i=1}^{4} Y_i\right) = \frac{1}{16}\sum_{i=1}^{4} Var(Y_i)$$

$$= \frac{1}{16} \times 4 \times \left(\frac{5}{4}\right)^2 = \frac{25}{64},$$

so that $\quad$ S.D. of $W = \frac{5}{8} = 0.625^{\circ}C$.

19. Five cards numbered 1,2,3,4,5 are shuffled and three are selected
at random without replacement. If X and Y denote respectively the
smallest and largest numbers selected, write down the joint
probability table for X and Y.
Derive the probability functions of (i) X, (ii) Y, (iii) Y−X and
find Var(Y−X).
Calculate Cov(X,Y), the covariance of X and Y, and verify that the
formula

$$Var(Y-X) = Var(Y) + Var(X) - 2Cov(X,Y)$$

holds in this case.

¶ There are 10 possible outcomes, namely 123,124,125,134,135,145,234,
235,245,345. The joint probability function is

		Y		
		3	4	5
X	1	$\frac{1}{10}$	$\frac{2}{10}$	$\frac{3}{10}$
	2	0	$\frac{1}{10}$	$\frac{2}{10}$
	3	0	0	$\frac{1}{10}$

The probability functions of X and Y are

x	1	2	3
p_x	$\frac{6}{10}$	$\frac{3}{10}$	$\frac{1}{10}$

and

y	3	4	5
p_y	$\frac{1}{10}$	$\frac{3}{10}$	$\frac{6}{10}$

It follows that $E(X) = 1.5$, $Var(X) = 0.45$,
$$E(Y) = 4.5, \quad Var(Y) = 0.45.$$

Y−X has the distribution

y−x	2	3	4
Prob	$\frac{3}{10}$	$\frac{4}{10}$	$\frac{3}{10}$

and
$$E(Y-X) = 3,$$
$$Var(Y-X) = 0.6.$$

Finally XY has the distribution

xy	3	4	5	8	10	15
Prob	$\frac{1}{10}$	$\frac{2}{10}$	$\frac{3}{10}$	$\frac{1}{10}$	$\frac{2}{10}$	$\frac{1}{10}$

and $E(XY) = 6.9$.

Thus
$$\begin{aligned}
Cov(X,Y) &= E(XY) - E(X)E(Y) \\
&= 6.9 - 1.5 \times 4.5 \\
&= 0.15.
\end{aligned}$$

Hence $Var(Y) + Var(X) - 2Cov(X,Y) = 0.45 + 0.45 - 2\times0.15$
$$= 0.6 \quad \text{as required.}$$

20. Let X and Y be discrete random variables with joint probability function $p(x,y)$.

Let $q_y = P(Y=y \mid X=x)$

for a fixed value x of X. Show that q_y satisfies the two properties of a probability function. (This probability function is called the *conditional probability function* of Y given X=x.)

¶ $q_y = P(Y=y \mid X=x) = \dfrac{P(Y=y, X=x)}{P(X=x)} = \dfrac{p(x,y)}{\displaystyle\sum_y p(x,y)}$

Since $p(x,y) \geqslant 0$ for all x,y, $q_y \geqslant 0$.

Further

$$\sum_y q_y = \frac{\sum\limits_y p(x,y)}{\sum\limits_Y p(x,y)} = 1 \quad \text{as required.}$$

21. Two fair dice are thrown. Let X and Y be respectively the smaller and larger values obtained. If the values are equal then X and Y are each given this value. Write down the joint probability table of X and Y and show that X and Y are dependent. Given that X=2, find the conditional probability function of Y and find its mean. (This mean is a *conditional mean* or *conditional expectation* and is written E(Y|X=2).) Compare its value with E(Y).

¶   X and Y have the joint probability table

Y

	1	2	3	4	5	6
1	$\frac{1}{36}$	$\frac{2}{36}$	$\frac{2}{36}$	$\frac{2}{36}$	$\frac{2}{36}$	$\frac{2}{36}$
2	0	$\frac{1}{36}$	$\frac{2}{36}$	$\frac{2}{36}$	$\frac{2}{36}$	$\frac{2}{36}$
3	0	0	$\frac{1}{36}$	$\frac{2}{36}$	$\frac{2}{36}$	$\frac{2}{36}$
4	0	0	0	$\frac{1}{36}$	$\frac{2}{36}$	$\frac{2}{36}$
5	0	0	0	0	$\frac{1}{36}$	$\frac{2}{36}$
6	0	0	0	0	0	$\frac{1}{36}$

(X labels the rows)

which follows immediately from the sample space of the 36 outcomes of tossing 2 dice.

X and Y are dependent since

$$P(X=2,Y=1) = 0 \neq P(X=2)P(Y=1)$$

$$P(Y=y|X=2) = \frac{P(X=2,Y=y)}{P(X=2)} = \frac{P(X=2,Y=y)}{9/36} = 4P(X=2,Y=y)$$

Hence the conditional probability function of Y given X=2 is

y	1	2	3	4	5	6
Prob	0	$\frac{1}{9}$	$\frac{2}{9}$	$\frac{2}{9}$	$\frac{2}{9}$	$\frac{2}{9}$

Thus $E(Y|X=2) = 1\times0 + 2\times\frac{1}{9} + \ldots + 6\times\frac{2}{9} = \frac{38}{9}$.

Y has the marginal distribution

y	1	2	3	4	5	6
p_y	$\frac{1}{36}$	$\frac{3}{36}$	$\frac{5}{36}$	$\frac{7}{36}$	$\frac{9}{36}$	$\frac{11}{36}$

and $E(Y) = 1\times\frac{1}{36} + 2\times\frac{3}{36} + \ldots + 6\times\frac{11}{36} = \frac{161}{36} \neq E(Y|X=2)$.

22. Children in a school are given a mathematics test. Each child is given one of the grades 1,2,3 or 4, 1 being the best and 4 the worst. The times taken to complete the test are recorded to the nearest 10 minutes.

Suppose that a randomly selected child obtains the grade X and completes the test in Y minutes. Further suppose X and Y have the following joint probability table.

		Y			
		30	40	50	60
	1	0.01	0.06	0.02	0.01
	2	0.03	0.16	0.09	0.02
X	3	0.04	0.14	0.21	0.01
	4	0.02	0.04	0.08	0.06

Find the marginal probability functions of X and Y. Find the conditional means $E(Y|X=x)$, for x=1,2,3 and 4, and comment on their values.

¶ The marginal probability functions of X and Y are

x	1	2	3	4
p_x	0.1	0.3	0.4	0.2

and

y	30	40	50	60
p_y	0.1	0.4	0.4	0.1

Using the same method as in Question 21, the conditional distribution of Y given X=1 is

y	30	40	50	60
p_y	$\frac{1}{10}$	$\frac{6}{10}$	$\frac{2}{10}$	$\frac{1}{10}$

so that $E(Y|X=1) = 30\times\frac{1}{10} + 40\times\frac{6}{10} + 50\times\frac{2}{10} + 60\times\frac{1}{10} = 43$.

Similarly the conditional distribution of Y given X=2 is

y	30	40	50	60
p_y	$\frac{1}{10}$	$\frac{8}{15}$	$\frac{3}{10}$	$\frac{1}{15}$

and $E(Y \mid X=2) = 43.3\dot{3}$.

Given X=3, the distribution of Y is

y	30	40	50	60
p_y	$\frac{1}{10}$	$\frac{7}{20}$	$\frac{21}{40}$	$\frac{1}{40}$

and $E(Y \mid X=3) = 44.75$.

Given X=4, the distribution of Y is

y	30	40	50	60
p_y	$\frac{1}{10}$	$\frac{1}{5}$	$\frac{2}{5}$	$\frac{3}{10}$

and $E(Y \mid X=4) = 49$.

On average, the worse the grade, the longer it takes to complete the test.

23. A group of mn people is to be screened for a certain disease by means of a blood test. In order to reduce the number of tests the group is divided at random into m subgroups of n people. The blood samples of the n people in a subgroup are pooled and analysed together. If the test of the pooled samples is negative then it can be concluded that all n members are disease-free and no further testing is needed. If the test is positive, however, than at least one person in the subgroups has the disease and in this case all n are tested individually, so that in all n+1 tests are made on that subgroup. This procedure is used for all subgroups. Assuming that the probability that a randomly selected person has the disease is 0.1, independently of other people, obtain an expression for the expected number of tests required to screen the whole group. Suppose that mn=100. Which of the possible choices for m gives the smallest expected number of tests? Is this necessarily the best choice from a practical point of view?

¶ Let X_i be the number of tests required to screen the ith subgroup.

$$X_i = 1 \quad \text{if all n are disease-free,}$$
$$= n+1 \quad \text{otherwise.}$$

Therefore $E(X_i) = 0.9^n + (n+1)(1-0.9^n)$ $\qquad (i = 1,2,\ldots,m)$.

Let X be the total number of tests required to screen the whole group. Then

$$X = \sum_{i=1}^{m} X_i$$

and

$$E(X) = E\left(\sum_{i=1}^{m} X_i\right) = \sum_{i=1}^{m} E(X_i)$$

$$= m(0.9^n + (n+1)(1-0.9^n)).$$

If mn = 100, the possible choices for m and the corresponding expected numbers of tests are as follows

m	n	E(X)
100	1	110
50	2	69
25	4	59.39
20	5	60.95
10	10	75.13
5	20	92.84
4	25	96.82
2	50	101.48
1	100	101.00

So the choice of 25 subgroups of 4 people gives the smallest expected number of tests though administrative convenience might call for a smaller number of subgroups to be used.

24. An absent-minded professor writes n letters and addresses n envelopes but he places the letters in the envelopes at random. He realises what he has done only after the letters have been posted. What is the expected number of people who receive the right letter? Calculate the variance of this number when (a) n=2, (b) n=3.

¶   For i = 1,2,...,n let

$\qquad X_i = 1$ if the ith person receives the right letter,

$\qquad \quad = 0$ if not.

$\qquad E(X_i) = 1 \times P(X_i = 1) = 1 \times \frac{1}{n} = \frac{1}{n}$

as there are n equally likely possibilities.

Let X be the number of people who receive the right letter.

$$\text{Then} \quad X = \sum_{i=1}^{n} X_i$$

$$\text{and } E(X) = E\left(\sum_{i=1}^{n} X_i\right) = \sum_{i=1}^{n} E(X_i) = n \times \frac{1}{n} = 1.$$

(a) n=2.

Here X = 0 or 2 as it is impossible for only one person to receive the correct letter.

Clearly $P(X=0) = P(X=2) = \frac{1}{2}$

and $\quad Var(X) = (0-1)^2 \times \frac{1}{2} + (2-1)^2 \times \frac{1}{2} = 1.$

(b) n=3.

Suppose the people are labelled A, B and C. There are 6 possibilities for the letters they receive, namely ABC, ACB, BAC, BCA, CAB, CBA. It follows that X has probability distribution

x	0	1	2	3
P_x	$\frac{2}{6}$	$\frac{3}{6}$	0	$\frac{1}{6}$

and $Var(X) = (0-1)^2 \times \frac{2}{6} + (1-1)^2 \times \frac{3}{6} + (3-1)^2 \times \frac{1}{6} = 1.$

(In fact it can be shown that Var(X) = 1 for all values of n.)

25. The height X and weight Y of a randomly chosen man both have normal distributions. It is known that 5% of men are shorter than 62 inches and 10% are taller than 72 inches. Further, 10% are lighter than 130 lbs and 15% are heavier than 185 lbs. Finally 1% are shorter than 60 inches and weigh less than 120 lbs. Are X and Y independent?

¶ It would be most surprising if X and Y were independent but dependence can be confirmed as follows.

Let X be $N(\mu_1, \sigma_1^2)$ and Y be $N(\mu_2, \sigma_2^2)$.

Since $\quad 0.05 = P(X < 62) = P\left(\frac{X-\mu_1}{\sigma_1} < \frac{62-\mu_1}{\sigma_1}\right) = \Phi\left(\frac{62-\mu_1}{\sigma_1}\right)$

we have $\quad 62-\mu_1 = -1.645\sigma_1.$ \hfill (1)

Also $\quad 0.1 = P(X > 72) = P\left(\frac{X-\mu_1}{\sigma_1} > \frac{72-\mu_1}{\sigma_1}\right) = 1 - \Phi\left(\frac{72-\mu_1}{\sigma_1}\right),$

so that $\quad \Phi\left(\frac{72-\mu_1}{\sigma_1}\right) = 0.9$

and $\qquad 72-\mu_1 = 1.282\sigma_1 \qquad\qquad$ (2)

Solving (1) and (2), $\mu_1 = 67.620$
$$\sigma_1 = 3.416.$$

Similarly $\qquad \Phi(\frac{130-\mu_2}{\sigma_2}) = 0.1$ and $\Phi(\frac{185-\mu_2}{\sigma_2}) = 0.85,$

so that $\qquad\qquad 130-\mu_2 = -1.282\sigma_2,$
$$185-\mu_2 = 1.036\sigma_2,$$

leading to $\qquad\qquad \mu_2 = 160.418,$
$$\sigma_2 = 23.727.$$

Now $\qquad P(X < 60) = \Phi(\frac{60-\mu_1}{\sigma_1}) = \Phi(-2.23) = 0.01287,$

$$P(Y < 120) = \Phi(\frac{120-\mu_2}{\sigma_2}) = \Phi(-1.703) = 0.04429.$$

Hence $P(X < 60, Y < 120) = 0.01 \neq P(X < 60)P(Y < 120).$
This is sufficient to show that X and Y are not independent.

26. Consider a sequence of Bernoulli trials with success probability p.
Let Y denote the number of trials necessary to obtain r successes,
for some positive integer r. Let X_i be the number of trials
required after the (i-1)th success to obtain the ith success, so
that
$$Y = \sum_{i=1}^{r} X_i.$$

By noting that the X_i are independent geometrically distributed
random variables (see Question 19 on page 124), show that
$$E(Y) = \frac{r}{p}$$
$$Var(Y) = \frac{r(1-p)}{p^2}.$$
(The mean and variance of the geometric distribution may be
assumed.)

¶ Because of the independence of the trials, the number of trials
required after the (i-1)th success to obtain the ith success has
the same distribution as the number to the first success, that is
a geometric distribution.
Using the results for a geometric distribution,
$$E(X_i) = \frac{1}{p}, \qquad Var(X_i) = \frac{1-p}{p^2} \qquad \text{for each i.}$$

Hence $\quad E(Y) = E(\sum_{i=1}^{r} X_i) = \sum_{i=1}^{r} E(X_i) = \frac{r}{p},$

$$\text{Var}(Y) = \text{Var}\left(\sum_{i=1}^{r} X_i\right) = \sum_{i=1}^{r} \text{Var}(X_i) = \frac{r(1-p)}{p^2}.$$

N.B. Y has a negative binomial distribution - see Question 25 on page 128.

27. When the manager of a high-street shop orders a batch of washing machines, he is equally likely to order 1, 2 or 3 machines. Upon delivery, each machine is found to be faulty with probability 1/4 independently of all other machines.

   If X denotes the number of machines ordered and Y denotes the number of faulty machines delivered, find

   (i)   the joint probability function of X,Y,

   (ii) the marginal probability function of Y,

   (iii) E(Y), Var(Y) and Cov(X,Y).

   The manufacturer's net profit on the order is £W, where

   $$W = 50X - 75Y.$$

   Calculate E(W) and Var(W).

¶   (i)   The joint probability table is

		Y = 0	Y = 1	Y = 2	Y = 3
X	1	$\frac{1}{4}$	$\frac{1}{12}$	0	0
	2	$\frac{9}{48}$	$\frac{6}{48}$	$\frac{1}{48}$	0
	3	$\frac{27}{192}$	$\frac{27}{192}$	$\frac{9}{192}$	$\frac{1}{192}$

For example $P(X=2, Y=1) = P(2 \text{ delivered } \& 1 \text{ faulty})$

$$= P(1 \text{ faulty} | 2 \text{ delivered}) P(2 \text{ delivered})$$

$$= \left(2 \times \frac{1}{4} \times \frac{3}{4}\right) \times \frac{1}{3} = \frac{6}{48}.$$

(ii) Y has the marginal probability function

y	0	1	2	3
p_y	$\frac{111}{192}$	$\frac{67}{192}$	$\frac{13}{192}$	$\frac{1}{192}$

(iii) Routine calculation gives $E(Y) = \frac{96}{192} = \frac{1}{2}$, $E(Y^2) = \frac{128}{192}$,

and $\text{Var}(Y) = \frac{80}{192} = \frac{5}{12}.$

By symmetry $E(X) = 2$.

$$E(XY) = (1\times1\times\tfrac{1}{12}) + (2\times1\times\tfrac{6}{48}) + (2\times2\times\tfrac{1}{48}) + (3\times1\times\tfrac{27}{192})$$

$$+ (3\times2\times\tfrac{9}{192}) + (3\times3\times\tfrac{1}{192})$$

$$= \frac{224}{192}.$$

Hence $Cov(X,Y) = E(XY) - E(X)E(Y)$

$$= \frac{224}{192} - \tfrac{1}{2}\times2 = \frac{32}{192} = \tfrac{1}{6}.$$

$$E(W) = 50E(X) - 75E(Y)$$

$$= 50\times2 - 75\times\tfrac{1}{2} = \frac{125}{2} = 62.5.$$

$$Var(W) = 50^2Var(X) + 75^2Var(Y) - 2\times50\times75Cov(X,Y)$$

Now $\quad Var(X) = (1-2)^2\times\tfrac{1}{3} + (2-2)^2\times\tfrac{1}{3} + (3-2)^2\times\tfrac{1}{3} = \tfrac{2}{3}$

as $\quad P(X = x) = \tfrac{1}{3}, \quad x = 1,2,3.$

Hence $\quad Var(W) = \frac{5000}{3} + 5625\times\frac{80}{192} - \frac{7500}{6}$

$$\approx 2760.4.$$

28. Two random variables, X,Y have the following joint distribution

		Y		
		−1	0	1
	0	0	a	0
X	1	b	0	c
	2	0	d	0

where a+d > 0 and b+c > 0.

Show that $Cov(X,Y) = 0$ if b=c or a=d but that there are no values of a,b,c and d for which X and Y are independent.

Consider the random variables U,V defined by

$$U = X + Y, \quad V = X - Y.$$

Show that if ad=bc then U and V are independent even though X and Y are dependent.

¶ $P(X=1) = b+c$ and $P(X=2) = d$, so that

$$E(X) = b + c + 2d$$

$$= 1 - a + d \quad \text{as } a+b+c+d = 1.$$

Similarly $\qquad E(Y) = c - b$

and $\qquad E(XY) = 1\times(-1)\times b + 1\times1\times c = c-b.$

Therefore $\qquad Cov(X,Y) = (c-b) - (c-b)(1-a+d) = (c-b)(a-d).$

Hence $\text{Cov}(X,Y) = 0$ if b=c or a=d.

Now $P(X=1,Y=0) = 0$ while $P(X=1)P(Y=0) = (b+c)(a+d) > 0$ by assumption, and so X and Y are dependent.

U and V have the following probability distributions.

u	0	2
p_u	a+b	c+d

v	0	2
p_v	a+c	b+d

Their joint probability table is

		V	
		0	2
U	0	a	b
	2	c	d

Now
$$P(U=0)P(V=0) = (a+b)(a+c) = a(a+b+c) + bc$$
$$= a(1-d) + bc = a + bc - ad$$
$$= a \qquad \text{if } ad=bc$$
$$= P(U=0,V=0).$$

Similarly $P(U=1)P(V=0) = P(U=1,V=0)$
$$P(U=0)P(V=1) = P(U=0,V=1)$$
$$P(U=1)P(V=1) = P(U=1,V=1).$$

Hence U and V are independent provided ad=bc.

29. Two dice are thrown ten times. Let X be the number of times no 1's occur and Y the number of times that two 1's occur. Write down the joint probability function of X and Y, and state whether or not X and Y are independent. Find the probability that
(i) X and Y are both less than 3,
(ii) X + Y = 5.

¶ When 2 dice are tossed
$$P(\text{no 1's occur}) = (\tfrac{5}{6})^2 = \tfrac{25}{36},$$

$$P(\text{one 1 occurs}) = 2 \times \tfrac{1}{6} \times \tfrac{5}{6} = \tfrac{10}{36},$$

$$P(\text{two 1's occur}) = (\tfrac{1}{6})^2 = \tfrac{1}{36},$$

so that $P(X=x,Y=y) = \dfrac{10!}{x!y!(10-x-y)!}(\tfrac{25}{36})^x (\tfrac{1}{36})^y (\tfrac{10}{36})^{10-x-y}$ \qquad (1) for x,y ⩾ 0 and x+y ⩽ 10   (see Question 34 on page 243.)

Clearly $P(X=6) > 0$, $P(Y=6) > 0$ but $P(X=6,Y=6) = 0$.

Hence X and Y are dependent.

(i) $P(X < 3, Y < 3) = p(0,0) + p(0,1) + p(0,2) + p(1,0) + p(1,1)$
$$+ p(1,2) + p(2,0) + p(2,1) + p(2,2)$$

where $p(x,y) = P(X=x,Y=y)$.

Repeated substitution in (1) gives
$$P(X < 3, Y < 3) = 0.00176.$$

(ii) Similarly $P(X+Y=5) = p(5,0) + p(4,1) + p(3,2) + p(2,3)$
$$+ p(1,4) + p(0,5)$$
$$= 0.08189.$$

30. A manufacturing company produces rods whose lengths are nominally
25 cm.   In fact the length of a randomly chosen rod has the normal
distribution N(25,1).   Rods between 24 and 26 cm in length are
accepted and make a profit of 5 pence.   Rods longer than 25 cm are
cut to the required length and make a profit of 3 pence.   Rods
shorter than 24 cm are scrapped and make a loss of 4 pence.

(i)   Find the expected profit per rod.

(ii) Find the probability that out of a sample of 10 such rods,
2 are scrapped and 3 have to be cut.

¶   Let X be the length of a randomly chosen rod.

Then $P(24 \leqslant X \leqslant 26) = \Phi(1) - \Phi(-1) = 0.68268$,
$$P(X \leqslant 24) = \Phi(-1) = 0.15866,$$
$$P(X \geqslant 26) = 0.15866 \quad \text{by symmetry.}$$

(i) $E(\text{profit}) = 5 \times 0.68268 + 3 \times 0.15866 - 4 \times 0.15866 = 3.25$ pence.

(ii) Using the multinomial distribution (see Question 34 below) the
probability that out of 10 rods 2 are scrapped and 3 have to
be cut is
$$\frac{10!}{5!2!3!}(0.68268)^5 \times (0.15866)^2 \times (0.15866)^3 = 0.03757.$$

31. A bag contains 12 red balls and 8 white balls. Three are chosen at
random without replacement.   Let X be defined by
$$X = 1 \quad \text{if the first ball chosen is red,}$$
$$= 0 \quad \text{otherwise,}$$
with Y defined similarly for the second ball and Z for the third.
List the possible values (x,y,z) of X,Y,Z and write down the

corresponding probabilities. Hence find the mean and variance of X+Y+Z. State the distribution of X+Y+Z if the selection is made with replacement and compare its mean and variance with the results obtained above.

¶ There are 8 possible values of (x,y,z).

x	y	z		Prob.	
0	0	0	$\frac{8}{20}\times\frac{7}{19}\times\frac{6}{18}$	=	$\frac{14}{285}$
0	0	1	$\frac{8}{20}\times\frac{7}{19}\times\frac{12}{18}$	=	$\frac{28}{285}$
0	1	0	$\frac{8}{20}\times\frac{12}{19}\times\frac{7}{18}$	=	$\frac{28}{285}$
1	0	0	$\frac{12}{20}\times\frac{8}{19}\times\frac{7}{18}$	=	$\frac{28}{285}$
0	1	1	$\frac{8}{20}\times\frac{12}{19}\times\frac{11}{18}$	=	$\frac{44}{285}$
1	0	1	$\frac{12}{20}\times\frac{8}{19}\times\frac{11}{18}$	=	$\frac{44}{285}$
1	1	0	$\frac{12}{20}\times\frac{11}{19}\times\frac{8}{18}$	=	$\frac{44}{285}$
1	1	1	$\frac{12}{20}\times\frac{11}{19}\times\frac{10}{18}$	=	$\frac{55}{285}$

Thus X+Y+Z has the distribution

x+y+z	0	1	2	3
prob.	$\frac{14}{285}$	$\frac{84}{285}$	$\frac{132}{285}$	$\frac{55}{285}$

Then E(X+Y+Z) = $\frac{513}{285}$ = 1.8,   E((X+Y+Z)^2) = $\frac{1107}{285}$

and Var(X+Y+Z) = 0.6442.

If the selection is made with replacement then on each occasion the probability that a red ball is chosen is 0.6. X+Y+Z is the total number of red balls chosen and so has a binomial distribution B(3,0.6).

Hence   E(X+Y+Z) = 3×0.6 = 1.8,

        Var(X+Y+Z) = 3×0.6×0.4 = 0.72.

32. A football team plays 10 matches. In each match it has probability 1/2 of winning, 1/6 of drawing and 1/3 of losing, independently of all other matches. Two points are obtained for a win, one for a draw and none for a defeat. Calculate the probability that the team

obtains (i) 0 points, (ii) 2 points, (iii) 10 points. Find also the mean number of points obtained.

¶ Let X be the number of wins and Y the number of draws in 10 matches. If N is the number of points then N = 2X + Y.
Now

$$p(x,y) = P(X=x, Y=y) = \frac{10!}{x!y!(10-x-y)!} (\tfrac{1}{2})^x (\tfrac{1}{6})^y (\tfrac{1}{3})^{10-x-y}$$

for $x, y \geqslant 0$, $x+y \leqslant 10$, as X and Y have a multinomial distribution (see Question 34).

To find $P(N=n)$ we sum $p(x,y)$ over the values of x and y which satisfy $2x+y = n$.

(i) $P(N=0) = p(0,0) = (\tfrac{1}{3})^{10} = 1.694 \times 10^{-5}$.

(ii) $P(N=2) = p(1,0) + p(0,2) = 4.445 \times 10^{-4}$.

(iii) $P(N=10) = p(0,10) + p(1,8) + p(2,6) + p(3,4) + p(4,2) + p(5,0)$
$$= 0.1157.$$

Let X_i be the number of points obtained in the ith match.

Then $E(X_i) = 2 \times \tfrac{1}{2} + 1 \times \tfrac{1}{6} + 0 \times \tfrac{1}{3} = \tfrac{7}{6}$.

Now $N = \displaystyle\sum_{i=1}^{10} X_i$

and so $E(N) = \displaystyle\sum_{i=1}^{10} E(X_i) = 10 \times \tfrac{7}{6} = \tfrac{35}{3}$.

33. $X_1, X_2, \ldots, X_n$ are n independent random variables, each with probability function
$$p_x = p^x(1-p), \quad x = 0, 1, \ldots$$
where $0 < p < 1$. Let Y be the random variable which takes the same value as the smallest of $X_1, X_2, \ldots, X_n$. Show that Y has a probability function of the above form but with a different parameter.

¶ For any i and any integer x, $P(X_i \geqslant x) = \displaystyle\sum_{y=x}^{\infty} p^y(1-p) = \frac{p^x(1-p)}{1-p} = p^x$.

Now $P(Y \geqslant x) = P(X_1 \geqslant x, X_2 \geqslant x, \ldots, X_n \geqslant x)$
$$= P(X_1 \geqslant x)P(X_2 \geqslant x)\ldots P(X_n \geqslant x)$$
$$= (p^x)^n$$
$$= p^{nx}.$$

So $\quad P(Y = x) = P(Y \geqslant x) - P(Y \geqslant x+1)$

$$= p^{nx} - p^{n(x+1)}$$

$$= (1 - p^n)p^{nx}$$

which is the same form as p_x but with p replaced by p^n.

34. An experiment has k outcomes $A_1, A_2, \ldots, A_k$. The experiment is performed n times and on each occasion the probability that outcome A_i occurs is p_i $(i=1,2,\ldots,k)$, independently of all other occasions. If X_i denotes the total number of times that outcome A_i occurs, show that

$$P(X_1=x_1, X_2=x_2, \ldots, X_k=x_k) = \frac{n!}{x_1! x_2! \ldots x_k!} p_1^{x_1} p_2^{x_2} \ldots p_k^{x_k}$$

for all non-negative integer values of $x_1, x_2, \ldots, x_k$ satisfying

$$\sum_{i=1}^{k} x_i = n. \quad \text{[This is called the } multinomial \text{ distribution.]}$$

¶ Consider the event $X_1=x_1, X_2=x_2, \ldots, X_k=x_k$, where each $x_i \geqslant 0$ and

$$\sum_{i=1}^{k} x_i = n.$$ Any sequence of outcomes with these values has

probability $\qquad p_1^{x_1} p_2^{x_2} \ldots p_k^{x_k}.$

The number of possible sequences with these values is

$$\frac{n!}{x_1! x_2! \ldots x_k!}$$

and so

$$P(X_1=x_1, X_2=x_2, \ldots, X_k=x_k) = \frac{n!}{x_1! x_2! \ldots x_k!} p_1^{x_1} p_2^{x_2} \ldots p_k^{x_k}.$$

35. X and Y are independent Poisson random variables with means λ and μ respectively and $Z=X+Y$. Show that the set of (X,Y) values which give rise to the event $\{Z=z\}$ is

$$\{(0,z), (1,z-1), (2,z-2), \ldots, (z,0)\}.$$

Hence show that

(i) $\quad P(Z=0) = e^{-(\lambda+\mu)}$,

(ii) $\quad P(Z=1) = (\lambda+\mu)e^{-(\lambda+\mu)}$,

(iii) $P(Z=2) = \dfrac{(\lambda+\mu)}{2!}e^{-(\lambda+\mu)}$.

Generalise these results to show that Z has a Poisson distribution with mean $\lambda+\mu$.

¶ If Z=z, then X+Y = z and since X ⩾ 0, Y ⩾ 0 the set of (X,Y) values leading to X+Y = z is

$$\{(0,z),(1,z-1),\ldots,(z,0)\}.$$

(i) $P(Z=0) = P(X=0,Y=0)$

$\qquad\qquad = P(X=0)P(Y=0)$ by independence

$\qquad\qquad = e^{-\lambda}e^{-\mu} = e^{-(\lambda+\mu)}.$

(ii) $P(Z=1) = P(X=0,Y=1) + P(X=1,Y=0)$

$\qquad\qquad = P(X=0)P(Y=1) + P(X=1)P(Y=0)$

$\qquad\qquad = e^{-\lambda}\mu e^{-\mu} + \lambda e^{-\lambda}e^{-\mu}$

$\qquad\qquad = (\lambda+\mu)e^{-(\lambda+\mu)}.$

(iii) $P(Z=2) = P(X=0)P(Y=2) + P(X=1)P(Y=1) + P(X=2)P(Y=0)$

$\qquad\qquad = e^{-\lambda}\dfrac{\mu^2 e^{-\mu}}{2} + \lambda e^{-\lambda}\mu e^{-\mu} + \dfrac{\lambda^2 e^{-\lambda}}{2}e^{-\mu}$

$\qquad\qquad = \dfrac{(\lambda+\mu)^2}{2!}e^{-(\lambda+\mu)}.$

For any non-negative integer z,

$$P(Z=z) = \sum_{x=0}^{z} P(X=x,Y=z-x) = \sum_{x=0}^{z} \frac{\lambda^x e^{-\lambda}}{x!}\cdot\frac{\mu^{z-x}e^{-\mu}}{(z-x)!}$$

$$= \frac{e^{-(\lambda+\mu)}}{z!}\sum_{x=0}^{z}\frac{z!}{x!(z-x)!}\lambda^x\mu^{z-x}$$

$$= \frac{e^{-(\lambda+\mu)}}{z!}(\lambda+\mu)^z \quad \text{by the binomial theorem}$$

and so Z has a Poisson distribution with mean $\lambda+\mu$.

36. The number X of telephone calls which arrive at a switchboard in an hour has a Poisson distribution with mean λ. Each call has a probability p, independently of all others, of being a wrong number. Let Y be the number of wrong numbers occuring in an hour. Write down an expression for $P(Y=y|X=x)$ and deduce that

$$P(X=x,Y=y) = \frac{e^{-\lambda}\lambda^x p^y(1-p)^{x-y}}{y!(x-y)!} \quad \begin{array}{l}\text{if } x=0,1,2,\ldots\ldots \\ y=0,1,2,\ldots\ldots,x.\end{array}$$

Hence show that the marginal probability function of Y is given by

$$P(Y=y) = \frac{e^{-p\lambda}(p\lambda)^y}{y!} \quad \text{if } y = 0,1,2,\ldots$$

What does this tell you about the number of wrong numbers obtained in an hour?

¶
$$P(X=x) = \frac{e^{-\lambda}\lambda^x}{x!} \qquad x = 0,1,2,\ldots\ldots$$

Given a number x of telephone calls, the number Y of wrong numbers will have a binomial distribution $B(x,p)$.

Hence
$$P(Y=y\,|\,X=x) = {}^xC_y p^y (1-p)^{x-y}, \qquad y = 0,1,\ldots,x.$$

It follows that
$$P(X=x,Y=y) = P(Y=y\,|\,X=x)\,P(X=x)$$
$$= \frac{e^{-\lambda}\lambda^x p^y (1-p)^{x-y}}{y!\,(x-y)!}$$

and
$$P(Y=y) = \sum_{x=y}^{\infty} P(X=x,Y=y) \qquad \text{as } X \geqslant Y$$

$$= \frac{e^{-\lambda}p^y \lambda^y}{y!} \sum_{x=y}^{\infty} \frac{\lambda^{x-y}(1-p)^{x-y}}{(x-y)!}$$

$$= \frac{e^{-\lambda}(\lambda p)^y}{y!} \sum_{z=0}^{\infty} \frac{(\lambda(1-p))^z}{z!} \qquad (z = x-y)$$

$$= \frac{e^{-\lambda}(\lambda p)^y e^{\lambda(1-p)}}{y!} = \frac{e^{-\lambda p}(\lambda p)^y}{y!}.$$

Hence the number of wrong numbers in an hour has a Poisson distribution with mean λp.

37. The numbers of butterflies and moths observed by a lepidopterist on a field trip are independent Poisson random variables with means λ and μ respectively. He captures every butterfly and every moth he sees and returns home with N lepidoptera in all. Let X be the number of butterflies and Y be the number of moths in his catch. Show that both X and Y are binomially distributed with means $\lambda N/(\lambda+\mu)$ and $\mu N/(\lambda+\mu)$ respectively.

¶ We know that $P(X=x) = \dfrac{e^{-\lambda}\lambda^x}{x!}$ and $P(Y=y) = \dfrac{e^{-\mu}\mu^y}{y!}$.

By the result of Question 35 above, if $Z=X+Y$ then
$$P(Z=N) = \frac{e^{-(\lambda+\mu)}(\lambda+\mu)^N}{N!}.$$

We require
$$P(X=x\,|\,Z=N) = \frac{P(X=x,Z=N)}{P(Z=N)} = \frac{P(X=x,Y=N-x)}{P(Z=N)}$$

$$= \frac{e^{-\lambda}\lambda^x}{x!} \cdot \frac{e^{-\mu}\mu^{N-x}}{(N-x)!} e^{(\lambda+\mu)} N!\,(\lambda+\mu)^{-N}$$

$$= {}^{N}C_x \left(\frac{\lambda}{\lambda+\mu}\right)^x \left(\frac{\mu}{\lambda+\mu}\right)^{N-x}.$$

Hence, given that $Z=N$, X has a binomial distribution $B\left(N, \frac{\lambda}{\lambda+\mu}\right)$.

Since $Y=N-X$, the result for Y follows immediately.

38. (a) N balls are distributed at random among N boxes, each box being large enough to contain all N balls.

If $\qquad X_i^{(r)} = 1 \quad$ if the ith box contains r balls,

$\qquad\qquad\qquad\quad = 0 \quad$ otherwise,

show that

$$E(X_i^{(r)}) = {}^{N}C_r \left(\frac{1}{N}\right)^r \left(1 - \frac{1}{N}\right)^{N-r}.$$

Use the fact that the number N_r of boxes containing r balls ($r=0,1,\ldots,N$) can be written in the form

$$N_r = \sum_{i=1}^{N} X_i^{(r)}.$$

to obtain an expression for $E(N_r)$.

(b) Show that when N is large the expected number of empty boxes is approximately Ne^{-1}.

(c) One thousand people take part in one thousand raffles and each person buys one ticket on each occasion. What is the expected number of people who fail to win even one first prize?

¶ (a) $\qquad X_i^{(r)} = 1 \quad$ if ith box contains r balls,

$\qquad\qquad\qquad\quad = 0 \quad$ otherwise.

Now each ball goes into box i with probability $\frac{1}{N}$ as there are N available boxes. Hence the number in box i has a binomial distribution $B(N,\frac{1}{N})$ and

$$P(X_i^{(r)}=1) = {}^{N}C_r \left(\frac{1}{N}\right)^r \left(1 - \frac{1}{N}\right)^{N-r}.$$

Hence $\qquad E(X_i^{(r)}) = P(X_i^{(r)}=1) = {}^{N}C_r \left(\frac{1}{N}\right)^r \left(1 - \frac{1}{N}\right)^{N-r}$.

Now N_r, the number of boxes containing r balls, is $\displaystyle\sum_{i=1}^{N} X_i^{(r)}$

and $\qquad E(N_r) = NE(X_i^{(r)}) = N \times {}^{N}C_r \left(\frac{1}{N}\right)^r \left(1 - \frac{1}{N}\right)^{N-r}$.

(b) The expected number of empty boxes is

$$E(N_0) = N \times {}^{N}C_0 \left(1 - \frac{1}{N}\right)^N = N\left(1 - \frac{1}{N}\right)^N$$

$$\approx Ne^{-1} \quad \text{as} \quad \left(1 - \frac{1}{N}\right)^N \approx e^{-1} \quad \text{for large N.}$$

(c) This problem is equivalent to the above if we replace the boxes by the people and the balls by first prizes. The expected number of people with no first prizes is then $1000e^{-1} = 367.9$ by (b).

39. (i) Let X,Y and Z be random variables. Show that if a,b and c are constants then
$$\text{Var}(aX+bY+cZ) = a^2\text{Var}(X) + b^2\text{Var}(Y) + c^2\text{Var}(Z)$$
$$+ 2ab\text{Cov}(X,Y) + 2ac\text{Cov}(X,Z) + 2bc\text{Cov}(Y,Z).$$

(ii) Suppose the distributions of three random variables X_1,X_2,X_3 are identical and define Y_1,Y_2,Y_3 by
$$Y_i = X_i - \bar{X} \quad (i=1,2,3)$$
where $\bar{X}$ is the arithmetic mean of X_1,X_2 and X_3.
Show that if X_1,X_2,X_3 are not independent then Y_1,Y_2,Y_3 are not necessarily identically distributed.

¶ (i) $\text{Var}(aX+bY+cZ) = \text{Var}(aX+bY) + \text{Var}(cZ) + 2\text{Cov}(aX+bY,cZ)$
Now $\text{Var}(aX+bY) = a^2\text{Var}(X) + b^2\text{Var}(Y) + 2ab\text{Cov}(X,Y)$
and $\text{Cov}(aX+bY,cZ) = E((aX+bY)cZ) - E(aX+bY)E(cZ)$
$$= ac(E(XZ)-E(X)E(Z)) + bc(E(YZ)-E(Y)E(Z))$$
$$= ac\text{Cov}(X,Z) + bc\text{Cov}(Y,Z).$$

Hence $\text{Var}(aX+bY+cZ) = a^2\text{Var}(X) + b^2\text{Var}(Y) + c^2\text{Var}(Z)$
$$+ 2ab\text{Cov}(X,Y) + 2ac\text{Cov}(X,Z) + 2bc\text{Cov}(Y,Z).$$

(ii)
$$Y_1 = X_1 - \frac{X_1+X_2+X_3}{3} = \frac{2X_1-X_2-X_3}{3},$$
and similarly $Y_2 = \frac{2X_2-X_1-X_3}{3}, \quad Y_3 = \frac{2X_3-X_1-X_2}{3}.$
$E(Y_1) = E(Y_2) = E(Y_3) = 0.$
However, if $\text{Var}(X_i) = \sigma^2$, $i=1,2,3$ and $\text{Cov}(X_i,Y_j) = \gamma_{ij}$ $(i\neq j)$, the result of (i) shows that
$$\text{Var}(Y_1) = \frac{6\sigma^2}{9} - \frac{4}{9}\gamma_{12} - \frac{4}{9}\gamma_{13} + \frac{1}{9}\gamma_{23},$$
$$\text{Var}(Y_2) = \frac{6\sigma^2}{9} - \frac{4}{9}\gamma_{12} - \frac{4}{9}\gamma_{23} + \frac{1}{9}\gamma_{13}.$$

Hence $\text{Var}(Y_1) - \text{Var}(Y_2) = \frac{5}{9}(\gamma_{23} - \gamma_{13})$

which is not necessarily zero. Hence Y_1 and Y_2 are not necessarily identically distributed.

40. X_1, X_2, X_3, X_4, X_5 are five independent random variables uniformly distributed on $[0,1]$. The random variable Y is defined by
$$Y = \text{Max}(X_1, X_2, X_3, X_4, X_5).$$
If $F(x)$, $G(y)$ denote respectively the cumulative distribution functions of the X's and of Y, show that
$$G(y) = [F(y)]^5.$$
Hence find the probability density function of Y, and deduce the mean and variance of Y.

How would these results change if we had n independent uniform random variables?

What is the least value of n for which the probability that Y exceeds 0.95 is greater than 0.9?

¶
$$\begin{aligned}
G(y) &= P(Y \leqslant y) \\
&= P(X_1 \leqslant y, X_2 \leqslant y, \ldots, X_5 \leqslant y) \\
&= P(X_1 \leqslant y)P(X_2 \leqslant y) \ldots P(X_5 \leqslant y) \quad \text{(by independence)} \\
&= [F(y)]^5.
\end{aligned}$$

As X_1 is uniform on $[0,1]$, it has probability density function
$$\begin{aligned}
f(x) &= 1 \quad \text{if } 0 \leqslant x \leqslant 1, \\
&= 0 \quad \text{otherwise.}
\end{aligned}$$

Hence if $0 \leqslant x \leqslant 1$,
$$F(y) = \int_0^y 1 \, dx = y$$

and
$$G(y) = y^5.$$

Thus Y has probability density function
$$\begin{aligned}
g(y) &= 5y^4 \quad \text{if } 0 \leqslant y \leqslant 1, \\
&= 0 \quad \text{otherwise.}
\end{aligned}$$

$$E(Y) = \int_0^1 y \cdot 5y^4 \, dy = \frac{5}{6}, \qquad E(Y^2) = \int_0^1 y^2 \cdot 5y^4 \, dy = \frac{5}{7},$$

so that
$$\text{Var}(Y) = \frac{5}{7} - \left(\frac{5}{6}\right)^2 = \frac{5}{252}.$$

If Y is the maximum of n independent uniform variables then
$$G(y) = [F(y)]^n = y^n \quad (0 \leqslant y \leqslant 1),$$

and
$$g(y) = ny^{n-1} \quad (0 \leqslant y \leqslant 1).$$

Then
$$E(Y) = \frac{n}{n+1}, \quad \text{Var}(Y) = \frac{n}{n+2} - \left(\frac{n}{n+1}\right)^2 = \frac{n}{(n+1)^2(n+2)}.$$

Now
$$P(Y > 0.95) = 1 - G(0.95) = 1 - 0.95^n,$$

so we require $1 - 0.95^n > 0.9$,
$$0.95^n < 0.1,$$

$$n \log 0.95 < \log 0.1,$$

that is
$$n > \frac{\log 0.1}{\log 0.95} = 44.89.$$

Hence the least value of n is 45.

Table 1. The Normal Cumulative Distribution Function

The function tabulated is $\Phi(x) = \frac{1}{\sqrt{2\pi}}\int_{-\infty}^{x} e^{-y^2/2}\,dy = P(X \leqslant x)$

where X is Normally distributed with zero mean and unit variance. The value of the function $\Phi(x)$ corresponds to the shaded area. For negative x the relation $\Phi(x) = 1 - \Phi(-x)$ should be used.

x	.00	.01	.02	.03	.04	.05	.06	.07	.08	.09
0.0	0.50000	0.50399	0.50798	0.51197	0.51595	0.51994	0.52392	0.52790	0.53188	0.53586
0.1	0.53983	0.54380	0.54776	0.55172	0.55567	0.55962	0.56356	0.56749	0.57142	0.57535
0.2	0.57926	0.58317	0.58706	0.59095	0.59483	0.59871	0.60257	0.60642	0.61026	0.61409
0.3	0.61791	0.62172	0.62552	0.62930	0.63307	0.63683	0.64058	0.64431	0.64803	0.65173
0.4	0.65542	0.65910	0.66276	0.66640	0.67003	0.67364	0.67724	0.68032	0.68439	0.68793
0.5	0.69146	0.69497	0.69847	0.70194	0.70540	0.70884	0.71226	0.71566	0.71904	0.72240
0.6	0.72575	0.72908	0.73237	0.73565	0.73891	0.74215	0.74537	0.74857	0.75175	0.75490
0.7	0.75804	0.76115	0.76424	0.76730	0.77035	0.77337	0.77637	0.77935	0.78230	0.78524
0.8	0.78814	0.79103	0.79389	0.79673	0.79955	0.80234	0.80511	0.80785	0.81057	0.81327
0.9	0.81594	0.81859	0.82121	0.82381	0.82639	0.82894	0.83147	0.83398	0.83646	0.83891
1.0	0.84134	0.84375	0.84614	0.84849	0.85083	0.85314	0.85543	0.85769	0.85993	0.86214
1.1	0.86433	0.86650	0.86864	0.87076	0.87286	0.87493	0.87698	0.87900	0.88100	0.88298
1.2	0.88493	0.88686	0.88877	0.89065	0.89251	0.89435	0.89617	0.89796	0.89973	0.90147
1.3	0.90320	0.90490	0.90658	0.90824	0.90988	0.91149	0.91308	0.91466	0.91621	0.91774
1.4	0.91924	0.92073	0.92220	0.92364	0.92507	0.92647	0.92785	0.92922	0.93056	0.93139
1.5	0.93319	0.93448	0.93574	0.93699	0.93822	0.93943	0.94062	0.94179	0.94295	0.94408
1.6	0.94520	0.94630	0.94738	0.94845	0.94950	0.95053	0.95154	0.95254	0.95352	0.95449
1.7	0.95543	0.95637	0.95728	0.95818	0.95907	0.95994	0.96080	0.96164	0.96246	0.96327
1.8	0.96407	0.96485	0.96562	0.96638	0.96712	0.96784	0.96856	0.96926	0.96995	0.97062
1.9	0.97128	0.97193	0.97257	0.97320	0.97381	0.97441	0.97500	0.97558	0.97615	0.97670
2.0	0.97725	0.97778	0.97831	0.97882	0.97932	0.97982	0.98030	0.98077	0.98124	0.98169
2.1	0.98214	0.98257	0.98300	0.98341	0.98382	0.98422	0.98461	0.98500	0.98537	0.98574
2.2	0.98610	0.98645	0.98679	0.98713	0.98745	0.98778	0.98809	0.98840	0.98870	0.98899
2.3	0.98928	0.98956	0.98983	0.99010	0.99036	0.99061	0.99086	0.99111	0.99134	0.99158
2.4	0.99180	0.99202	0.99224	0.99245	0.99266	0.99286	0.99305	0.99324	0.99343	0.99361
2.5	0.99379	0.99396	0.99413	0.99430	0.99446	0.99461	0.99477	0.99492	0.99506	0.99520
2.6	0.99534	0.99547	0.99560	0.99573	0.99585	0.99598	0.99609	0.99621	0.99632	0.99643
2.7	0.99653	0.99664	0.99674	0.99683	0.99693	0.99702	0.99711	0.99720	0.99728	0.99736
2.8	0.99744	0.99752	0.99760	0.99767	0.99774	0.99781	0.99788	0.99795	0.99801	0.99807
2.9	0.99813	0.99819	0.99825	0.99831	0.99836	0.99841	0.99846	0.99851	0.99856	0.99861
3.0	0.99865	0.99869	0.99874	0.99878	0.99882	0.99886	0.99889	0.99893	0.99896	0.99900
3.1	0.99903	0.99906	0.99910	0.99913	0.99916	0.99918	0.99921	0.99924	0.99926	0.99929
3.2	0.99931	0.99934	0.99936	0.99938	0.99940	0.99942	0.99944	0.99946	0.99948	0.99950
3.3	0.99952	0.99953	0.99955	0.99957	0.99958	0.99960	0.99961	0.99962	0.99964	0.99965
3.4	0.99966	0.99968	0.99969	0.99970	0.99971	0.99972	0.99973	0.99974	0.99975	0.99976
3.5	0.99977	0.99978	0.99978	0.99979	0.99980	0.99981	0.99981	0.99982	0.99983	0.99983
3.6	0.99984	0.99985	0.99985	0.99986	0.99986	0.99987	0.99987	0.99988	0.99988	0.99989
3.7	0.99989	0.99990	0.99990	0.99990	0.99991	0.99991	0.99992	0.99992	0.99992	0.99992
3.8	0.99993	0.99993	0.99993	0.99994	0.99994	0.99994	0.99994	0.99995	0.99995	0.99995
3.9	0.99995	0.99995	0.99996	0.99996	0.99996	0.99996	0.99996	0.99996	0.99997	0.99997

Table 2. The Binomial Cumulative Distribution Function

The function tabulated is $F(x;n,p) = \sum_{r=0}^{x} {}^{n}C_{r}p^{r}(1-p)^{n-r} = P(X \leqslant x)$

where X is binomially distributed with parameters n and p. For p>0.5, the relation $F(x;n,p) = 1-F(n-x-1;n,1-p)$ should be used. For n>100, approximate values can be obtained using either the Normal or Poisson approximations, whichever is appropriate.

x \ p		0.05	0.10	0.15	0.20	0.25	0.30	0.35	0.40	0.45	0.50
n=2	0	0.90250	0.81000	0.72250	0.64000	0.56250	0.49000	0.42250	0.36000	0.30250	0.25000
	1	0.99750	0.99000	0.97750	0.96000	0.93750	0.91000	0.87750	0.84000	0.79750	0.75000
	2	1.00000	1.00000	1.00000	1.00000	1.00000	1.00000	1.00000	1.00000	1.00000	1.00000
n=3	0	0.85738	0.72900	0.61413	0.51200	0.42188	0.34300	0.27463	0.21600	0.16638	0.12500
	1	0.99275	0.97200	0.93925	0.89600	0.84375	0.78400	0.71825	0.64800	0.57475	0.50000
	2	0.99988	0.99900	0.99663	0.99200	0.98438	0.97300	0.95713	0.93600	0.90858	0.87500
	3	1.00000	1.00000	1.00000	1.00000	1.00000	1.00000	1.00000	1.00000	1.00000	1.00000
n=4	0	0.81451	0.65610	0.52201	0.40960	0.31641	0.24010	0.17851	0.12960	0.09151	0.06250
	1	0.98598	0.94770	0.89048	0.81920	0.73828	0.65170	0.56298	0.47520	0.39098	0.31250
	2	0.99952	0.99630	0.98802	0.97280	0.94922	0.91630	0.87352	0.82080	0.75852	0.68750
	3	0.99999	0.99990	0.99949	0.99840	0.99609	0.99190	0.98499	0.97440	0.95899	0.93750
	4	1.00000	1.00000	1.00000	1.00000	1.00000	1.00000	1.00000	1.00000	1.00000	1.00000
n=5	0	0.77378	0.59049	0.44371	0.32768	0.23730	0.16807	0.11603	0.07776	0.05033	0.03125
	1	0.97741	0.91854	0.83521	0.73728	0.63281	0.52822	0.42842	0.33696	0.25622	0.18750
	2	0.99884	0.99144	0.97339	0.94208	0.89648	0.83692	0.76483	0.68256	0.59313	0.50000
	3	0.99997	0.99954	0.99777	0.99328	0.98438	0.96922	0.94598	0.91296	0.86878	0.81250
	4	1.00000	0.99999	0.99992	0.99968	0.99902	0.99757	0.99475	0.98976	0.98155	0.96875
	5	1.00000	1.00000	1.00000	1.00000	1.00000	1.00000	1.00000	1.00000	1.00000	1.00000
n=6	0	0.73509	0.53144	0.37715	0.26214	0.17798	0.11765	0.07542	0.04666	0.02768	0.01563
	1	0.96723	0.88574	0.77648	0.65536	0.53394	0.42018	0.31908	0.23328	0.16357	0.10938
	2	0.99777	0.98415	0.95266	0.90112	0.83057	0.74431	0.64709	0.54432	0.44152	0.34375
	3	0.99991	0.99873	0.99411	0.98304	0.98240	0.92953	0.88258	0.82080	0.74474	0.65625
	4	1.00000	0.99995	0.99960	0.99840	0.99536	0.98907	0.97768	0.95904	0.93080	0.89063
	5		1.00000	0.99999	0.99994	0.99976	0.99927	0.99816	0.99590	0.99170	0.98438
	6			1.00000	1.00000	1.00000	1.00000	1.00000	1.00000	1.00000	1.00000
n=7	0	0.69834	0.47830	0.32058	0.20972	0.13348	0.08235	0.04902	0.02709	0.01522	0.00781
	1	0.95562	0.85031	0.71658	0.57672	0.44495	0.32942	0.23380	0.15863	0.10242	0.06250
	2	0.99624	0.97431	0.92623	0.85197	0.75641	0.64707	0.53228	0.41990	0.31644	0.22656
	3	0.99981	0.99727	0.98790	0.96666	0.92944	0.87396	0.80015	0.71021	0.60829	0.50000
	4	0.99999	0.99982	0.99878	0.99533	0.98712	0.97120	0.94439	0.90374	0.84707	0.77344
	5	1.00000	0.99999	0.99993	0.99963	0.99866	0.99621	0.99099	0.98116	0.96429	0.93750
	6		1.00000	1.00000	0.99999	0.99994	0.99978	0.99936	0.99836	0.99626	0.99219
	7				1.00000	1.00000	1.00000	1.00000	1.00000	1.00000	1.00000
n=8	0	0.66342	0.43047	0.27249	0.16777	0.10011	0.05765	0.03186	0.01680	0.00837	0.00391
	1	0.94276	0.81310	0.65718	0.50332	0.36708	0.25530	0.16913	0.10638	0.06318	0.03516
	2	0.99421	0.96191	0.89479	0.79692	0.69854	0.55177	0.42781	0.31539	0.22013	0.14453
	3	0.99963	0.99493	0.97865	0.94372	0.88618	0.80590	0.70640	0.59409	0.47696	0.36328
	4	0.99998	0.99957	0.99715	0.98959	0.97270	0.94203	0.89391	0.82633	0.73952	0.63672
	5	1.00000	0.99998	0.99976	0.99877	0.99577	0.98871	0.97468	0.95019	0.91154	0.85547
	6		1.00000	0.99999	0.99992	0.99962	0.99871	0.99643	0.99148	0.98188	0.96484
	7			1.00000	1.00000	0.99998	0.99993	0.99977	0.99934	0.99832	0.99609
	8					1.00000	1.00000	1.00000	1.00000	1.00000	1.00000

Table 2   The Binomial Cumulative Distribution Function

x \ p	0.05	0.10	0.15	0.20	0.25	0.30	0.35	0.40	0.45	0.50
n=9 0	0.63025	0.38742	0.23162	0.13422	0.07508	0.04035	0.02071	0.01008	0.00461	0.00195
1	0.92879	0.77484	0.59948	0.43621	0.30034	0.19600	0.12109	0.07054	0.03852	0.01953
2	0.99164	0.94703	0.85915	0.73820	0.60068	0.46283	0.33727	0.23179	0.14950	0.08984
3	0.99936	0.99167	0.96607	0.91436	0.83427	0.72966	0.60889	0.48261	0.36138	0.25391
4	0.99997	0.99911	0.99437	0.98042	0.95107	0.90119	0.82828	0.73343	0.62142	0.50000
5	1.00000	0.99994	0.99937	0.99693	0.99001	0.97471	0.94641	0.90065	0.83418	0.74609
6		1.00000	0.99995	0.99969	0.99866	0.99571	0.98882	0.97479	0.95023	0.91016
7			1.00000	0.99998	0.99989	0.99957	0.99860	0.99620	0.99092	0.98047
8				1.00000	1.00000	0.99998	0.99992	0.99974	0.99924	0.99805
9						1.00000	1.00000	1.00000	1.00000	1.00000
n=10 0	0.59874	0.34868	0.19687	0.10737	0.05631	0.02825	0.01346	0.00605	0.00253	0.00098
1	0.91386	0.73610	0.54430	0.37581	0.24403	0.14931	0.08595	0.04636	0.02326	0.01074
2	0.98850	0.92981	0.82020	0.67780	0.52559	0.38278	0.26161	0.16729	0.09956	0.05469
3	0.99897	0.98720	0.95003	0.87913	0.77588	0.64961	0.51383	0.38228	0.26604	0.17188
4	0.99994	0.99837	0.99013	0.96721	0.92187	0.84973	0.75150	0.63310	0.50440	0.37695
5	1.00000	0.99985	0.99862	0.99363	0.98027	0.95265	0.90507	0.83376	0.73844	0.62305
6		0.99999	0.99987	0.99914	0.99649	0.98941	0.97398	0.94524	0.89801	0.82813
7		1.00000	0.99999	0.99992	0.99958	0.99841	0.99518	0.98771	0.97261	0.94531
8			1.00000	1.00000	0.99997	0.99986	0.99946	0.99832	0.99550	0.98926
9						1.00000	0.99999	0.99997	0.99990	0.99966	0.99902
10						1.00000	1.00000	1.00000	1.00000	1.00000
n=11 0	0.56830	0.31381	0.16734	0.08590	0.04224	0.01977	0.00875	0.00363	0.00139	0.00049
1	0.89811	0.69736	0.49219	0.32212	0.19710	0.11299	0.06058	0.03023	0.01393	0.00586
2	0.98476	0.91044	0.77881	0.61740	0.45520	0.31274	0.20013	0.11892	0.06522	0.03271
3	0.99845	0.98147	0.93056	0.83886	0.71330	0.56956	0.42555	0.29628	0.19112	0.11328
4	0.99980	0.99725	0.98411	0.94959	0.88537	0.78970	0.66831	0.53277	0.39714	0.27441
5	0.99999	0.99970	0.99734	0.98835	0.96567	0.92178	0.85132	0.75350	0.63312	0.50000
6	1.00000	0.99998	0.99968	0.99803	0.99244	0.97838	0.94986	0.90065	0.82620	0.72559
7		1.00000	0.99997	0.99976	0.99881	0.99571	0.98776	0.97072	0.93904	0.88672
8			1.00000	0.99998	0.99987	0.99942	0.99796	0.99408	0.98520	0.96729
9				1.00000	0.99999	0.99995	0.99979	0.99927	0.99779	0.99414
10					1.00000	1.00000	0.99999	0.99996	0.99985	0.99951
11							1.00000	1.00000	1.00000	1.00000
n=12 0	0.54036	0.28243	0.14224	0.06872	0.03168	0.01384	0.00569	0.00218	0.00077	0.00024
1	0.88164	0.65900	0.44346	0.27498	0.15838	0.08503	0.04244	0.01959	0.00829	0.00317
2	0.98043	0.88913	0.73582	0.55835	0.39068	0.25282	0.15129	0.08344	0.04214	0.01929
3	0.99776	0.97436	0.90779	0.79457	0.64878	0.49252	0.34665	0.22534	0.13447	0.07300
4	0.99982	0.99567	0.97608	0.92744	0.84236	0.72366	0.58335	0.43818	0.30443	0.19385
5	0.99999	0.99946	0.99536	0.98059	0.94560	0.88215	0.78726	0.66521	0.52693	0.38721
6	1.00000	0.99995	0.99933	0.99610	0.98575	0.96140	0.91537	0.84179	0.73931	0.61279
7		1.00000	0.99993	0.99942	0.99722	0.99051	0.97449	0.94269	0.88826	0.80615
8			0.99999	0.99994	0.99961	0.99831	0.99439	0.98473	0.96443	0.92700
9			1.00000	1.00000	0.99996	0.99979	0.99915	0.99719	0.99212	0.98071
10					1.00000	0.99998	0.99992	0.99968	0.99892	0.99683
11						1.00000	1.00000	0.99998	0.99993	0.99976
12								1.00000	1.00000	1.00000
n=13 0	0.51334	0.25419	0.12091	0.05498	0.02376	0.00969	0.00370	0.00131	0.00042	0.00012
1	0.86458	0.62135	0.39828	0.23365	0.12671	0.06367	0.02958	0.01263	0.00490	0.00171
2	0.97549	0.86612	0.69196	0.50165	0.33260	0.20248	0.11319	0.05790	0.02691	0.01123
3	0.99690	0.96584	0.88200	0.74732	0.58425	0.42061	0.27827	0.16858	0.09292	0.04614
4	0.99971	0.99354	0.96584	0.90087	0.79396	0.65431	0.50050	0.35304	0.22795	0.13342
5	0.99998	0.99908	0.99247	0.96996	0.91979	0.83460	0.71589	0.57440	0.42681	0.29053
6	1.00000	0.99990	0.99873	0.99300	0.97571	0.93762	0.87053	0.77116	0.64374	0.50000
7		0.99999	0.99984	0.99875	0.99435	0.98178	0.95380	0.90233	0.82123	0.70947
8		1.00000	0.99998	0.99983	0.99901	0.99597	0.98743	0.96792	0.93015	0.86658
9			1.00000	0.99998	0.99987	0.99935	0.99749	0.99221	0.97966	0.95336
10				1.00000	0.99999	0.99993	0.99965	0.99868	0.99586	0.98877
11					1.00000	1.00000	0.99997	0.99986	0.99948	0.99829
12							1.00000	0.99999	0.99997	0.99988
13								1.00000	1.00000	1.00000

Table 2   The Binomial Cumulative Distribution Function

x	p	0.05	0.10	0.15	0.20	0.25	0.30	0.35	0.40	0.45	0.50
n=14	0	0.48768	0.22877	0.10277	0.04398	0.01782	0.00678	0.00240	0.00078	0.00023	0.00006
	1	0.84701	0.58463	0.35667	0.19791	0.10097	0.04748	0.02052	0.00810	0.00299	0.00092
	2	0.96995	0.84164	0.64791	0.44805	0.28113	0.16084	0.08393	0.03979	0.01701	0.00647
	3	0.99583	0.95587	0.85349	0.69819	0.52134	0.35517	0.22050	0.12431	0.06322	0.02869
	4	0.99957	0.99077	0.95326	0.87016	0.74153	0.58420	0.42272	0.27926	0.16719	0.08978
	5	0.99997	0.99853	0.98847	0.95615	0.88833	0.78052	0.64051	0.48585	0.33732	0.21198
	6	1.00000	0.99982	0.99779	0.98839	0.96173	0.90672	0.81641	0.69245	0.54612	0.39526
	7		0.99998	0.99967	0.99760	0.98969	0.96853	0.92466	0.84986	0.74136	0.60474
	8		1.00000	0.99996	0.99962	0.99785	0.99171	0.97566	0.94168	0.88114	0.78802
	9			1.00000	0.99995	0.99966	0.99833	0.99396	0.98249	0.95738	0.91022
	10				1.00000	0.99996	0.99975	0.99889	0.99609	0.98857	0.97131
	11					1.00000	0.99997	0.99986	0.99939	0.99785	0.99353
	12						1.00000	0.99999	0.99994	0.99975	0.99908
	13							1.00000	1.00000	0.99999	0.99994
	14									1.00000	1.00000
n=15	0	0.46329	0.20589	0.08735	0.03518	0.01336	0.00475	0.00156	0.00047	0.00013	0.00003
	1	0.82905	0.54904	0.31859	0.16713	0.08018	0.03527	0.01418	0.00517	0.00169	0.00049
	2	0.96380	0.81594	0.60423	0.39802	0.23609	0.12683	0.06173	0.02711	0.01065	0.00369
	3	0.99453	0.94444	0.82266	0.64816	0.46129	0.29687	0.17270	0.09050	0.04242	0.01758
	4	0.99939	0.98728	0.93829	0.83577	0.68649	0.51549	0.35194	0.21728	0.12040	0.05923
	5	0.99995	0.99775	0.98319	0.93895	0.85163	0.72162	0.56428	0.40322	0.26076	0.15088
	6	1.00000	0.99969	0.99639	0.98194	0.94338	0.86886	0.75484	0.60981	0.45216	0.30362
	7		0.99997	0.99939	0.99576	0.98270	0.94999	0.88677	0.78690	0.65350	0.50000
	8		1.00000	0.99992	0.99922	0.99581	0.98476	0.95781	0.90495	0.81824	0.69638
	9			0.99999	0.99989	0.99921	0.99635	0.98756	0.96617	0.92397	0.84912
	10			1.00000	0.99999	0.99988	0.99933	0.99717	0.99065	0.97453	0.94077
	11				1.00000	0.99999	0.99991	0.99952	0.99807	0.99367	0.98242
	12					1.00000	0.99999	0.99994	0.99972	0.99889	0.99631
	13						1.00000	1.00000	0.99997	0.99988	0.99951
	14								1.00000	0.99999	0.99997
	15									1.00000	1.00000
n=20	0	0.35849	0.12158	0.03876	0.01153	0.00317	0.00080	0.00018	0.00004	0.00001	0.00000
	1	0.73584	0.39175	0.17556	0.06918	0.02431	0.00764	0.00213	0.00052	0.00011	0.00002
	2	0.92452	0.67693	0.40490	0.20608	0.09126	0.03548	0.01212	0.00361	0.00093	0.00020
	3	0.98410	0.86705	0.64773	0.41145	0.22516	0.10709	0.04438	0.01596	0.00493	0.00129
	4	0.99743	0.95683	0.82985	0.62965	0.41484	0.23751	0.11820	0.05095	0.01886	0.00591
	5	0.99967	0.98875	0.93269	0.80421	0.61717	0.41637	0.24540	0.12560	0.05533	0.02069
	6	0.99997	0.99761	0.97806	0.91331	0.78578	0.60801	0.41663	0.25001	0.12993	0.05766
	7	1.00000	0.99958	0.99408	0.96786	0.89819	0.77227	0.60103	0.41589	0.25201	0.13159
	8		0.99994	0.99867	0.99002	0.95907	0.88667	0.76238	0.59560	0.41431	0.25172
	9		0.99999	0.99975	0.99741	0.98614	0.95204	0.87822	0.75534	0.59136	0.41190
	10		1.00000	0.99996	0.99944	0.99606	0.98286	0.94683	0.87248	0.75071	0.58810
	11			1.00000	0.99990	0.99906	0.99486	0.98042	0.94347	0.86924	0.74828
	12				0.99998	0.99982	0.99872	0.99398	0.97897	0.94197	0.86841
	13				1.00000	0.99997	0.99974	0.99843	0.99353	0.97859	0.94234
	14					1.00000	0.99996	0.99969	0.99839	0.99357	0.97931
	15						0.99999	0.99995	0.99968	0.99847	0.99409
	16						1.00000	0.99999	0.99995	0.99972	0.99871
	17							1.00000	0.99999	0.99996	0.99980
	18								1.00000	1.00000	0.99998
	19										1.00000

Table 2 The Binomial Cumulative Distribution Function

	x \ p	0.05	0.10	0.15	0.20	0.25	0.30	0.35	0.40	0.45	0.50
n=25	0	0.27739	0.07179	0.01720	0.00378	0.00075	0.00013	0.00002	0.00000	0.00000	0.00000
	1	0.64238	0.27121	0.09307	0.02739	0.00702	0.00157	0.00030	0.00005	0.00001	0.00000
	2	0.87289	0.53709	0.25374	0.09823	0.03211	0.00896	0.00213	0.00043	0.00007	0.00001
	3	0.96591	0.76359	0.47112	0.23399	0.09621	0.03324	0.00968	0.00237	0.00048	0.00008
	4	0.99284	0.90201	0.68211	0.42067	0.21374	0.09047	0.03205	0.00947	0.00231	0.00046
	5	0.99879	0.96660	0.83848	0.61669	0.37828	0.19349	0.08262	0.02936	0.00860	0.00204
	6	0.99983	0.99052	0.93047	0.78004	0.56110	0.34066	0.17340	0.07357	0.02575	0.00732
	7	0.99998	0.99774	0.97453	0.89088	0.72651	0.51185	0.30608	0.15355	0.06385	0.02164
	8	1.00000	0.99954	0.99203	0.95323	0.85056	0.67693	0.46682	0.27353	0.13398	0.05388
	9		0.99992	0.99786	0.98267	0.92867	0.81056	0.63031	0.42462	0.24237	0.11476
	10		0.99999	0.99951	0.99445	0.97033	0.90220	0.77116	0.58578	0.38426	0.21218
	11		1.00000	0.99990	0.99846	0.98927	0.95575	0.87458	0.73228	0.54257	0.34502
	12			0.99998	0.99963	0.99663	0.98253	0.93956	0.84623	0.69368	0.50000
	13			1.00000	0.99992	0.99908	0.99401	0.97454	0.92220	0.81731	0.65498
	14				0.99999	0.99979	0.99822	0.99069	0.96561	0.90402	0.78782
	15				1.00000	0.99996	0.99955	0.99706	0.98683	0.95604	0.88524
	16					0.99999	0.99990	0.99921	0.99567	0.98264	0.94612
	17					1.00000	0.99998	0.99982	0.99879	0.99417	0.97836
	18						1.00000	0.99997	0.99972	0.99836	0.99268
	19							0.99999	0.99995	0.99962	0.99796
	20							1.00000	0.99999	0.99993	0.99954
	21								1.00000	0.99999	0.99992
	22									1.00000	0.99999
	23										1.00000
n=30	0	0.21464	0.04239	0.00763	0.00124	0.00018	0.00002	0.00000			
	1	0.55354	0.18370	0.04803	0.01052	0.00196	0.00031	0.00004	0.00000	0.00000	
	2	0.81218	0.41135	0.15140	0.04418	0.01060	0.00211	0.00035	0.00005	0.00001	
	3	0.93923	0.64744	0.32166	0.12271	0.03745	0.00932	0.00190	0.00031	0.00004	0.00000
	4	0.98436	0.82451	0.52447	0.25523	0.09787	0.03015	0.00752	0.00151	0.00024	0.00003
	5	0.99672	0.92681	0.71058	0.42751	0.20260	0.07659	0.02326	0.00566	0.00109	0.00016
	6	0.99943	0.97417	0.84742	0.60697	0.34805	0.15952	0.05857	0.01718	0.00398	0.00072
	7	0.99992	0.99222	0.93022	0.76079	0.51429	0.28138	0.12377	0.04352	0.01210	0.00261
	8	0.99999	0.99798	0.97222	0.87135	0.67360	0.43152	0.22470	0.09401	0.03121	0.00806
	9	1.00000	0.99955	0.99034	0.93891	0.80341	0.58881	0.35754	0.17629	0.06941	0.02139
	10		0.99991	0.99706	0.97438	0.89427	0.73037	0.50776	0.29147	0.13504	0.04937
	11		0.99998	0.99921	0.99051	0.94934	0.84068	0.65482	0.43109	0.23269	0.10024
	12		1.00000	0.99981	0.99689	0.97841	0.91553	0.78021	0.57847	0.35918	0.18080
	13			0.99996	0.99910	0.99182	0.95995	0.87369	0.71450	0.50248	0.29233
	14			0.99999	0.99977	0.99725	0.98306	0.93481	0.82463	0.64494	0.42777
	15			1.00000	0.99995	0.99918	0.99363	0.96992	0.90294	0.76909	0.57223
	16				0.99999	0.99978	0.99788	0.98764	0.95189	0.86440	0.70767
	17				1.00000	0.99995	0.99937	0.99550	0.97876	0.92861	0.81920
	18					0.99999	0.99984	0.99855	0.99170	0.96656	0.89976
	19					1.00000	0.99996	0.99959	0.99715	0.98616	0.95063
	20						0.99999	0.99990	0.99914	0.99499	0.97861
	21						1.00000	0.99998	0.99978	0.99843	0.99194
	22							1.00000	0.99995	0.99958	0.99739
	23								0.99999	0.99990	0.99928
	24								1.00000	0.99998	0.99984
	25									1.00000	0.99997
	26										1.00000
n=35	0	0.16608	0.02503	0.00339	0.00041	0.00004	0.00000	0.00000			
	1	0.47203	0.12238	0.02430	0.00396	0.00054	0.00006	0.00001			
	2	0.74577	0.30625	0.08704	0.01904	0.00334	0.00047	0.00005	0.00000		
	3	0.90425	0.53099	0.20882	0.06052	0.01361	0.00243	0.00037	0.00006	0.00000	
	4	0.97097	0.73075	0.38075	0.14349	0.04101	0.00912	0.00159	0.00022	0.00002	0.00000
	5	0.99275	0.86836	0.56886	0.27209	0.09762	0.02690	0.00575	0.00095	0.00012	0.00001
	6	0.99848	0.94482	0.73484	0.43284	0.19198	0.06500	0.01695	0.00340	0.00052	0.00006
	7	0.99973	0.98001	0.85619	0.59933	0.32228	0.13265	0.04194	0.01017	0.00187	0.00025
	8	0.99996	0.99370	0.93114	0.74501	0.47430	0.23412	0.08903	0.02595	0.00573	0.00094
	9	0.99999	0.99826	0.97082	0.85427	0.62632	0.36458	0.16510	0.05753	0.01522	0.00299
	10	1.00000	0.99958	0.98902	0.92529	0.75808	0.50996	0.27160	0.11225	0.03541	0.00834
	11		0.99991	0.99632	0.96564	0.85789	0.65156	0.40192	0.19517	0.07294	0.02048
	12		0.99998	0.99890	0.98582	0.92443	0.77293	0.54228	0.30574	0.13436	0.04477
	13		1.00000	0.99971	0.99474	0.96367	0.86495	0.67599	0.43614	0.22326	0.08773
	14			0.99993	0.99825	0.98423	0.92693	0.78913	0.57275	0.33757	0.15525
	15			0.99998	0.99948	0.99382	0.96412	0.87442	0.70026	0.46850	0.24978
	16			1.00000	0.99986	0.99782	0.98404	0.93182	0.80652	0.60241	0.36794
	17				0.99997	0.99930	0.99358	0.96637	0.88569	0.72486	0.50000
	18				0.99999	0.99980	0.99767	0.98497	0.93847	0.82505	0.63206
	19				1.00000	0.99995	0.99924	0.99394	0.96995	0.89839	0.75022
	20					0.99999	0.99978	0.99780	0.98674	0.94640	0.84475
	21					1.00000	0.99994	0.99928	0.99474	0.97446	0.91227
	22						0.99999	0.99979	0.99813	0.98896	0.95523
	23						1.00000	0.99995	0.99941	0.99582	0.97952
	24							0.99999	0.99983	0.99858	0.99166
	25							1.00000	0.99996	0.99958	0.99701
	26								0.99999	0.99989	0.99906
	27								1.00000	0.99998	0.99975
	28									1.00000	0.99994
	29										0.99999
	30										1.00000

Table 2   The Binomial Cumulative Distribution Function

n=40

x	0.05	0.10	0.15	0.20	0.25	0.30	0.35	0.40	0.45	0.50
0	0.12851	0.01478	0.00150	0.00013	0.00001	0.00000				
1	0.39906	0.08047	0.01211	0.00146	0.00014	0.00001	0.00000			
2	0.67674	0.22281	0.04860	0.00794	0.00102	0.00010	0.00001			
3	0.86185	0.42313	0.13017	0.02846	0.00470	0.00060	0.00006	0.00000		
4	0.95197	0.62902	0.26332	0.07591	0.01604	0.00256	0.00031	0.00003	0.00000	
5	0.98612	0.79373	0.43250	0.16133	0.04327	0.00862	0.00129	0.00014	0.00001	
6	0.99661	0.90048	0.60666	0.28589	0.09622	0.02376	0.00436	0.00059	0.00006	0.00000
7	0.99929	0.95810	0.75593	0.43715	0.18195	0.05528	0.01240	0.00205	0.00025	0.00002
8	0.99987	0.98450	0.86460	0.59313	0.29983	0.11101	0.03025	0.00606	0.00088	0.00009
9	0.99998	0.99494	0.93278	0.73178	0.43954	0.19593	0.06444	0.01557	0.00273	0.00034
10	1.00000	0.99853	0.97008	0.83923	0.58390	0.30874	0.12149	0.03522	0.00742	0.00111
11		0.99962	0.98803	0.91249	0.71514	0.44061	0.20528	0.07095	0.01789	0.00321
12		0.99991	0.99569	0.95676	0.82087	0.57718	0.31431	0.12851	0.03859	0.00829
13		0.99998	0.99860	0.98059	0.89677	0.70325	0.44077	0.21116	0.07506	0.01924
14		1.00000	0.99959	0.99208	0.94556	0.80745	0.57208	0.31743	0.13260	0.04035
15			0.99989	0.99706	0.97376	0.88485	0.69464	0.44022	0.21421	0.07693
16			0.99997	0.99901	0.98844	0.93669	0.79776	0.56813	0.31855	0.13409
17			0.99999	0.99970	0.99535	0.96805	0.87615	0.68852	0.43906	0.21480
18			1.00000	0.99991	0.99829	0.98522	0.93008	0.79107	0.56505	0.31791
19				0.99998	0.99943	0.99375	0.96371	0.87023	0.68441	0.43731
20				0.99999	0.99983	0.99758	0.98272	0.92565	0.78696	0.56269
21				1.00000	0.99995	0.99915	0.99247	0.96083	0.86686	0.68209
22					0.99999	0.99973	0.99700	0.98109	0.92332	0.78520
23					1.00000	0.99992	0.99891	0.99166	0.95947	0.86591
24						0.99998	0.99964	0.99665	0.98042	0.92307
25						0.99999	0.99989	0.99878	0.99139	0.95965
26						1.00000	0.99997	0.99960	0.99657	0.98076
27							0.99999	0.99988	0.99877	0.99171
28							1.00000	0.99997	0.99960	0.99679
29								0.99999	0.99989	0.99889
30								1.00000	0.99997	0.99966
31									0.99999	0.99991
32									1.00000	0.99998
33										1.00000

n=50

x	0.05	0.10	0.15	0.20	0.25	0.30	0.35	0.40	0.45	0.50
0	0.07694	0.00515	0.00030	0.00001	0.00000					
1	0.27943	0.03379	0.00291	0.00019	0.00001					
2	0.54053	0.11173	0.01419	0.00129	0.00009	0.00000				
3	0.76041	0.25029	0.04605	0.00566	0.00050	0.00003	0.00000			
4	0.89638	0.43120	0.11211	0.01850	0.00211	0.00017	0.00001			
5	0.96222	0.61612	0.21935	0.04803	0.00705	0.00072	0.00005	0.00000		
6	0.98821	0.77023	0.36130	0.10340	0.01939	0.00249	0.00022	0.00001		
7	0.99681	0.87786	0.51875	0.19041	0.04526	0.00726	0.00080	0.00006	0.00000	
8	0.99924	0.94213	0.66810	0.30733	0.09160	0.01825	0.00248	0.00023	0.00001	
9	0.99984	0.97546	0.79109	0.44374	0.16368	0.04023	0.00670	0.00076	0.00006	0.00000
10	0.99997	0.99065	0.88008	0.58356	0.26220	0.07885	0.01601	0.00220	0.00020	0.00001
11	1.00000	0.99678	0.93719	0.71067	0.38162	0.13904	0.03423	0.00569	0.00063	0.00005
12		0.99900	0.96994	0.81394	0.51099	0.22287	0.06613	0.01325	0.00177	0.00015
13		0.99971	0.98683	0.88941	0.63704	0.32788	0.11633	0.02799	0.00449	0.00047
14		0.99993	0.99471	0.93928	0.74808	0.44683	0.18778	0.05396	0.01038	0.00130
15		0.99998	0.99805	0.96920	0.83692	0.56918	0.28010	0.09550	0.02195	0.00330
16		1.00000	0.99934	0.98556	0.90169	0.68388	0.38886	0.15609	0.04265	0.00767
17			0.99979	0.99374	0.94488	0.78219	0.50597	0.23688	0.07653	0.01642
18			0.99994	0.99749	0.97127	0.85944	0.62159	0.33561	0.12735	0.03245
19			0.99998	0.99907	0.98608	0.91520	0.72644	0.44648	0.19737	0.05946
20			1.00000	0.99968	0.99374	0.95224	0.81395	0.56104	0.28617	0.10132
21				0.99990	0.99738	0.97491	0.88126	0.67014	0.38996	0.16112
22				0.99997	0.99898	0.98772	0.92904	0.76602	0.50191	0.23994
23				0.99999	0.99963	0.99441	0.96036	0.84383	0.61341	0.33591
24				1.00000	0.99988	0.99763	0.97933	0.90219	0.71604	0.44386
25					0.99996	0.99907	0.98996	0.94266	0.80337	0.55614
26					0.99999	0.99966	0.99546	0.96859	0.87207	0.66409
27					1.00000	0.99988	0.99809	0.98397	0.92204	0.76006
28						0.99996	0.99925	0.99238	0.95562	0.83888
29						0.99999	0.99973	0.99664	0.97646	0.89868
30						1.00000	0.99991	0.99863	0.98840	0.94054
31							0.99997	0.99948	0.99470	0.96755
32							0.99999	0.99982	0.99776	0.98358
33							1.00000	0.99994	0.99913	0.99233
34								0.99998	0.99969	0.99670
35								1.00000	0.99990	0.99870
36									0.99997	0.99953
37									0.99999	0.99985
38									1.00000	0.99995
39										0.99999
40										1.00000

Table 2 The Binomial Cumulative Distribution Function

x	0.05	0.10	0.15	0.20	0.25	0.30	0.35	0.40	0.45	0.50
n=100 0	0.00592	0.00003								
1	0.03708	0.00032	0.00000							
2	0.11826	0.00194	0.00002							
3	0.25784	0.00784	0.00009							
4	0.43598	0.02371	0.00043	0.00000						
5	0.61600	0.05758	0.00155	0.00002						
6	0.76601	0.11716	0.00470	0.00008						
7	0.87204	0.20605	0.01217	0.00028	0.00000					
8	0.93691	0.32087	0.02748	0.00086	0.00001					
9	0.97181	0.45129	0.05509	0.00233	0.00004					
10	0.98853	0.58316	0.09945	0.00570	0.00014	0.00000				
11	0.99573	0.70303	0.16349	0.01257	0.00039	0.00001				
12	0.99854	0.80182	0.24730	0.02533	0.00103	0.00002				
13	0.99954	0.87612	0.34743	0.04691	0.00246	0.00006				
14	0.99986	0.92743	0.45722	0.08044	0.00542	0.00016	0.00000			
15	0.99996	0.96011	0.56832	0.12851	0.01108	0.00041	0.00001			
16	0.99999	0.97940	0.67246	0.19234	0.02111	0.00097	0.00002			
17	1.00000	0.98999	0.76328	0.27119	0.03763	0.00216	0.00005			
18		0.99542	0.83717	0.36209	0.06301	0.00452	0.00014	0.00000		
19		0.99802	0.89346	0.46016	0.09953	0.00889	0.00034	0.00001		
20		0.99919	0.93368	0.55946	0.14883	0.01646	0.00078	0.00002		
21		0.99969	0.96072	0.65403	0.21144	0.02883	0.00169	0.00004		
22		0.99989	0.97786	0.73893	0.28637	0.04787	0.00343	0.00011		
23		0.99996	0.98811	0.81091	0.37108	0.07553	0.00662	0.00025	0.00000	
24		0.99999	0.99392	0.86865	0.46167	0.11357	0.01213	0.00056	0.00001	
25		1.00000	0.99703	0.91252	0.55347	0.16313	0.02114	0.00119	0.00003	
26			0.99862	0.94417	0.64174	0.22440	0.03514	0.00240	0.00007	
27			0.99939	0.96585	0.72238	0.29637	0.05581	0.00460	0.00016	0.00000
28			0.99974	0.97998	0.79246	0.37678	0.08482	0.00843	0.00036	0.00001
29			0.99989	0.98875	0.85046	0.46234	0.12360	0.01478	0.00076	0.00002
30			0.99996	0.99394	0.89621	0.54912	0.17302	0.02478	0.00154	0.00004
31			0.99998	0.99697	0.93065	0.63311	0.23311	0.03985	0.00297	0.00009
32			0.99999	0.99845	0.95540	0.71072	0.30288	0.06150	0.00550	0.00020
33			1.00000	0.99926	0.97241	0.77926	0.38029	0.09125	0.00976	0.00044
34				0.99966	0.98357	0.83714	0.46243	0.13034	0.01653	0.00089
35				0.99985	0.99059	0.88392	0.54584	0.17947	0.02724	0.00176
36				0.99994	0.99482	0.92012	0.62692	0.23861	0.04290	0.00332
37				0.99998	0.99725	0.94695	0.70245	0.30681	0.06507	0.00602
38				0.99999	0.99860	0.96602	0.76987	0.38219	0.09514	0.01049
39				1.00000	0.99931	0.97901	0.82759	0.46208	0.13425	0.01760
40					0.99968	0.98750	0.87498	0.54329	0.18306	0.02844
41					0.99985	0.99283	0.91232	0.62253	0.24149	0.04431
42					0.99994	0.99603	0.94057	0.69674	0.30865	0.06661
43					0.99997	0.99789	0.96109	0.76347	0.38277	0.09667
44					0.99999	0.99891	0.97540	0.82110	0.46133	0.13563
45					1.00000	0.99946	0.98499	0.86891	0.54132	0.18410
46						0.99974	0.99116	0.90702	0.61956	0.24206
47						0.99988	0.99498	0.93621	0.69312	0.30865
48						0.99995	0.99725	0.95770	0.75957	0.38218
49						0.99998	0.99855	0.97290	0.81727	0.46021
50						0.99999	0.99926	0.98324	0.86542	0.53979
51						1.00000	0.99964	0.98999	0.90405	0.61782
52							0.99983	0.99424	0.93383	0.69135
53							0.99992	0.99680	0.95589	0.75794
54							0.99997	0.99829	0.97161	0.81590
55							0.99999	0.99912	0.98236	0.86437
56							0.99999	0.99956	0.98943	0.90333
57							1.00000	0.99979	0.99389	0.93339
58								0.99990	0.99660	0.95569
59								0.99996	0.99818	0.97156
60								0.99998	0.99906	0.98240
61								0.99999	0.99953	0.98951
62								1.00000	0.99978	0.99398
63									0.99990	0.99668
64									0.99996	0.99824
65									0.99998	0.99911
66									0.99999	0.99956
67									1.00000	0.99980
68										0.99991
69										0.99996
70										0.99998
71										0.99999
72										1.00000

Table 3. The Poisson Cumulative Distribution Function

The function tabulated is $F(x,\lambda) = \sum_{r=0}^{x} \dfrac{\lambda^r e^{-\lambda}}{r!} = P(X \leqslant x)$ where X is Poisson

distributed with mean λ. For $\lambda > 10$, use the Normal approximation

$F(x,\lambda) \approx \Phi\left(\dfrac{x+\frac{1}{2}-\lambda}{\sqrt{\lambda}}\right)$ where Φ is defined in Table 1.

x \ λ	0.1	0.2	0.3	0.4	0.5	0.6	0.7	0.8	0.9	1.0
0	0.90484	0.81873	0.74082	0.67032	0.60653	0.54881	0.49659	0.44933	0.40657	0.36788
1	0.99532	0.98248	0.96306	0.93845	0.90980	0.87810	0.84419	0.80879	0.77248	0.73576
2	0.99985	0.99885	0.99640	0.99207	0.98561	0.97688	0.96586	0.95258	0.93714	0.91970
3	1.00000	0.99994	0.99973	0.99922	0.99825	0.99664	0.99425	0.99092	0.98654	0.98101
4		1.00000	0.99998	0.99994	0.99983	0.99961	0.99921	0.99859	0.99766	0.99634
5			1.00000	1.00000	0.99999	0.99996	0.99991	0.99982	0.99966	0.99941
6					1.00000	1.00000	0.99999	0.99998	0.99996	0.99992
7							1.00000	1.00000	0.99999	0.99999
8									1.00000	1.00000

x \ λ	1.1	1.2	1.3	1.4	1.5	1.6	1.7	1.8	1.9	2.0
0	0.33287	0.30119	0.27253	0.24660	0.22313	0.20190	0.18268	0.16530	0.14957	0.13534
1	0.69903	0.66263	0.62682	0.59183	0.55783	0.52493	0.49325	0.46284	0.43375	0.40601
2	0.90042	0.87949	0.85711	0.83350	0.80885	0.78366	0.75722	0.73062	0.70372	0.67668
3	0.97426	0.96623	0.95690	0.94627	0.93436	0.92119	0.90681	0.89129	0.87470	0.85712
4	0.99456	0.99225	0.98934	0.98575	0.98142	0.97632	0.97039	0.96359	0.95592	0.94735
5	0.99903	0.99850	0.99777	0.99680	0.99554	0.99396	0.99200	0.98962	0.98678	0.98344
6	0.99985	0.99975	0.99960	0.99938	0.99907	0.99866	0.99812	0.99743	0.99655	0.99547
7	0.99998	0.99996	0.99994	0.99989	0.99983	0.99974	0.99961	0.99944	0.99921	0.99890
8	1.00000	0.99999	0.99999	0.99998	0.99997	0.99995	0.99993	0.99989	0.99984	0.99976
9		1.00000	1.00000	1.00000	1.00000	0.99999	0.99999	0.99998	0.99997	0.99995
10						1.00000	1.00000	1.00000	0.99999	0.99999
11									1.00000	1.00000

x \ λ	2.1	2.2	2.3	2.4	2.5	2.6	2.7	2.8	2.9	3.0
0	0.12246	0.11080	0.10026	0.09072	0.08208	0.07427	0.06721	0.06081	0.05502	0.04979
1	0.37961	0.35457	0.33085	0.30844	0.28730	0.26738	0.24866	0.23108	0.21459	0.19915
2	0.64963	0.62271	0.59604	0.56971	0.54381	0.51843	0.49362	0.46945	0.44596	0.42319
3	0.83864	0.81935	0.79935	0.77872	0.75758	0.73600	0.71409	0.69194	0.66962	0.64723
4	0.93787	0.92750	0.91625	0.90413	0.89118	0.87742	0.86291	0.84768	0.83178	0.81526
5	0.97955	0.97509	0.97002	0.96433	0.95798	0.95096	0.94327	0.93489	0.92583	0.91608
6	0.99414	0.99254	0.99064	0.98841	0.98581	0.98283	0.97943	0.97559	0.97128	0.96649
7	0.99851	0.99802	0.99741	0.99666	0.99575	0.99467	0.99338	0.99187	0.99012	0.98810
8	0.99966	0.99953	0.99936	0.99914	0.99886	0.99851	0.99809	0.99757	0.99694	0.99620
9	0.99993	0.99990	0.99986	0.99980	0.99972	0.99962	0.99950	0.99934	0.99914	0.99890
10	0.99999	0.99998	0.99997	0.99996	0.99994	0.99991	0.99988	0.99984	0.99978	0.99971
11	1.00000	1.00000	0.99999	0.99999	0.99999	0.99998	0.99997	0.99996	0.99995	0.99993
12			1.00000	1.00000	1.00000	1.00000	0.99999	0.99999	0.99999	0.99998
13							1.00000	1.00000	1.00000	1.00000

Table 3   The Poisson Cumulative Distribution Function

x \ λ	3.2	3.4	3.6	3.8	4.0	4.2	4.4	4.6	4.8	5.0
0	0.04076	0.03337	0.02732	0.02237	0.01832	0.01500	0.01228	0.01005	0.00823	0.00674
1	0.17120	0.14684	0.12569	0.10738	0.09158	0.07798	0.06630	0.05629	0.04773	0.04043
2	0.37990	0.33974	0.30275	0.26890	0.23810	0.21024	0.18514	0.16264	0.14254	0.12465
3	0.60252	0.55836	0.51522	0.47348	0.43347	0.39540	0.35945	0.32571	0.29423	0.26503
4	0.78061	0.74418	0.70644	0.66784	0.62884	0.58983	0.55118	0.51323	0.47626	0.44049
5	0.89459	0.87054	0.84412	0.81556	0.78513	0.75314	0.71991	0.68576	0.65101	0.61596
6	0.95538	0.94215	0.92673	0.90911	0.88933	0.86746	0.84365	0.81803	0.79080	0.76218
7	0.98317	0.97693	0.96921	0.95989	0.94887	0.93606	0.92142	0.90495	0.88667	0.86663
8	0.99429	0.99171	0.98833	0.98401	0.97864	0.97207	0.96420	0.95493	0.94418	0.93191
9	0.99824	0.99729	0.99597	0.99420	0.99187	0.98887	0.98511	0.98047	0.97486	0.96817
10	0.99950	0.99919	0.99873	0.99807	0.99716	0.99593	0.99431	0.99222	0.98958	0.98630
11	0.99987	0.99978	0.99963	0.99941	0.99908	0.99863	0.99799	0.99714	0.99601	0.99455
12	0.99997	0.99994	0.99990	0.99983	0.99973	0.99957	0.99934	0.99902	0.99858	0.99798
13	0.99999	0.99999	0.99997	0.99995	0.99992	0.99987	0.99980	0.99969	0.99953	0.99930
14	1.00000	1.00000	0.99999	0.99999	0.99998	0.99997	0.99994	0.99991	0.99985	0.99977
15			1.00000	1.00000	0.99999	0.99999	0.99998	0.99997	0.99996	0.99993
16					1.00000	1.00000	1.00000	0.99999	0.99999	0.99998
17								1.00000	1.00000	0.99999
18										1.00000

x \ λ	5.5	6.0	6.5	7.0	7.5	8.0	8.5	9.0	9.5	10.0
0	0.00409	0.00248	0.00150	0.00091	0.00055	0.00034	0.00020	0.00012	0.00007	0.00005
1	0.02656	0.01735	0.01128	0.00730	0.00470	0.00302	0.00193	0.00123	0.00079	0.00050
2	0.08838	0.06197	0.04304	0.02964	0.02026	0.01375	0.00928	0.00623	0.00416	0.00277
3	0.20170	0.15120	0.11185	0.08177	0.05959	0.04238	0.03011	0.02123	0.01486	0.01034
4	0.35752	0.28506	0.22367	0.17299	0.13206	0.09963	0.07436	0.05496	0.04026	0.02925
5	0.52892	0.44568	0.36904	0.30071	0.24144	0.19124	0.14960	0.11569	0.08853	0.06709
6	0.68604	0.60630	0.52652	0.44971	0.37815	0.31337	0.25618	0.20678	0.16495	0.13014
7	0.80948	0.74398	0.67276	0.59871	0.52464	0.45296	0.38560	0.32390	0.26866	0.22022
8	0.89436	0.84724	0.79157	0.72909	0.66197	0.59255	0.52310	0.45565	0.39182	0.33282
9	0.94622	0.91607	0.87738	0.83049	0.77641	0.71662	0.65297	0.58741	0.52183	0.45793
10	0.97475	0.95738	0.93316	0.90148	0.86224	0.81589	0.76336	0.70599	0.64533	0.58304
11	0.98901	0.97991	0.96612	0.94665	0.92076	0.88808	0.84866	0.80301	0.75199	0.69677
12	0.99555	0.99117	0.98397	0.97300	0.95733	0.93620	0.90908	0.87577	0.83643	0.79155
13	0.99831	0.99637	0.99290	0.98719	0.97843	0.96582	0.94859	0.92615	0.89813	0.86446
14	0.99940	0.99860	0.99704	0.99428	0.98974	0.98274	0.97257	0.95853	0.94001	0.91654
15	0.99980	0.99949	0.99884	0.99759	0.99539	0.99177	0.98616	0.97796	0.96652	0.95126
16	0.99994	0.99982	0.99957	0.99904	0.99804	0.99628	0.99338	0.98889	0.98227	0.97296
17	0.99998	0.99994	0.99985	0.99964	0.99921	0.99840	0.99700	0.99468	0.99107	0.98572
18	0.99999	0.99998	0.99995	0.99987	0.99969	0.99935	0.99870	0.99757	0.99571	0.99281
19	1.00000	0.99999	0.99998	0.99995	0.99989	0.99975	0.99946	0.99894	0.99803	0.99654
20		1.00000	0.99999	0.99998	0.99996	0.99991	0.99979	0.99956	0.99914	0.99841
21			1.00000	0.99999	0.99998	0.99997	0.99992	0.99982	0.99964	0.99930
22				1.00000	0.99999	0.99999	0.99997	0.99993	0.99985	0.99970
23					1.00000	1.00000	0.99999	0.99997	0.99994	0.99988
24							0.99999	0.99999	0.99998	0.99995
25							1.00000	0.99999	0.99999	0.99998
26								1.00000	0.99999	0.99999
27									1.00000	0.99999
28										1.00000

Titles in the RND Statistical Series:

Statistical Tables   *ISBN 0-9506719-0-8*

Introductory Statistics   *ISBN 0-9506719-1-6*
Volume 1 - Probability and Distribution Theory

Worked Examples in Probability and
Distribution Theory   *ISBN 0-9506719-2-4*